58p

To love, honour and cherish...always?

Husbands
& *Wives*

THE ULTIMATE BETRAYAL
by
Michelle Reid

MARRIAGE IN JEOPARDY
by
Miranda Lee

SAVAGE OBSESSION
by
Diana Hamilton

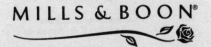

MILLS & BOON®

*MILLS & BOON and MILLS & BOON with the Rose Device
are registered trademarks of the publisher.*
*Harlequin Mills & Boon Limited,
Eton House, 18-24 Paradise Road, Richmond, Surrey, TW9 1SR*

HUSBANDS & WIVES
© by Harlequin Enterprises II B.V., 2000

The Ultimate Betrayal, Marriage in Jeopardy and Savage Obsession were
first published in Great Britain by Harlequin Mills & Boon Limited in
separate, single volumes.

The Ultimate Betrayal © Michelle Reid 1995
Marriage in Jeopardy © Miranda Lee 1993
Savage Obsession © Diana Hamilton 1992

ISBN 0 263 82421 7

05-1100

*Printed and bound in Spain
by Litografia Rosés S.A., Barcelona*

Michelle Reid grew up on the southern edges of Manchester, the youngest in a family of five lively children. But now she lives in the beautiful county of Cheshire with her busy executive husband and two grown-up daughters. She loves reading, the ballet, and playing tennis when she gets the chance. She hates cooking, cleaning, and despises ironing! Sleep she can do without and produces some of her best written work during the early hours of the morning.

Look out for THE SPANISH HUSBAND
by Michelle Reid
in Modern Romance™, December 2000

THE ULTIMATE BETRAYAL

by

MICHELLE REID

CHAPTER ONE

THE telephone started ringing as Rachel was coming downstairs after putting the twins to bed. She muttered something not very complimentary, hitched six-month-old Michael further up her hip, and rushed the final few steps which brought her to the hall extension—then stopped dead with her hand hovering half an inch above the telephone receiver, her attention caught by the reflection in the mirror on the wall behind the telephone table.

God, you look a mess! she told herself in disgust. Half her pale blonde hair was hanging in damp twists around her neck and face while the rest of it spewed untidily from a lopsided knot to one side of the top of her head. Her cheeks were flushed, her light blue overshirt darkened in huge patches where bathtime for three small children had extended its wetness to her also. And Michael was determinedly trying to wreak its final destruction by tugging at the buttons in an effort to expose her breast. A greedy child at the best of times, he was also tired and impatient now.

'No,' she scolded, gently but firmly forestalling his forage by disentangling his fingers from her blouse. 'Wait.' And she kissed the top of his downy head as she picked up the telephone receiver while still frowning at her own reflection.

'Hello?' she murmured, sounding distracted—which she certainly was.

So distracted, in fact, that she missed the tense little pause before the person on the other end answered cautiously, 'Rachel? It's Amanda.'

5

'Oh, hi, Mandy!' Rachel watched pleased surprise ease the frown from her face, and only realised as she did so that she had been frowning. That brought the frown back, a perplexed one this time, because she had caught herself doing that a lot recently. 'Michael, please wait a little longer!' she sighed at the small boy grappling with her blouse.

He scowled at her and she sent him a teasing scowl back, her blue eyes alight with love and amusement. He might be the most bad-tempered and demanding of her three children, but she adored him just the same—how could she not when she only had to look into those dove-grey eyes and see Daniel looking back at her?

'Aren't those brats in bed yet?' Amanda sighed in disgust. She made no secret of the fact that she found the children an irritant. But then Mandy was the epitome of made-it-in-a-man's-world woman. She had no time for children. She was a tall, willowy red-head who strode through her highly polished life on a different plane from the one Rachel existed on. She was the sophisticate while Rachel was the comfortable, stay-at-home wife and mother.

She was also Rachel's best friend. Well, maybe that was going a bit far, she acknowledged. She was the only friend Rachel had kept in touch with from her school days. The only one of the crowd who now lived in London like herself and Daniel. The others, as far as she knew, had made their lives back home in Cheshire.

'Two down, one to go,' she told her friend. 'Michael wants feeding but he can wait,' she added, for the baby's benefit as much as Amanda's.

'And Daniel?' Amanda asked next. 'Is he home yet?'

Rachel detected more disapproval in her friend's tone and smiled at it. Amanda did not get on with Daniel. They struck uncomfortably hostile sparks off each other whenever they were in the same company.

So, 'No,' Rachel said, adding ruefully, 'So you're safe to call him all the rotten names you like. He won't overhear you.'

It had been meant as a joke, and not a very new one either. Rachel had always given Amanda leave to vent her opinion of Daniel when he wasn't around. It allowed her friend to get off her chest all those things she would have loved to say to his face only she never quite had the courage to. But this time just an odd silence followed the invitation, and Rachel felt a sudden and unaccountable tension fizz down the line towards her.

'Is something wrong?' she asked sharply.

'Damn,' Mandy muttered. 'Yes. You could say that. Listen, Rachel. I'm going to feel an absolute heel for doing this, but you have a right to—'

Just then, a pair of Postman Pat pyjamas came gliding down the stairs, the small figure within making out he was a fighter pilot, firing his forward guns. Michael shrieked with glee, his eyes lighting up as he watched his big brother come hurtling down towards them.

'Drink of water,' the pilot informed the questioning look in his mother's eyes as he reached the hallway, and flew off in the direction of the kitchen.

'Look—' Mandy sounded impatient '—I can hear you're busy. 'I'll call you back later—tomorrow maybe. I—'

'No!' Rachel cut in quickly. 'Don't you dare ring off!' She might be distracted, but not so much that she hadn't picked up on the fact that whatever Mandy wanted to say was important. 'Just hang on a moment while I sort this lot out.'

She put the receiver down on the table then went after her eldest son, her long, beautifully slender legs moulded in white Lycra leggings which finished several inches above white rolled-down socks and white trainers. She was not tall, but she was incredibly slender and her figure was tight—surprisingly tight considering the fact that she'd carried and borne three children. But then she worked out regularly at the local sports centre—swimming, aerobics, the occasional game of badminton when she could find the time.

'Caught you red-handed!' she accused her six-year-old, who had his hand lost in the biscuit barrel. Rachel sent him a fierce look while he went red, then sighed an impatient, 'Oh, go on then—and take one for Kate—but no crumbs in the beds!' she called after him as Sammy shot off with a whoop of triumph before she could change her mind.

The kitchen was big and homely, big enough to house the netted play-pen hugging one corner of the room. She popped Michael into it and gave him something messy to suck at while she went back to the phone.

'Right,' she said, dragging the twisted telephone cord behind her as she went to make herself comfortable on the bottom stair. 'Are you still there, Mandy?'

'Yes.' The answer was gruff and terse. 'Why don't you employ someone to help you with those kids?' Mandy asked irritably. 'They're an absolute pain in the neck sometimes!'

'I'll tell Daniel you said that,' Rachel threatened, not taking offence. So Mandy was not the maternal type; she could accept that. Rachel was very maternal, and was not ashamed to admit it. 'And we do employ help,' she defended that criticism. 'It's just that I like the house to myself in the evenings, that's all. Live-in help feels as though you've got permanent guests. I can't relax around them.'

'Become any more relaxed,' Mandy mocked acidly, 'and

you'll be asleep! For goodness' sake, Rachel! Will you stop emulating Sleeping Beauty and wake up?'

'Wake up to what?' She frowned, totally bewildered as to why Mandy felt this sudden need to attack her.

A harsh sigh rattled down the line to her eardrum. 'Rachel,' she said, 'where is Daniel tonight?'

The frown deepened. 'Working late,' she answered.

'He's been doing a lot of that recently, hasn't he?'

'Well, yes—but he's been very busy with that take-over thing with Harveys. You know about it, don't you?' she prompted. 'I'm sure I heard you both discussing it the last time you came to dinner...'

'The Harvey thing was over months ago, Rachel!' Mandy sighed.

Months? Had it really been months since Mandy had come to dinner? Rachel pouted, thinking back. Michael had been about—three months old, she recalled. That was three months ago! My God, where had the days, weeks—months gone to?

'Hey!' she exclaimed. 'You'll have to come to dinner again soon. I hadn't realised it was so long since I'd seen you! I'll talk to Daniel and see which night would be—'

'Rachel!' The sheer exasperation in Mandy's voice cut her short. 'For goodness sake—I didn't call you to wheedle a dinner invitation out of you! Though your dinners are worth attending when you bother to put one on,' she added, with yet more criticism spicing her tone. 'Not that I know how you find the time, what with a house and three crazy kids to take care of, not to mention a selfish swine like...'

She was off on her usual soap-box, Rachel acknowledged, switching off. Mandy hated the way Rachel liked to run her home virtually single-handed, and she thought Daniel contributed little or nothing. She did not understand how busy he was, how hard it had been for him to scramble his way to the top and support a young family at the same time. Nor did she understand that Rachel did not mind the long hours he had to work, that she understood that he was doing it for them, herself and the children, for their future security.

'…and I just can't let it go on any longer without telling you, Rachel. You are my friend, after all, not him. And it's time someone woke you up to what's going on under your very nose…'

'Hey, back up a little, will you?' Rachel had switched her attention back to what Mandy was saying only to find she had completely lost the thread of the conversation. 'I think I missed something there along the way. What's going on right under my nose that you think I should know about?'

'See?' Mandy cried impatiently. 'There you go again! Switching off when someone is trying to tell you something important. Wake up, for God's sake, Rachel. Wake up!'

'Wake up to what?' Like Mandy, she was beginning to get impatient herself.

'To that bastard you're married to!' Mandy cried. 'Dammit, Rachel—he's playing you for a fool! He isn't working late. He's out with another woman!'

The words cracked like a whip, bringing Rachel jerking to her feet. 'What, tonight?' she heard herself say stupidly.

'No, not tonight in particular,' Mandy answered heavily, obviously thinking the question as stupid as Rachel thought it. 'Some nights,' she adjusted. 'I don't know how often! I just know that he is having an affair, and all of London seems to know about it except for you!'

Silence. Rachel was having difficulty functioning on any conscious level. Her breath was lying frozen inside her lungs, as pins and needles—like a deadening drug administered to ward off impending shock—gathered in her throat and made their tingling way down to her feet.

'I'm so sorry, Rachel...' Sensing her shock, Mandy's voice softened and became husky. 'Don't think I'm enjoying this, no matter how...' She had been going to say how much she resented Daniel and would enjoy seeing the mighty fall. But she managed to restrain herself. Mandy disliked Daniel. Daniel disliked Mandy. Neither of them had ever made a secret of the fact that they put up with each other only for Rachel's sake. 'And don't think I'm telling you this without being sure of my facts,' she added defiantly to Rachel's continuing silence. 'They've been seen around town. In restaurants—you know—being too intimate with each other for a business relationship. But worse than that, I've seen them with my own eyes. My latest has a flat in the same building as Lydia Marsden,' she explained. 'I've seen them coming and going...'

Rachel had stopped listening. Her mind had turned entirely inwards, seeing things—pointers that made everything Mandy was saying just too probable to be dismissed as malicious gossip. Things she should have picked up on weeks ago, but she had been too busy, too wrapped up in her own hectic routine to notice, too trusting of the man whose love for herself and the children she had never questioned.

But she was seeing now. His frequent grim moods recently. The way he snapped at her and the children, the many times he had remained downstairs in his study working instead of coming to bed with her—making love with her.

Sickness swam like a wave over her, making her sway, close her eyes, see other times when he had tried to make love with her only to find her too tired and unresponsive. Weeks—months—of bitter frustration when she had been willing enough to give but he had been unwilling to take without knowing he was giving back in return.

But she'd thought they'd sorted that problem out! She'd thought over the last week or two—since Michael had been sleeping through the night and she had been feeling more rested—that everything was getting back to normal again.

And it was only a few nights ago that they had made love so beautifully that Daniel had trembled in her arms afterwards...

God...!

'Rachel...'

No! She couldn't listen to any more. 'I have to go,' she said huskily. 'Michael needs me.' Couldn't, because she was remembering one other pointer that was far more damning than any weak points of irritability or even poor sexual performances! She was remembering the delicate scent of an expensive perfume emanating from one of his shirts one morning as she prepared it for washing. It had clung to the fine white cotton, all over it. The collar, the shoulders, the two front sections. It had been the same delicate scent she had smelled but not quite picked up on each time she had kissed him when he came home at night—on his late nights. On his lean cheek. In his hair.

Fool!

'No—Rachel, please wait. I—'

The receiver dropped noisily on to its rest and she sank, leaden-bodied, back on to the stairs. Seeing Daniel. Daniel with another woman. Daniel having an affair. Daniel making love, drowning in another woman's...

She retched nauseously, a hand going up to cover her mouth, turning into a white-knuckled fist to press her cold and trembling lips painfully against her clenched teeth.

The phone began ringing again. A tired cry coming from the kitchen joined the shrill sound, and she stood up, a strange kind of calmness settling over her as she first picked up the receiver, then dropped it immediately back on its rest. Then, with that same odd calmness which actually spoke of reeling shock, she lifted it off again and left it off, then walked towards the kitchen.

Michael went straight to sleep after his feed. He curled himself up into his habitual ball with his padded bottom stuck up in the air and his small teddy tucked beneath his chubby cheek. Rachel stood for a long time just staring down at him—not really seeing him, not seeing anything much.

Her mind seemed to have gone a complete blank.

She checked the twins' rooms as she passed by. Sammy was fast asleep with his covers kicked off as usual, arms thrown out across his pillow in abandonment. She bent to drop a soft kiss on her eldest son's cheek before gently pulling the covers over him. Sam was more like his father than the other two, dark-haired and determined-chinned. Tall for his age, too, and sturdy. Daniel had looked like him at that age; she had seen snaps of him in his mother's photograph album. And Sam showed a stubbornness of purpose in that six-year-old face—just like his adored father.

Her heart wrenched, but she ignored the ugly feeling, turning instead to go to the other room where she stood staring down at the sleeping figure of her daughter. Kate was a different proposition entirely from her twin. You could come into this room in the morning almost guaranteed to find her sleeping in exactly the same position you had left her in the night before. Kate, with her silky hair like sunshine on her pillow. The apple of her father's eye. She could wheedle more out of Daniel than anyone else in the family could. He openly and unashamedly adored his blue-eyed princess. And the precocious little madam knew it—and exploited it to its fullest degree.

Would Daniel so much as consider doing anything which could hurt his little girl? Or lower his stature in the eyes of his adoring eldest son? Would he dare place all of this in jeopardy over something so basic as sex?

Sex? A terrifying shiver went skittering down her spine. Maybe it was more than sex. Maybe he couldn't help himself. Maybe it was love—the real thing. Love. The kind of love men were willing to betray everything for.

Maybe this was all just a stupid lie. A dark and cancerous bloody lie! And she was doing him the worst indignity of all by even considering it as the truth!

Then she remembered the perfume. And the times he had stayed out all night—blaming it on the Harvey contract.

The damned Harvey contract.

She reeled away and walked blindly out of Kate's room and across the landing into their bedroom where, only last week, they had found each other again. Made love beautifully for the first time in months.

Last week. So what had happened last week to make him suddenly turn to her again? She had made an effort; that was what had happened. She'd been worried about the way their relationship was going, and she'd made an effort. Sent the children to stay with his mother for the night. Cooked his favourite meal, laid the table with their best china and lit candles, and greeted him home in a slinky black dress and with a kiss that promised so much...

So much, in fact, that she'd not even noticed the clenching of his jaw and the sudden twitch of that little nerve beside his mouth which was always a dead give-away that he was labouring under severe stress. But she noticed it now, with aching hindsight. She closed her eyes tightly in the silence of their bedroom and saw his lean face clench, his tanned skin pale, that little nerve begin to work as she wound her arms around his neck and leaned provocatively against him.

God. The nausea came back, almost overwhelming her, and she stumbled blindly out of the room and down the stairs to their sitting-room, seeing so much—so much that she had been foolishly blind to until now—that she was barely aware of what she was doing.

The tension with which he had held her shoulders, trying to put some distance between them. The pained bleak look in his grey eyes as he had stared down at her inviting mouth. The sigh which had rasped from him and the shudder which had shaken him when she'd murmured, 'I love you, Daniel. I'm so sorry I've been such a pain to live with.'

He'd closed his eyes tightly, swallowed tightly, clenched his lips, and clenched his hands on her shoulders until she'd actually winced in pain. Then he'd pulled her close, hugged her to him, burying his face in her throat, and said not a word, not a single word. No answering apology, no answering declaration of love. Nothing.

But they had made love beautifully, she remembered now, with an ache which echoed deep into her being. Whatever else Daniel was getting from this other woman, he could still want her with a passion no man could fake—surely?

Or could he? she wondered now. What did she know of men and how their sex-drives worked? She had been just seventeen when she met Daniel. He had been her first lover—her only lover. She knew nothing—nothing about men.

Not even her own husband, seemingly.

Her eye was caught by her own reflection in the mirror set above the white marble fireplace, and she stared numbly at herself. She looked pale, she noted, a trifle tense around the mouth, but otherwise normal. No blood evident. No scars. Just Rachel Masterson *née* James. Twenty-four years old. Mother. Wife—in that order. She smiled bitterly at that. Facing the truth of it in a way she had never allowed herself to do before.

You wanted him, she told her reflection. And my God, you got him—and all in the space of six short months, too! Not bad going for a sweet naïve seventeen-year-old. Daniel had been all of twenty-four. Far too worldly-wise, surely, she mocked her reflection cynically, to be caught out by the oldest trick in the book!

Then the cynicism left her, because it had not been a trick, and she had no right denigrating herself by calling it one. She had been seventeen and utterly innocent when she met Daniel at her very first visit to a real nightclub, with a crowd of girls from school who thought it hilarious that she was frightened they would ask her her age and discover she was not old enough to enter their establishment.

'Come on, Rachel!' they'd mocked her. 'If they ask you, you lie, like we do!' And they had given her a new date of birth which she repeated over and over to herself until she was safely inside the glittering dimness of the night-club. And even then she had jumped like a terrified rabbit every time someone so much as brushed by her, half-expecting to be thrown out by one of the big burly bouncers dotted around the place. Then, slowly, she had relaxed, begun to enjoy herself along with the rest of them, dancing to the disco music and sipping white wine and feeling less inhibited as the evening went on.

She was aware of Daniel from the moment he stepped into the club. He carried that kind of charisma with him. A big, lean man with neat dark hair and the kind of clean good looks film stars were made of. The others noticed him too, and giggled when he seemed to be taking an inordinate interest in their dancing group. But it was Rachel he was looking at. Rachel with her long, pale blonde hair billowing in its natural spiralling curls around her shoulders and pretty face, expertly made-up by the far more experienced Julie, and her slender body encased in one of Julie's tight black mini-skirts and a red cropped vest top which gave tantalising glimpses of her flat stomach as she gyrated to the disco music. If her parents had seen her dressed like that, they'd have died of horror. But she had been staying with Julie while her parents went off to visit relatives that weekend, and they had no idea what their only child, born very late in their lives, was up to while they were away.

And it was to Rachel that Daniel came when the music changed to a lazy smooch, his hand light on her shoulder as he turned her to face him, his smile, like the rest of him, smooth, confident, charismatic. Aware of the other girls' envy, she let him take her in his arms without a word of protest, could still remember those first tingles of shy awareness that fizzed up inside her at his touch, his closeness, the hard smooth line of male brushing against soft and sensitive female.

They danced for ages before he spoke. 'What's your name?' he asked simply.

'Rachel,' she told him, shy-eyed and breathless. 'Rachel James.'

'Hello, Rachel James,' he murmured. 'Daniel Masterson,' he announced himself. Then, while she was still absorbing the sexy resonance of his beautifully modulated voice, he slid his hand beneath the cropped top, making her gasp at the hot stinging sensation of his smooth touch against her bare skin, and pulled her closer.

He made no attempt to kiss her, or talk her into leaving with him instead of her friends. But he did take her telephone number and promised to call her soon, and she spent the next week camped by the phone, waiting—yearning for him to call.

He took her for a drive on their first real date. He drove a red Ford. 'Firm's car,' he explained, with a wry smile she never quite understood. Then gently, but with an intensity which kept her on the edge of her seat with breathless anticipation, he made her talk about herself. About her family, her friends. Her likes and dislikes, and her ambitions to take art at college with a view to going into advertising. He frowned at that, then quietly asked her how old she was. Unable to lie, she flushed guiltily and told him the truth. His frown deepened, and he was rather quiet after that while she chewed on her bottom lip, knowing achingly that she'd blown it. Which seemed to be confirmed when he took her back home and just murmured an absent goodnight as she got out of the car. She'd been devastated. For several days she'd barely eaten, could not sleep, and was in dire danger of wasting away by the time he called her again a week later.

He took her to the cinema that night, sitting beside her in the darkness staring at the big screen while she did the same, only without seeing a single thing, her attention fixed exclusively on his closeness, the subtle tangy smell of him, his hard thigh mere inches away from her own, his shoulder brushing against hers. Dry-mouthed, tense, and terrified of making a single move in case she blew it a second time, she therefore actually cried out when he reached over and picked up one of her hands. His expression was grave as he gently prised her fingers out of the white-knuckled clench she had them in. 'Relax,' he murmured. 'I'm not going to bite you.'

The trouble was, she'd wanted him to bite. Even then, as naïve as they came and with no real idea of what it meant to be with a man, she had wanted him with a desperation which must have shown in her face, because he muttered something and tightened his grip on her hand, holding it trapped in his own while he forced his own attention back to the film. That night he kissed her hard and hungrily, the power of it taking her to the edge of fear before he drew angrily away and made her get out of the car.

The next time he took her out it was to a quiet restaurant, where his eyes lingered broodingly on her through the meal while he told her about himself. About his job as a sales-man for a big computer firm which, by the nature of the job, meant he travelled all over the country touting for new business and could mean his being out of the area for weeks on end sometimes. He told her of his ambition to own his own company one day. How he dabbled in stocks and shares with his commission and lived on a shoe-string to do it. He spoke levelly and softly so that she had to lean forward a little to catch his words, and all the time his eyes never left her face, not just brooding, but seeming to con-sume her, so by the time he drove her home that night she was in danger of exploding at the sexual tension he had developed around them both. Yet still it was just the one hungry kiss before he was sending her into the house and driving away. It went like that for perhaps half a dozen more dates before eventually, inevitably, she supposed, his control snapped and, instead of taking her to the cinema as they had planned, he took her to his flat.

After that, they rarely went anywhere else. Being alone together, making love together, became the most important thing in her life. Daniel became the most important thing in her life, over her A-levels, over her ambitions, over the disapproval her parents made no bones about voicing but which made no difference to the way she felt.

Three months later—and after he had been away in

London for almost two weeks—she had been waiting for him at his flat door when he returned.

'What are you doing here?' he asked, and it was only now, almost seven years later, that she realised he had been far from pleased to find her there. His face had been tired and tense—just as it had looked over these last few months, she thought, on another pained realisation.

'I had to see you,' she'd explained, slipping her hand trustingly into his as he walked into the flat. Inevitably they had made love, then she made some coffee while he showered and they drank in silence, he lounging in a lumpy old easy-chair wearing only his terry bathrobe, she curled at his feet between his parted knees as she always was.

It was then she had told him she was pregnant. He hadn't moved or said anything, and she had not looked at him. His hand had stroked absently at her hair and her cheek rested comfortably on his thigh.

After a while, he had sighed, long and heavy, then bent to lift her on to his lap. She had curled into him there, too. Like a child, she thought now. As Kate does when she goes to her daddy for love and comfort.

'How sure are you?' he had asked then.

'Very sure,' she had answered, snuggling closer because he was the axis her whole world turned upon. 'I bought one of those pregnancy test things when I missed my period this month. It showed positive. Do you think there could be a mistake?' she had asked guilelessly then. 'Shall I go and get a proper test from the doctor before we decide what to do?'

'No.' He had rejected that idea. 'So, you're only just pregnant. I wonder how that happened?' he had pondered thoughtfully.

That made her chuckle. 'Your fault,' she had reminded him. 'You're supposed to take care of all that.'

'So I was and so it is,' he had conceded. 'Well, at least we have time to get married without the whole town knowing why we're having to do it.'

And that had been it. The decision made as, really, she had expected it to be. With Daniel making all the arrangements, shielding her from any unpleasantness, handling her parents and their natural hurt and disappointment in her.

Again, it was only now, seven years later, that she took the words he had spoken and looked at them properly. 'We have time to get married without the whole town knowing why we're having to do it' he had said. And it hit her for the first time that Daniel would not have married her otherwise.

She had trapped him. With her youth, her innocence, with her childlike trust and blind adoration. Daniel had married her because he felt he had to.

Love had never come into it.

The sound of a key turning in the front door lock brought her jolting back to the present, and she turned, feeling oddly calm, yet lead-weighted, to glance at the brass carriage-clock sitting on the sideboard. It was only eight-thirty. Daniel had not been due home for hours yet. A business dinner, he'd called it. Now she bitterly mocked that excuse as she went to stand by the open sitting-room door.

His back was towards her. She could see the tension in him, in his neck muscles and in the stiffness of his shoulders beneath the padding of his black overcoat.

He turned slowly to send her a brief glance. She looked at his face, saw the lines of strain etched there, the greyish pallor. He moved his gaze to where the phone still lay off its rest and went over to it, putting his black leather brief-case down on the floor before picking up the receiver. His hand was trembling as he settled it back on its rest.

Mandy must have called him. She would have panicked

when Rachel refused to answer the phone, and rung Daniel
to tell him what she had done. Rachel would have liked to
have listened in to that conversation, she decided. The cut
and parry of confession, accusation, condemnation and defence.

He looked back at her through eyes heavily hooded by
thick dark lashes, and she let him have his moment's private communion as he ran that gaze over the mess she must
look. Then, without a word, she turned and went back into
the sitting-room.

He was guilty. It was written all over him. Guilty as sin.

CHAPTER TWO

SEVERAL minutes passed by before he joined her. Minutes he needed, to compose himself for what was to come, while she sat patiently waiting for him.

Strangely, she felt incredibly calm. Disconnected almost. Her heart was pumping quite steadily, and her hands lay relaxed on her lap.

He came in—minus his overcoat and jacket, his tie loosened around his neck and the top few buttons of his crisp white shirt tugged undone. He didn't glance at her but made straight for the drinks cabinet where his usual bottle of good whisky waited for him.

'Want one?' he asked.

She shook her head. He must have sensed her refusal because he didn't repeat the enquiry, nor did he look at her. He poured himself a large measure, then came to drop down in the chair opposite her.

He took a large gulp at the spirit. 'Loyal friend you've got,' was his opening gambit.

Loyal husband, she countered, but didn't bother saying it.

His eyes were closed. He had not looked directly at her once since coming into the room. His long legs were stretched out in front of him, whisky glass held loosely between both sets of fingers—long, strong fingers, with blunted nails kept beautifully clean. Like the rest of him, she supposed: long-limbed, strong-bodied and always kept scrupulously clean. Good suits, shoes, hand-made shirts and expensive silk ties. His face was paler than usual, strain finely etched into his lean bones, but it was still a very attractive face, with clean-cut squared-off lines to complement the chiselled shape of his nose and slim, determined mouth. Thirty-one now—going on thirty-two—he had always been essentially a masculine kind of man, but through the years other facets of his character had begun to write themselves into his features: an inner strength which perhaps always came with maturity, confidence, a knowledge of self-worth. The signs of power and an ability to wield it efficiently all had a place in his face now—nothing you could actually point to and say, You have that because you're successful and know it, but just a general air about the man, which placed him up there among the special set.

And controlled, she realised now. Daniel had always possessed an impressive depth of self-control, rarely lost his temper, rarely became irritated when things did not quite go his way. He had this rare ability to look at a problem and put aside its negative sides to deal only with the positive.

Which was probably what he was doing now—searching through the debris of what one phone call had done to his marriage and looking for the positive aspects he could sift out from it.

That, she supposed, epitomised Daniel Masterson, head of Master Holdings, an organisation which had over the last few years grown at a phenomenal pace, gobbling up smaller companies then spitting them out again as better, far more commercially profitable appendages to their new father company.

And he had done it all on his own, too. Built his mini-empire by maintaining that fine balance between success and disaster without once placing his family and what he had got for them at risk. He had surrounded her with luxury, cherished her almost—as a man would a possession he had a sentimental attachment to.

'What now?' he asked suddenly, lifting those darkly fringed eyelids to reveal the dove-grey beauty of his eyes to her.

So, he wasn't going to try denying it. Something inside her quivered desperately for expression, but she squashed it down. 'You tell me,' she shrugged, still with that amazingly calm exterior.

Mandy must have told him exactly what she'd done. She must have worried herself sick afterwards that the silly blind Rachel had gone and done something stupid, like hanged herself or taken a bottle of pills. How novel, she thought. How very dramatic. Poor Mandy, she mused, without an ounce of sympathy, she must have been really alarmed to dare confess to Daniel of all people!

'She's a bitch!' Daniel ground out suddenly, his own thoughts obviously not that far away from Rachel's own. He lurched forward in his chair, hands tightening around the whisky glass. Face clenched too. That tell-tale nerve jumping in his jaw. Elbows pressing into his knees as he glared furiously at the carpet between his spread feet. 'If she hadn't stuck her twisted nose in, you could have been spared all of this! It was over!' he shot out thickly. 'And if she'd only kept her big mouth shut she would have seen it was over! The bitch has always had it in for me. She's been waiting—waiting for me to slip up so she could get her claws into me! But I never thought she'd sink so low as to do it through you!'

That's right, thought Rachel. Blame Mandy. Blame everything and anything so long as it is not yourself.

'Say something, for God's sake!' he ground out, making her blink, because Daniel rarely raised his voice to her like that. And she realised that she had been sitting here just staring blankly at him but not really seeing him. Her eyes felt stuck, fixed in a permanent stare which refused to focus properly—like her emotions—locked on hold until something or someone hit the right button to set them free. She hoped it didn't happen. She had an idea she might fall apart when that happened.

It must feel like this, she pondered flatly, when someone you love dearly dies.

'I want a divorce,' she heard herself say, and was as surprised by the statement as Daniel was, because the idea of divorce hadn't so much as entered her head before she'd said it. 'You can get out. I'll keep the house and the children. You can easily afford to support us.' Another shrug, and she was amazed at her own calmness when she knew she should really be screeching at him like a fishwife.

'Don't be damned stupid!' he ground out. 'That's no damned answer and you know it.'

'Don't shout,' she censured. 'You'll wake the children.'

That seemed to do it, lift the top right off his self-control, and he surged to his feet. The glass was slapped down on the mantel top, whisky slopping over the side to splash on to white marble.

He tried to glare at her but could not hold her steady gaze long enough to gain the upper hand, so he threw himself away instead, his shoulders hunching in the white shirt so that the material became stretched taut across his back, while his hands were thrust angrily into his trouser pockets.

'Look...' he said after a moment, struggling to get hold of himself. 'It wasn't what you think—what that bitch made it out to be! It was just—' he swallowed tensely '—a flash in the pan thing—over before it really began!' He slashed violently at the air with his hand, and Rachel thought, Poor Lydia, guillotined just like that. 'I was under pressure at work. The Harvey take-over was threatening to kill everything I had worked for.' He reached out for his glass of whisky, gulping at the contents like a man with a severe thirst. 'I found I had to work night and day just to keep one step ahead of them. You were still recovering from the bad time you'd had carrying Michael, and I seemed to be spending more time with her than with you. Then the twins got measles—you wouldn't even let me employ a nurse to help you!' he flung at her in accusation. 'So you looked worn out most of the time, and I was worried about you, the sick twins, Michael who refused to sleep more than half an hour at a time, work was getting on top of me and it seemed easier on you if I made myself scarce here, kept my problems confined to the office...' He was talking about a period several months ago when she had believed that everything that could go wrong had gone wrong. She had never so much as considered adding her husband taking up with another woman to her list of problems. It had never entered her head!

'Rachel...' he murmured huskily. 'I never meant to do it. I never even wanted to do it! But she was there when I needed someone and you were not, and I just—'

'Oh—do shut up!'

Nausea hit, and she had to thrust her fist into her mouth to stop herself being sick all over their beautiful Wilton carpet. She crawled to her feet, swaying, sending him a look of hostile warning when he instinctively reached out to steady her, and he flinched away, going grey. She stumbled over to the drinks cabinet and, with her hands shaking violently, poured herself some of his whisky. She hated the stuff, but at that moment felt a dire need to feel its burning vapours shoot through her blood.

He was standing there just watching her, his pose one of violent helplessness as he watched her throw the drink to the back of her throat then stand with her head flung back, eyes closed, while she fought to maintain some control over herself.

But it was all beginning to happen now. Her body was becoming racked by a whole sea of tearing emotions. Her heart was stammering out of rhythm; she wanted to suck in some deep steadying breaths of air but found her lungs unwilling to comply. They were locked up along with the torment. Stomach muscles, ribs, all were paralysed by re-action, while her brain was the opposite, opening up and letting out all the suppressed pain and anguish, letting it taunt her, sniggering and sneering at her until she thought she would pass out.

'It's over, Rachel!' he repeated hoarsely, appealing to her in a voice she had never heard before. 'For God's sake, it's over!'

'And when was it over?' Tipping her head upright, she shrivelled him with a look. 'When my body became yours to indulge yourself in once again? Poor Lydia,' she drawled, the whisky having the desired effect and numbing her from the neck down. 'I wonder which one of us you played for the bigger fool?'

He shook his head, refusing to get into that one. 'It hap-pened,' he stated grimly, raking a shaky hand through his neat dark hair. 'I wish it hadn't, but I can't turn back the clock, no matter how much I want to. If it helps any, I'll admit to feeling utterly ashamed of myself. But as God is my witness,' he added huskily, 'I give you my word that it will never happen again.'

'Until the next time,' she muttered, and was suddenly moving to get out of the room before all the ugly feelings working inside her overflowed in a storm of bitter bile.

'No!' He made a grab for her arm, his fingers biting into her flesh as he pulled her roughly against him, hugging her close while she fought to be free. 'We have to talk this through!' he pleaded thickly. 'Please, I know you're hurting but we need—'

'How many times?' she threw at him, grinding out the words on a complete loss of control. 'How many times did you come home with the scent of her still clinging to your skin? How many times did you have to f-force yourself to make love to me after losing yourself in her!'

'No, no *no!*' he groaned, his arms like steel around her while she struggled angrily to be free. 'No, Rachel! Never! I never let it get that far!' Her huff of scornful disbelief sent him white. 'I love you, Rachel,' he stated hoarsely. 'I love you!'

For some reason that strangled declaration tipped her right over the edge and, on a totally alien burst of violence, she brought her hand up and hit him right across his unfaithful face.

It rocked him—enough to make him let go of her. Rachel stepped back out of reach, her eyes at that moment revealing a murderous kind of hatred that no one who knew her would ever have believed her capable of. And Daniel stood stock-still, digesting the full horror of that look, and was silent.

Without another word she turned and left the room. At the door to their bedroom she paused, then moved away, towards Michael's room.

The child didn't stir when she entered. Rachel walked over to him, leaned gently on the side of the cot and just stared blindly down at her younger son, wondering if the intolerable ache inside her could actually make her physically ill.

Then the dam burst, and on a sob she only just managed to contain while she stumbled over to the single bed which would be Michael's when he grew older, she crawled beneath the Paddington Bear duvet to muffle the sounds of

her wretched sobs, sobs which went on and on until she
slid into a dark dull sleep.

Morning came with the gurgling of Michael, awake but
content at the moment to kick playfully in his cot. And it
took Rachel several moments to remember why she was
sleeping in his room rather than in her own bed with
Daniel.

There was a single crashing feeling inside her as memory
returned, then she felt herself go calm again, last night's
storm of weeping seeming to have emptied her clean of
everything.

She got up, grimacing when she realised she was still
wearing the same clothes she'd had on when Mandy called.
A hand went to her head, finding the elastic band still partly
holding a clump of hair in a tangle of silky knots. She
tugged it out then shook her long tresses free. She looked
a mess, felt a mess—she hadn't even bothered removing
her trainers! She did that now, sitting down on the bed to
pull the hot and uncomfortable shoes from her feet just as
the baby noticed her and let out a delighted shriek.

She went to bend over his cot, his welcoming smile a
balm to her aching heart. And for a while she just immersed
herself in enjoying him, tickling his tummy and murmuring
all those little nothings mothers shared with their babies,
which only babies and mothers understood.

This was hers, she thought wretchedly. No matter what
else life wanted to take from her, it could never take away
the love of her children.

This, she declared silently, is mine.

He was soaking wet, and she stripped him before attempting to lift him from his cot. Michael was always lively
in the mornings, chirping away to himself, bouncing up and
down against her while she carried him through to the small

bathroom to run the few inches of bath water needed to freshen him up for the day.

She took him, wrapped snugly in a towel, back to his room to dress him. Normally she would then take him downstairs for his breakfast without bothering to get dressed herself. That usually waited until they were all out of the way—at work or at school—but there was no way she could greet the twins looking as she did. They were just too sharp not to wonder out loud why she was still wearing the same clothes she'd had on the night before.

But it took a great gathering together of her courage to enter the room where she knew Daniel would only just be stirring from sleep. She let herself in quietly, searching the gloom for a glimpse of his lean bulk huddled beneath the duvet.

He wasn't there, and it was then that she heard the telltale sounds coming from the bathroom. He appeared a moment later, already dressed in a clean white shirt and the trousers of his iron-grey suit. He saw her almost at once and came to an abrupt halt.

In all the years of knowing him, she had never felt so vulnerable in his presence, or so aware of her tumbled appearance: her puffy eyes, made so by too much weeping, her tousled hair hanging limp and untidy around her pale face.

Nor so aware of him: his height, the length of his long, straight body and the tightness of its superbly honed muscles. Wide chest, flat stomach, narrow hips, long powerful legs with...

No. Dry-mouthed, she flicked her gaze warily up to clash with his.

He looked tired, as though he hadn't slept much. He would have been thinking, working things out, trying to find the right solution to an impossible situation. He was good at that—making a success out of a disaster. It was the most fundamental source of his outstanding business success.

His gaze lingered on her face, his own a defensive mask. He had just shaved; his stubborn chin looked clean and shiny-smooth. Rachel caught the familiar scent of his aftershave, and felt her senses stir in response to it. Sexual magnetism held no boundaries, she acknowledged bitterly. Even now, while she was hating and despising him, she was disturbingly aware of him as the man she had loved for so long and so blindly.

Shifting jerkily, she moved over to the bed, lifting a knee on to the soft mattress so that she could lay Michael in the middle. It was only then that she realised that the bed had not been slept in, and the only evidence that Daniel had used it at all was in the imprint of his body on the smooth peach duvet.

Michael was kicking madly, trying to catch his father's attention—attention that was firmly fixed on Rachel. The baby let out a frustrated cry, going red in the face in his effort to pull himself into a sitting position, and Rachel smiled instinctively at his efforts, capturing a waving hand and feeling the instant tug as the child tried to use it for leverage.

Daniel came over to the bed, stretching out to recline on the other side of their son and automatically reaching for the other small hand, which was all Michael needed to lever himself into a sitting position.

'Da!' he said triumphantly, twisting free of both of them so that he could pat his satisfaction on the soft duvet.

Rachel kept her eyes firmly on her son while she felt the searing appeal in Daniel's gaze sting into her pale cheeks. 'Rachel please look at me.' It was a gruff plea that twisted at something wretched inside her, but one she refused to comply with, shaking her head.

'No,' she whispered, keeping her voice level with effort, and Daniel sighed heavily, then reached for Michael, lifting him to kiss the soft baby cheek before placing him further up the bed.

Alerted, Rachel moved to get up, but Daniel was too quick for her, his hand circling her wrist and pulling gently until he had hauled her across the small gap separating them, then enclosing her in the warm strength of his arms.

It's not fair! she thought piteously as her insides dipped and dived with a need to immerse herself in the comfort he was offering her. Her chest became tight, then began to throb with the need to weep, and she let free a constricted gulp in an effort to stop the flood.

'Don't,' he murmured unsteadily.

It had been the wrong thing to say, because the instant he showed her tenderness her control went haywire and she was sobbing deeply into his shoulder. He tightened his arms around her, and lowered his head on to hers. 'Sorry,' he kept saying, over and over. 'Sorry, sorry, sorry...'

But it wasn't enough, was it? It would never be enough. He had killed everything. Love, faith, trust, respect—all gone, and sorry would never bring them back to life again.

'I'm all right now,' she mumbled, making the monumental effort to pull herself together and draw away from him.

But his hold tightened. 'I know I've hurt you unbearably, Rachel,' he murmured, trying to keep a rein on his own distress. She could feel the tension in his chest, in the erratic thump of his heart. 'But don't make any rash decisions while you're in such an...' Emotional state, she guessed he was going to say, but he stopped himself. 'We have everything going for us if you'll just give it another chance.

Don't throw it all away because of one stupid mistake on my part. You can't throw it all away!' he insisted thickly.

'I didn't do the throwing away,' she countered, and this time, when she pulled, he let her go, his eyes dark and bleak as he watched her get up from the bed to begin moving around the room searching out fresh clothes, an electric current of suppressed emotion following her as she went from wardrobe to drawers then back again without really being aware of what she was choosing to wear.

All those years of blind trust she had given him, years of quiet understanding and acceptance of his deep personal need to achieve his ambitions. Through all those years she had stayed at home like some pampered pet dog and, so long as he gave her frequent pats of affection, fed the few basic needs she had, like food to eat and water to drink and the occasional trip out in the evening, she had been quite content with her lot.

What a pathetic creature you are! she jeered at herself now. What an utter bore!

Michael let out a wail, and they both started. He wanted his breakfast, and the playful game he had been having with himself had now turned into a demand for some attention.

Rachel stood hovering in the middle of the room, with her clean clothes clutched in her hands while her bemused mind grappled with the problem of what she should do next. Get dressed first or see to Michael first. A simple choice, but she couldn't seem to make it.

It was, in the end, Daniel who lifted the baby into his arms and walked towards the bedroom door. 'I'll see to him,' he said. 'Take your time. It's still quite early.' He let himself out, and Rachel literally sagged beneath the strain of it all.

Breakfast was awful. She seemed intent on flying off the handle at the slightest provocation: from Kate for talking too much, Sam for not putting enough milk on his Weetabix so the biscuits congealed in his dish like two cement bricks which he proceeded to hack at with zeal. She put too much coffee in the filter bag so that it tasted so bitter it was barely drinkable. In the end, angry with herself for over-reacting to everything, frustrated with her inability to cope with her own distraught emotions, she turned on Sam, remembering that he had left his computer out the night before with his selection of games spread all over the floor. By the time she'd finished Sam was stiff and pale, Kate was appalled, Michael silenced and Daniel... Well, Daniel just looked grim. The rest of the morning routine went off in total silence. The children looking openly re-lieved when Daniel eventually sent them off to their rooms to collect their school things.

'There was absolutely no reason for you to let fly at Sam like that!' Daniel gritted as soon as there was only Michael left to listen. 'You know as well as I do that he's usually the tidiest one of us all! You'll have all three of them a bag of nerves if you don't watch out,' he warned. 'They're good kids. Well-behaved kids for most of the time. I won't let you take it out on them because you're angry with me!'

She whirled on him. 'And since when are you around enough to know how they behave?' she threw at him, see-ing to her deep and bitter satisfaction that he stiffened as the thrust went home. 'You see them at breakfast, but only from behind your precious *Financial Times*! You don't even know you have three children most of the time! Y-You love them like you l-love that...Lowry painting you bought—when you remember you've got them, that is. So don't...don't you dare start telling me how to bring up *my* children when as a father you're damned useless!'

What was happening to her? she wondered as she took a jerky step back and Daniel lurched angrily to his feet, glowering at her across the kitchen table and looking fit to hit her. I'm cracking up! she realised dizzily. I'm going to shatter into a million tiny pieces and I don't know if I can stop it!

'You can accuse me of many things, Rachel,' Daniel was murmuring roughly. 'And most of them I probably deserve. But you cannot accuse me of not loving *our* children!'

'Really?' she questioned in sarcastic scorn. 'You only married me in the first place because you got me pregnant with the twins! And even little Michael was a mistake you took your time coming to terms with—!'

His fist slamming down on the table-top stopped her in mid-flow, and her eyelashes flickered nervously as she watched him swing his long body around the table, shifting the heavy pine a good foot off its usual setting when his thigh caught the corner in his haste to reach her. The violence in the air was tangible. Rachel could taste it on her suddenly dry lips as he approached her with his hands outstretched as if he intended throttling her.

As the very last second he changed his mind and grabbed her shoulders instead. It cost him an effort; she could feel him trembling with the need to choke the bitterness right out of her even as he suppressed the urge. 'He's too young to understand the implications of what you've just said,' he rasped out harshly, nodding towards a fascinated Michael. 'But if the twins overheard you, if you've given them any reason at all to think I don't love them, I'll…'

He didn't finish—didn't need to. Rachel knew exactly what he was threatening. He glared at her for a moment longer, then unclipped his hands from her and turned to walk out of the room.

Rachel gulped in a deep breath of air and it was only as she did so that she realised she had stopped breathing altogether. It was pure instinctive need for comfort that made her pick Michael up and cuddle him close.

She felt ashamed of herself, and angry, too, because in lashing out wildly at Daniel like that she had given him the right to attack her when, until that moment, she'd had everything stacked her way.

CHAPTER THREE

IT WAS the weekend before the twins really began to notice that things weren't quite as they were used to seeing them. And as usual it was the sharp-eyed and more outspoken Kate who wanted to know the reason why.

'Why are you sleeping in Michael's room, Mummy?' she demanded on Sunday morning while they all lingered around the breakfast table, as was their habit on the one day they had to be lazy in the morning.

They had only discovered her new sleeping arrangements because Michael had slept later this morning and, stupidly, Rachel had overslept along with him. Several nights of restless turning in the small bed while her mind tormented her with everything painful and self-pitying it could throw at her had left her exhausted, and last night when she had crawled beneath the Paddington Bear duvet she had achieved—to her relief—an instant black-out, which remained deep and dreamless right up until Sammy came to bounce on her to wake her up.

She still felt haggard, because what the sleep had made up for in hours, it had not made up for in spiritual relief. Wherever her dreams had gone off to last night, they had not eased her aching heart, or her anger, or the waves of bitterness and the soul-crushing self-abhorrence she was experiencing at the way she was letting the whole thing just drag on without doing something about it. Daniel had advised her to make no decisions until she was feeling less emotional and, like the pathetic creature she was, she had used that advice as an excuse to fall into a state of limbo where life had taken on colourless shapes of muted greys and nothing came into full focus any more.

Daniel looked no better, the same strain pulling at the clean-cut lines of his face too. He had been home by six-thirty every night since their cosy world had exploded around them. She suspected that the reason for this was her criticism of him as a father rather than a means to prove to her that his affair was over. She knew she'd hit him on the raw there.

So now he came home early enough to take over the bathing and putting to bed of the children while Rachel prepared their dinner. And on the surface everything appeared perfectly normal, as they both made an effort to hide their colossal problems from their children.

Until quietness engulfed the house—then they would eat their prepared meal in stiff silence, Daniel's few attempts at conversation quashed by her refusal to take him up on them. So he would disappear into his study as soon as he possibly could, and she would clear the remnants of a poorly eaten meal, feed her bleeding emotions on unreserved bouts of self-pity, then go to bed in Michael's room, feeling lonelier and more depressed as the days went by.

She was still labouring beneath the weight of a nullifying shock. She could acknowledge that even as she continued in her zombie-like existence. And Daniel just watched, grim-faced and silent, waiting, she knew, for the moment when she would crack wide apart.

Now she had her daughter's curious enquiry to deal with, and as the truth flooded into her mind and sent what vestige of colour she had left fleeing from her face, she managed an acceptable reply. 'Michael is teething again.'

The corner of Daniel's Sunday paper twitched, and Rachel knew he was listening, maybe even watching her over the top of that twitched corner. She didn't glance his way to find out. She didn't really care what he was doing.

Blonde-haired, blue-eyed, the uncanny image of her mother, Kate nodded understandingly. Michael's teeth had been the scourge of their nights' rest before—although Rachel had not so much as considered swapping beds to be closer to him then. But that did not seem to occur to Kate, who was already turning her attention to her darling daddy.

'I bet you miss having Mummy to cuddle, Daddy,' she remarked, getting down from her chair to go and climb on to Daniel's knee, her long hair flying as she blithely shoved his newspaper aside and made herself comfortable in those big, infinitely secure arms, with the certain knowledge that she was welcome. 'If you'd just told me,' she murmured, with typical Kate guile, 'I would have come and cuddled you instead.'

Tension leaped to life, unspoken words and acid replies flying about the room without being captured.

'That's nice of you, princess.' Daniel folded his paper away so that he could give his adored daughter his full attention. 'But I think I can manage for a little while longer without feeling completely rejected.'

If that last remark had been meant as a message to Rachel, she ignored it, and sat there sipping at her coffee without revealing the effort it cost her to do it.

He was sitting there dressed only in his blue towelling robe, and the cluster of dark hair at his chest curled upwards from between the gaping lapels. He dropped a kiss on his daughter's silky cheek, his smile so openly loving that Rachel felt her stomach tighten then sink, as jealousy, like nothing she had ever experienced before, shot through her, forcing her abruptly to her feet, appalled by what was going on inside her!

Jealous of your own daughter! she castigated herself. How bitter and twisted can you get?

Sheer desperation made her start gathering pots together. Daniel's watchful gaze lifted to her face, and she couldn't stop herself from looking back at him. Something must have shown in the bitter blue glint of her eyes, because his own narrowed speculatively before she spun away and deliberately ruined the relaxed atmosphere by banging around the kitchen, clearing up.

She became even more embittered when her tactics to shift them all didn't work. In fact they simply ignored her as Sam was drawn into conversation with Kate and Daniel, and even Michael, when he insisted on coming out of his high-chair, was promptly placed on Daniel's spare knee where he chattered blithely away to them all in his usual gibberish.

She couldn't stand it. Something in the cosy little scene gnawed into her ragged nerves. She felt left out, alienated by her inability to go over there and join in as she would normally have done. Lydia stood in her way like some huge unscalable wall, blocking her off from her family, from the love and affection she had always taken for granted as her right.

Giving up on clearing up before she broke something, she turned and left the room with a mumbled, 'I'm going to make the beds,' knowing no one heard her, and feeling even more cast out.

She was standing in the middle of their bedroom, just staring blankly into space, when Daniel came in. With a nervy jerk she moved off towards the *en suite* bathroom, trying to look as if that had been where she was making for when he opened the door. When she came out again Daniel was still there, standing at the window with his hands thrust into the deep pockets of his robe. He was big and lean and looked so damned appealing that she wanted to throw something at him—anything to ease this awful ache she was suffering inside.

Forcing herself to ignore him, she began tidying things away. She wanted to make his bed but was now avoiding so much as looking at it while he was present. It had taken on the proportions of a monster since Mandy's call, and each morning she'd had to force herself to come in here to fluff up the pillows and shake out the duvet. It smelled of Daniel—that clean male smell that was uniquely his. It ignited senses she would far rather remained dormant, especially since she wanted to believe he had killed them. But, if anything, her awareness of anything purporting to Daniel seemed to have been intensified rather than dulled. She had found betrayal fed a hateful awareness inside her, and anger fed desire, and pain fed her ability to torment herself with all those feelings she had previously taken for granted.

He turned slightly, watching her in silence as she moved around the room. After a while, when the throbbing silence threatened to choke the very atmosphere in the room, he came to stand in front of her, blocking her path. 'Rachel…' he said gently, willing her to look at him while she was equally determined not to. She looked at the floor between them instead. 'You have remembered I'm in Birmingham all next week?'

No, she had not remembered. But she did so now. Anger at his daring to put his business first, while his private life was in crisis, took the form of ice-cold efficiency. 'What shall I pack?' Was Lydia going? Was it to be a nice cosy double room for two for a week, with no hostile atmosphere to spoil their fun?

Her heart slammed against her breast and she had to fight not to take a step back from him. It would be like conceding some small if obscure point to him to back away, so she stood stiffly, eyes lowered, face a wretched blank.

Physically, it was the closest they'd been to each other since the night the bomb fell on her, and she was tingling all over with that bitter sense of awareness of him.

'Anything,' he dismissed impatiently. She had always packed his case for him when he went off on one of his trips—lovingly folding freshly laundered shirts and carefully counted socks, underwear, handkerchiefs, ties, several suits to wear. And even now, while she silently prayed for him to move out of her way so that she could put a safer distance between them, and her mood wanted to tell him to pack his own bloody case, she was making a mental list of everything he usually required.

Conditioned you are, Rachel! she scoffed at herself. Expertly programmed.

He didn't move, and the tension between them became intolerable. 'Will you be all right?' he asked at last, as though the question was a reluctant one, one he did not want to voice in case she used it as an excuse to attack him. He had been very careful this week to give her nothing which could start the avalanche. 'I...I could get my mother to come and stay if you feel the need for company or—'

'And why should I be in need of company?' She flashed him a bitter look. 'I've managed before when you've been away and I shall manage this time, no doubt, without the need of a baby-sitter.'

He took the taunt about her being one of his helpless children with a tightening of his jaw but without taking her up on it. 'I was not questioning your ability to cope,' he said quietly. 'But you look—tired. And I just wondered if—with everything—you would rather not be on your own right now, that's all.'

Tired, she repeated inside her head. She didn't just look

tired, she looked haggard! 'Is your secretary going with you?' Damn, she hadn't meant to ask that question. In fact, she had been determined not to so much as breathe it!

'Yes, but—'

'Then I won't have to concern myself about your comfort, will I?'

'Rachel,' he sighed, 'Lydia isn't—'

'I don't want to know.' She pushed by him, preferring to let her body brush against his than to stand here any longer enduring this kind of conversation.

'Why did you ask the damned question, then?' he barked, then made a concerted effort to control himself again. 'Rachel, we *have* to talk about this!'

She was making the bed now, gritting her teeth and getting on with the job because it was the only thing left in the room to do.

'It can't go on any longer.' He appealed for common sense. 'You must see that! Kate has noticed, which means she'll be on the alert from now on, watching, calculating how long you stay in Michael's room when—'

'And we must not upset your darling Kate, must we?' she flashed, then almost cried out in horror at herself. How could she be feeling jealous of her own child! Blindly, horribly jealous of that poor sweet child who possessed her father's love by right!

'Uncalled for, Rachel,' Daniel grimly rebuked, and she agreed, sickeningly so.

The bed was made. Now she could get out of...

'Let me just explain about Lydia,' Daniel said carefully. 'She isn't—'

'Are you planning on being here for the rest of the day?'

That threw him. It shut him up about his precious Lydia, too. 'Yes.' He frowned in puzzlement. 'Why?'

'Because I want to go out, and if you're here it saves me

having to ask your mother to come and mind the children.'
Why she had said that, Rachel had no idea. It had not been
a conscious decision to go anywhere. But, once said, she
found the idea of being on her own for a while—completely
on her own—something that was suddenly vital to her sanity.

She made a dive for the wardrobe, trembling in her sudden urgency to get out of the house and away from them
all. She dragged out the first thing that came to hand—her
rainproof anorak. Daniel seemed momentarily stunned, and
just stood there staring at her for the time it took her to
shrug the coat on.

Then he sprang to life. 'If you want to go out somewhere,
Rachel, you only had to say so!'

The zip was being stubborn and she stood, head bent,
grappling with it. It was so hot in here today! Struggling
with the zip was making her hot. Was it possible to suffocate in one's emotions? she wondered frantically. Because that was what she felt she was doing. People closing
her in, walls...feelings.

'Give me ten minutes while I get dressed myself, then
we'll all go out together...'

Shoes! She hadn't put on any shoes! On another jerk,
she was crouching on the floor and scrabbling around in
the bottom of her wardrobe while Daniel seemed glued to
the spot in stunned confusion.

She found her black leather boots and sat down on the
carpet to pull them on, tucking the bottoms of her narrow
jeans inside with fingers that shook.

'Rachel...don't do this!' It must have hit him then that
she really meant to go out alone because his voice was
rough and urgent. 'You've never gone out without us before,' he rasped. 'Wait until we can all...'

She was vaguely listening to him, though only from behind a wall of dark self-absorption. But one small part of what he had said got through. Daniel was right, and she never did go anywhere without one or all of them accompanying her! If it wasn't Daniel, then it was the children—or his mother! All her adult life she had lived beneath the protective wing of others. Her parents first, her more outward-going friends, Daniel! Mostly Daniel.

She was almost twenty-five years old, for God's sake! And here she was, a dowdy little housewife with three children and a husband who...

'I'm going alone!' she raked at him. 'It won't hurt you to have the children to yourself for once!'

'I never said it would!' he sighed impatiently. 'But Rachel, you've never—'

'Exactly!' Jumping up she spun away from him when he made a grab for her, concern raking at his taut face. 'While you've been busy making your fortune, chasing your personal rainbows and having your affairs,' she threw at him bitterly, 'I've been quietly sitting here in this damned house—stagnating!'

'Don't be stupid!' He made another lunge for her wrist and caught it this time. 'This is ridiculous. You're behaving like a child! It—'

'But that's just it, Daniel, don't you see?' she cried, appealing for his understanding even while rebellion ran crazily through her veins. 'That is exactly what I am—a child! A very spoiled, very overprotected child! I never grew up because I've never been given the chance to grow up! I was seventeen when I married you!' she choked out wretchedly. 'Still at school! And, before you came along, my parents used to wrap me in cotton wool! My God, what a shock it must have been to them when they discovered their sweet little innocent daughter had been sleeping with the big bad wolf without them knowing it!'

He laughed; she knew he couldn't help it because her description of himself was so damned accurate that it was either laugh or weep.

'So, I get pregnant,' she went on tightly, 'and swap one set of parents for another set—you and your mother!'

'Now that's not true, Rachel,' Daniel protested. 'I've never looked on you as a child. I—'

'Liar!' she declared. 'You damned hypocritical liar! And you know what makes you a liar, Daniel?' she demanded shrilly. 'It's the way you're beginning to panic because I want to spend some time on my own—because it could be Kate making the demand by the way you're reacting!'

'This is crazy!' he breathed, shaking his dark head as though he couldn't believe this conversation was taking place.

'Crazy?' she repeated. 'You think it's crazy? Well, how the hell do you think I feel knowing that I let you do this to me? I actually sat back and let you treat me like this— and look where it's got me! I've ended up a twenty-four-year-old has-been with three children and a husband who's already bored out of his mind with me! Oh, please let me go!'

On a wretched sob she twisted herself free, and made for the door. And it was with the walls around her looking strangely topsy-turvy that she stumbled down the stairs and through the front door, only just aware enough of what she was doing to remember to snatch up her purse from the hall table as she flew past it.

Her white Escort was blocked in by Daniel's black BMW so she simply ran off down the drive, away from the smart modern detached house that had been brand-new when they moved into it five years ago, one of a set built on a small but exclusive estate in one of London's executive belts. A house she had loved from the moment she walked into it because it offered them all so much more space after the tiny inner-city terraced house they had rented before.

Now she wanted only to get as far away from it as she could, and she hurried down the quiet tree-lined street and on to the main road, aware that Daniel would not come after her. It would take him ages to dress himself and three children before he could bundle them in the car to come looking for her. But knowing that did not stop her jumping on the first bus which came along.

Central London it was making for, so central London was where she was going to go. She sat staring miserably out of the bus window, where dust and grime and dried raindrops formed unsightly patterns across her vision. She could just make out the park where she often took the children to play—or was it they who took her? She didn't know any more. She didn't feel as if she knew anything for a certainty any more.

Collar turned up against the cool, late September air, hands stuffed into her pockets, blond head lowered, she walked the Sunday-quiet streets of London, lost inside a great pitiless sea of misery, her feelings becoming more battered as that cruel inner eye opened wider and wider to give her a ruthlessly honest look at who the real Rachel Masterson was.

She was a twenty-four-year-old woman who had become emotionally stuck at the age of seventeen, she decided. She, in her fantasy-like existence, had believed Daniel loved her because he made love to her, and she had never once questioned that love.

But she did now. And, though it galled her to do it, she found he had to be admired for the way he had calmly accepted responsibility when she became pregnant.

Daniel had simply paid his dues for getting himself involved with a young innocent. And if he did lead a separate life outside the one he shared with her, then maybe he considered that his due.

And a separate life it was, she accepted grimly. For it was only now, as she felt her cosy world rocking precariously on the very axis which supported it, that she realised that he hadn't ever drawn her into sharing with him that faster, more exciting life he led beyond the confines of his neat, well-ordered marriage. A marriage he had created for her to play at being housewife and mother to his children because it was what she'd wanted to do.

Did she only play? She didn't even know that any more.

Hours she walked, hours and hours without noticing them drift by. Hours just thinking, hurting, fielding the wretchedness of her own misery, until sheer exhaustion turned her feet towards home.

She caught a taxi, because she was tired, and because she was cold, and because home was suddenly the one place in the world she most wanted to be.

Which left her feeling somewhat defeated, because it also meant that her short grasp for freedom had done her no good at all.

CHAPTER FOUR

DANIEL was sprawled out on the sitting-room sofa when she entered the room. He had a book thrust in front of his face and was giving a good impression of someone who had not shifted his position in hours. He made no effort to acknowledge her, and after a short pause while she waited in defiance for the expected explosion which never came, she shut the door and went into the kitchen. She was smiling to herself as she went though, because he hadn't fooled her for a moment with that air of indifference—she had seen the sitting-room curtain twitch as she paid the cabby. For some reason his need to hide his concern put a lighter step in her walk.

The coffee dripped through its filter into the jug and Rachel watched it absently. Her coat was thrown across the back of one of the kitchen chairs, her boots standing neatly by the door.

He entered like a cat stalking its prey on silent tread, shoeless, his casual trousers a snug fit to his flat hips, his dark green fleeced cotton shirt tucked loosely into them.

'You'd better call Mandy,' he muttered, kicking out a chair and dropping into it.

'Why?' Rachel glanced at him and then away again, her tone lacking a single spark of interest in his reply.

'Because I've been giving her hell all day, believing you were there and she wasn't telling me.'

'And how do you know for sure it wasn't exactly like that?'

There was a pause before he said reluctantly, 'Because I

50

got my mother to watch the children and went round to her flat to see for myself.'

'So now both your mother and Mandy know I escaped for the day,' she noted drily. The coffee was ready, and she lifted a pretty painted mug down from the rack.

'You can't blame me for worrying about you when you went off half-cocked like that,' he grunted, looking uncomfortable.

Good! she thought. That should teach him not to treat me like a child. I might be one, but it doesn't mean I want to be treated like one. And, anyway, it might do him some good to realise that his predictable little wife is not so predictable after all.

She sat down opposite him, hugging the hot mug in her hands because they still felt cold. Daniel slouched in his chair, his forearms resting on the table and his fingers twining tensely as though he was struggling with something uncomfortable inside. His head was bent, his hair untidy—as though he had spent the day raking his fingers through the thick black mass.

She had never seen him like this before, lacking his usual poise.

'Your parents know too,' he said suddenly. 'I rang them when I couldn't think of anywhere else you could have gone. They've been expecting you to turn up in Altrincham all afternoon. You'd better give them a ring to let them know you're OK.'

So, it needed just three places to check before he ran out of ideas where to look for her. What did that tell her about herself? Having done enough self-analysis for one day, she decided to put that one in abeyance for the time being.

'I'll tell you what, Daniel,' she suggested instead. 'Why don't *you* call them back, since it was you who worried them all in the first place? Call your mother—and Mandy too while you're at it. I have no wish to speak to her personally,' she added coolly.

'Who—my mother?' He sounded startled.

'Mandy,' she drawled sarcastically, surprised, because he had to be feeling knocked off balance a bit to make that kind of mistake. Daniel was not usually stupid. 'You brought her back into this mess after making much of her learning to mind her own business, so you call her back, if you think she's that bothered.'

'We were all bothered!' he snapped, sweeping her an angry glance.

'I'm not suicidal, you know,' she informed him levelly, sipping at her coffee and feeling more at ease the more tense he became. 'I might have been a dumb-brained fool where you're concerned, but I won't be forfeiting the rest of my life because of it.'

'I never so much as considered you were!' he grunted, adding gruffly, 'I never considered you dumb-brained either.'

'Of course you did,' she argued. 'When you bothered wasting valuable time considering me at all, that is,' she added witheringly.

He sucked in a short breath, fighting not to rise to the bait. 'Where did you go?' he asked.

'To London,' she told him, bringing his head up sharply.

'Where in London?' he demanded. 'Doing what? You've been out since ten o'clock this morning. That's almost twelve hours! What the hell did you find to do in London with all the stores closed that could take twelve bloody hours?'

'Maybe I found myself a man!' she taunted, watching with a mild fascination as his face drained of all colour. 'It isn't that difficult to pick one up, you know.' She twisted the knife while he was still off balance from her first stab at him. 'Maybe I decided to take a leaf out of your book and go in search of some—comfort, because the going at home suddenly got tough!'

He shot to his feet, knocking the chair to the ground with a clatter. 'Stop it!' he rasped, raking a hand through his tousled hair. 'Stop trying to score points off me, Rachel! It isn't like you to take pleasure in hurting others.'

No, it wasn't, she agreed. Funny really, how one's nature could alter virtually overnight. Whereas once she would never have dreamed of striking out at anyone, she was suddenly consumed with the desire to cut to the raw! She didn't even care that her parents would be worrying about her. Or that Daniel's mother was probably sitting in her flat not a mile away from here on tenterhooks, waiting to hear that her darling Rachel had returned safely to the fold.

'Then go and make your phone calls,' she advised, returning her attention to the drink in her hands. 'Then you won't have to listen, will you?'

He glared at her across the length of the kitchen table, looking ready to reach across and shake her if she provoked him so much as an inch further. Then, surprisingly, he sighed harshly and turned and walked out of the room. She heard his study door close with a suppressed violence and grimaced to herself.

She went upstairs to use the bathroom while he was busy on the telephone, stuffing her long hair into a shower-cap and taking a quick shower, only then remembering, as she was hurriedly tying her fluffy long white bathrobe around her so that she could get out of the bedroom before he came up, that she had not packed his case.

On a silent curse she hurried into the bedroom, to dig out his soft black leather all-purpose suit-bag, and laid it on the bed to unbuckle the straps.

'You don't need to do that,' his tight voice informed her from the bedroom doorway. 'I cancelled this afternoon.'

'Oh, dear,' she drawled as he closed the bedroom door. 'Lydia will be disappointed.'

That's it! he might as well have shouted, the way his lean body jerked as though someone had cracked a whip at him. Rachel knew a moment's real panic as she stared into his face, white with angry frustration, then was given no opportunity to do anything other than gasp as he reached her in two strides and dragged her against him.

'I can't take any more of this,' he muttered. 'Nothing I can say or do is going to change your mind about me!'

'But I have changed my mind about you!' she countered, afraid of the hectic glitter she could see burning in his eyes, but refusing to show it. 'I used to think you were a saint, but now I know you're a bastard!'

'Then a bastard I will be!' he snarled, and dropped his mouth down on to hers.

He used no persuasion, no gentle coaxing to get what he wanted from her, but just forced her tight lips apart by sheer brute force. She groaned in protest, his fingers like clamps on her aching shoulders, holding her up to him while the rest of her body curved frantically away from him in an effort not to come into full contact with his traitorous frame.

His tongue snaked into her mouth and she tried to bite down on it, but he was expecting it, and just increased the pressure against her lips until they were pressed hard back against her teeth, then slid his tongue sensually over hers. She shuddered, her hands closing into fists that she pushed into his muscled ribcage in a hopeless attempt to try to stem the unbidden firing in her blood which told her she was vulnerable to him; even though she hated him to the very depths of her being, she was still vulnerable to this.

Another groan, and she kicked out at him with a bare foot. It made no difference. He was not going to release her, and her straining body was simply a supple wand he bent to his will. Taking one hand off her shoulder to loop it around her slender waist, he moved the other to her hair, winding the long silken swath around his fingers in a tight coil before he tugged cruelly to keep her mouth turned up to receive his kiss.

She was burning up inside her thick towelling robe, her body stinging with a prickly heat that made it all the more sensitive to the hard body now clamped tightly against her. And it wasn't just her temperature that had gone haywire, it was her senses—her senses firing out of control, wanting this, swarming towards it like bees to the sweetest honey ever made on this earth.

It's not fair! she thought wretchedly, it's just not fair that he can still do this to me! She hated herself—and despised him for making her acknowledge her own weakness.

'Damn you!' she cursed, when at last he came up for air. His cheeks were flushed, his eyes dark pools of bitter frustration as they glared down at her.

'Yes,' he agreed on a raw, driven hiss. 'Damn me to hell! But you want me, Rachel. You want me so badly that you're literally choking on it. So what does that make you in this nightmare?'

She flinched, the full bitter truth in his cruel taunt making something she had been holding on to for days now snap inside her—she actually felt it give, and she leaned back against his constricting arm, careless of the painful pull it placed on her scalp, careless of everything now as, with an animal growl that was as alien to her as it was to the man who was goading her, she went for him with her nails.

Good reflexes saved his face from serious damage. His head snapped back out of harm's way just in time, and her nails only managed to graze his neck from jawbone to the open collar of his shirt.

'You little cat!' he choked, long strands of strong silken hair clinging to his fingers when he released her to put his hand to his scratched neck.

'I hate you!'

'Good,' he grunted, and he pulled her back against him. 'That will make it easier when I take you, when the method of taking will make no difference to how you feel about me.'

'That's right!' she jeered. 'Why not add rape to adultery?'

'Rape?' he derided harshly. 'Since when did I ever have to resort to rape with you?' His tone sent shivers of self-revulsion rushing through her. 'In all my life I've never known a more sexually eager woman than you!'

'What—even Lydia?'

She was thrust unceremoniously away from him, his arms raking a wide, defeated arc before both hands went up to grip his nape as if he had to hold on to something or hit her. And he stared at her with something close to torment burning in his eyes. 'Stop it, Rachel,' he whispered thickly. 'Stop trying to rile me into doing something we'll both regret!'

Was that what she was doing? Riling him like some she-devil, wanting him to take her in anger—to prove to her totally that he was all the rotten things she was thinking about him?

Yes, she realised, that was exactly what she was doing as she continued to stand there, goading him with the hot glitter of her eyes when really she should be getting out of here while the chance to escape was good. She wanted to feed the hatred she felt towards him—the anguish, the bitter disappointment she was feeling, and last of all the great lump of pain that had not shifted from the centre of her chest since Mandy called.

And she heard herself, as if from the other end of a long dark tunnel, goad him further. 'Then get out!' she told him shrilly. 'Why don't you just do the honourable thing, Daniel, and get the hell out of here! No one's making you stay! There's nothing left here to stop you going to your precious Lydia!'

'Will you stop mentioning her bloody name?' he grated.

'Lydia,' she chanted instantly. 'Lydia—Lydia—*Lydia*!'

Something flared in his eyes—anguish?—gone before it could be proved. Then he was reaching for her again, top lip curling bitterly as he pulled her hard against him.

'No,' he muttered. 'You—you—*you*!'

And in a single swift movement he had turned them both and tipped them off balance so that they landed in a tangle of limbs on the bed behind them.

What followed was less loving than anything could be. It was a battle. A battle to see who could arouse whom more. A battle of the senses where each deliberate caress was answered by a matching one, each clash of their hot angry eyes taunted—scorned. The more aroused the one became, the more the other fed it, driving each other on some crazy helter-skelter ride of pained, fractured emotions.

There was a moment within it all when Daniel seemed to make a flailing grab for sanity, snatching at his self-control and making to move away from her. But Rachel saw it coming, and on a flash of blinding panic which seemed to have its roots in a terrible fear of losing him altogether, she reached for him, her mouth finding his with an urgency that made him groan out her name in a wretched plea against her marauding lips. But she took no notice. And it was suddenly Rachel playing the seducer, Rachel

conducting things from desperate beginning to wild tumultuous end, leaving the man beneath her shaken and spent
while she could only crawl away to huddle in a ball of
miserable frustration, her senses clawing for a release they
had been denied. And she felt appalled, disgusted with herself.

So who won the battle? she asked herself bleakly. Neither had won, she concluded. She just felt sickened by her
own wanton behaviour and the knowledge that she had
been driven to it by a fear of losing him—no matter what
he had done—and another driving need to feel him lose
himself completely in her. It had been essential—essential
to her sanity to know that, no matter how many Lydias
there had been for him, she, little boring Rachel, could still
turn him inside out with desire for her.

And, she had to acknowledge finally, she had wanted
him, wanted him with a need which had left no room for
pride or self-respect. But in the end even that had not been
enough to help her find at least some release from the pressures that had been culminating inside her over the last
terrible week. It was as though her wounded soul refused
to let her give him that final conquest. Would it ever again?

A single tear slid out from the corner of each staring eye
and ran their slow meandering way down her pale cheeks.
She, in her twisted need to prove some obscure point to
herself, had lost in the end, because what she had gained
in discovering she could still rock him she had lost in her
own failure to respond. Her blind trust in him had gone,
and taken with it her right to love and respond freely.

It hurt, it frightened her, and it left her feeling more
lonely than she could have felt if he'd just walked out and
left her. Because she didn't know how she was ever going
to be any different with him now.

'Rachel?' She turned her head on the pillow to find him

watching her, his eyes two dark and sombre points in the darkness. 'I'm sorry,' he said quietly.

Sorry for failing her just now in this bed? she wondered. Or sorry for the whole damned blasted mess in its entirety? In the end, she decided, it didn't really matter. Nothing seemed to matter any more. She was an empty husk, lost and alone, and no amount of sorrys was ever going to make her feel any better.

The tears glazed her eyes again, seeping in a wretched spill on to her lashes. 'I'm ashamed of myself,' she told him, in a voice thick and quivering.

Something suspiciously like moisture swam across his eyes and his answering sigh was decidedly shaky. 'Come here,' he said, and reached out to pull her to him. His arms enfolded her, his body drawing into a curve which almost totally cocooned her. 'On the vow of a man who has never felt so wretched in his life, Rachel,' he murmured into the tangled silk of her hair, 'I swear I will never do anything that could hurt you like this again.'

Could she afford to believe him? she wondered bleakly. It would be easy enough to let herself believe him. Forgive and forget and shove it all to the back of her mind in the hope that it would take the hurt with it.

'I love you,' he told her huskily. 'I do love you, Rachel.'

'No!' She stiffened violently at that, all thoughts of forgiving gone with the utterance of those three false words. She had believed them once before and look where it had got her! 'Don't speak of love to me,' she choked out angrily. 'Love had nothing to do with what happened just now—or why you married me at all for that matter!'

Breakfast the next morning was an awkward affair. The twins kept sending her glances which were both troubled and curious. She knew they must be wondering about her sudden disappearance yesterday, but it was obvious they were under orders from Daniel not to question her. She even allowed herself a small smile when Kate opened her mouth to ask something, only to close it again with a mutinous snap at the warning look Daniel sent her. Sam was different. He kept frowning at her but otherwise said nothing, and that was the worry—he hadn't spoken a single word since coming down to breakfast.

'Eat up, Sammy,' Rachel said gently to him after watching him toy with his Weetabix for long enough. 'You'll be complaining of being hungry by mid-morning if you don't.'

Those eyes beneath their frowning brows, so like his father's, glanced at her. 'Where did you go yesterday!' he burst out suddenly, sending a wary look towards his father's pink newspaper.

Rachel glanced at it too. 'I—took the day off,' she answered lightly, smiling at him to show him everything was all right. 'You didn't mind, did you?'

He shifted uncomfortably, and Rachel felt her heart squeeze for him. He wasn't like his irrepressible twin, who did her worrying all up front. Sammy did it all within himself, and for him to speak out like this meant he had to be really bothered about her sudden out-of-character move. 'But—where did you go?' he persisted.

Rachel sighed inwardly, instinctively reaching across the table to comb her fingers through his ruthlessly flattened-down hair. He did not jerk away or protest at her messing him about, as he would usually have done.

'I was—tired,' she explained, floundering in her effort to offer a reason fit for a six-year-old to understand. 'Feeling—all shut-in and restless. So I went out on my own for a while, that's all.'

'But you aren't used to going out without one of us to

look after you!' he said, glaring at the lowering pink paper, almost warning his father to stay out of this.

'Who says?' she teased, trying to make a joke of it when in actual fact she was appalled to realise that even her six-year-old son thought her incapable of looking after herself! 'I am all grown-up, you know. And quite capable of looking after myself.'

'But Daddy said you weren't,' chipped in Kate. 'He told Grandma. He stormed around the house. Up and down, in and out.' As blithe as can be, Kate spoke about the forbidden and brought the newspaper all the way down. 'And he kept on shouting down the phone at Aunty Mandy.'

'That's enough, Kate,' Daniel said quietly, but his tone was enough to bring those wide innocent eyes around to his in surprise.

'But you did!' she insisted. 'You were behaving like a—a mad bull!'

'A what?' Daniel choked.

'A mad bull,' she repeated poutingly. 'That's what my teacher calls us when we charge around all over the place. "Mad bulls belong in fields," she says.' Kate gave a very good impression of her teacher's firm voice. 'Well, you charged around here yesterday, didn't you? And see—' she smiled one of her deliberately beguiling smiles, usually guaranteed to have her father eating out of her hand '—Mummy came back all safe and sound, just like I said she would!'

So at least one of her family thought her capable of looking after herself! Thanks, Kate, Rachel thought drily. 'Eat your breakfast,' was what she actually said. 'As you all can see, I returned safe and sound, so let's forget it, shall we?'

'You can go to Birmingham if you want to,' she told Daniel as soon as the children went off to collect their school things.

He was checking his briefcase, folding away his news-paper and placing it inside when she spoke. He paused, his long fingers stilling on the leather lid, then continued to close and lock the case.

He looked every bit the successful businessman this morning in his crisp white shirt and charcoal suit—sud-denly very out of place in this homely kitchen with its mad clutter of family living. He would look just perfect in the breakfast-room of an elegant Georgian manor house, sur-rounded by rich mahogany furniture with the weak morning sunlight spilling in through a deep bay window. And it hit her suddenly that, while she had been standing still for the last seven years, Daniel had been growing further and fur-ther away.

'It's no longer necessary for me to go.' He declined her offer coolly. 'Jack Brice can handle things as well as I could.'

Then why wasn't he going in the first place? she wanted to ask, but didn't because the answer could only hinge upon Lydia.

'Are you worried that I might walk out on you if you do go?' she asked, with a genuine interest in his reply. Daniel cared for her and the children, she knew, but would it be that much of a tragedy if they were no longer a part of his life?

He spun away to go and stand by the kitchen window that overlooked the toy-cluttered rear garden, his hands lost in his trouser pockets. 'Yes,' he admitted grimly at last.

And Rachel was shocked by the overwhelming sense of relief she experienced at his answer—which in turn made her angry, because it only exposed her own weakness. 'It isn't my place to leave,' she pointed out. 'You must know that prerogative is all yours.'

'Yes.' His dark head dipped for a moment before he

turned back to the table. He didn't look at her, but made a play of checking his briefcase again. 'I know that if I had a self-respecting bone left in my body, I would be shifting my stuff out of here and leaving you with some semblance of pride intact. But I don't want to leave. I don't want to break up what we have—had,' he corrected grimly. 'I know I have to prove myself to you again. I know it's going to take time. But I won't give in, Rachel.' He looked at her at last, his eyes dark and determined. 'You can throw what the hell you like at me, but it won't be me who will do the walking.'

'I could slap a separation order on you,' she hit out at him suddenly, aware that she was only doing it to hide her own weak fears. 'Make you move out.'

Daniel frowned at her. 'How the hell could you know about things like that?' he demanded. He was wondering if she had already taken legal advice from somewhere. He didn't really think her capable of it, but he wasn't sure.

She liked to see him looking uncertain. It lifted her ego, so she just shrugged indifferently and said with heavy sarcasm, 'I watch a lot of TV.'

'And are you going to?' he asked. 'Begin the end of our marriage?'

He was clever; she had to give it him. With one blunt question he had neatly dropped the responsibility into her lap. 'You began the deterioration of this marriage, Daniel,' she threw back levelly. 'But—no,' she answered his question. 'I'm not intending doing anything about the situation—just yet.'

'Then why not now?' he sighed out wearily, unhooking his jacket from the back of the chair and shrugging it on. Rachel watched him, saw the flash of gold on his left hand, put there all those millions of years ago. It was nothing but a slender band of gold, very plain, very cheap. They had not been able to afford anything better. She had a matching one of her own—and an engagement ring bought for her several years after they were married and finances were beginning to get a little easier. It was just a single diamond solitaire, small but neat on her slender finger.

He had told her he loved her then, she recalled. 'I love you, Rachel,' he'd said as he slid the little ring on her finger. 'Without you and the twins, all the hard work would have no meaning.'

But he was wrong. Without them, Daniel would be twice the success he was today; she was sure of it.

He was studying her now with that shuttered look while he waited for her to answer his question. She found his eyes, and held on to them for a moment before dropping her gaze to her cup. 'I don't know,' she answered honestly. 'But I think I want to see you bleed.'

Surprisingly, he smiled, a hand going to his neck where the evidence of her attack last night just showed above the collar of his shirt. 'I thought you'd already done that,' he said ruefully.

'Not enough,' she said, flushing slightly despite her determination not to apologise for that particular attack.

'Ah,' he said.

'Yes,' she agreed. 'Ah.'

'So I am about to enter a period of—retribution.' He smiled again, then bent to drop a kiss on top of Michael's golden head. 'So be it,' he said, and strode arrogantly from the room, leaving Rachel feeling ever so slightly—flattened.

But, oddly, it didn't quite work like that. Instead of meeting him with a cold face and a biting tongue, she found herself avoiding anything that could even hint at trouble. And over the next few weeks they seemed to slip into a weird kind of limbo, as though their marriage had fallen into a coma—a period where they were being given time to recover a little before having to face the future for what it was to be.

She did not go back to sleeping in Michael's room. But she didn't know why she went back to sleeping with Daniel. Neither did she refuse him when he would reach for her in the dark silences their nights had become. But even though they shared a kind of loving, it never quite managed to reach any real level of satisfaction for either of them, she guessed. She would go with him, move with him, and travel that long sensual path towards fulfilment—want to travel it! But suddenly she would see herself in her mind's eye, entwined and pulsing with desire in his arms, feel his body trembling against her own, his breath just soft gasps of sensual urgency against her sensitised flesh—then see Lydia in her place, Lydia in his arms, Lydia driving him to the same state of mindless passion. And she would pull frantically away from him, halting their loving as effectively as switching off the power that drove them.

Then she would lie, curled up and away from him, shivering her distress in lonely torment while Daniel would lie beside her, an arm covering his face, knowing, even though they never spoke about it—never tried to resume making love—that Lydia had come between them as surely as if she'd crawled into the bed with them. The hurt and betrayal, the cruel twist of jealousy would all rush back to flay her, and Rachel could not bear him so much as to touch her. And Daniel never tried.

She spent her days worrying about it, frightened because she knew that if anything was likely to send him back into Lydia's arms, then it was surely her stupid if unintentional hot and cold tactics.

That Daniel saw this as the form her retribution was to take only made her feel worse, because retribution was the very last thing on her mind when he would reach for her in the night.

And knowing this only made her more tense, more aware of how her own self-respect suffered every time she let him try to love her, because she knew she should be scorning him even before it started. Yet she needed him, even while her ability to respond was sadly retarded, she needed what small amount of succour she could glean from his loving— and she needed to know that Daniel needed her.

CHAPTER FIVE

DANIEL'S mother began spending more time with her during the day. She never mentioned the Sunday Rachel had escaped, but it was always there in the careful guard she kept on her expression, in the stealthy way she trod around certain subjects.

Jenny Masterson was proud of her son. He had dragged himself up from lean beginnings, made a success of his career when all the advantages had been stacked against him. But she wasn't blind to what temptation could be put in the way of a man of Daniel's calibre. He was quick, shrewd, and clever. He was nearly thirty-two years old and already a respected member of the business community. The whiz-kid who had to be watched.

Star quality, with the looks to go with the label.

Women had to be interested in him because those dark good looks and his ability to make money out of nothing made him interesting to them. And, although nothing had been said to her as to why her son's marriage was suddenly very rocky, Jenny was no fool, and most probably had had a fairly accurate idea of the truth. So she spent more time with Rachel, offering moral support in her quiet solid way, and Rachel was grateful, for she had also come to the bleak realisation that Jenny was her only friend in this new alien world she was living in right now.

Which in turn made her feel restless, utterly dissatisfied with herself and the empty person she had allowed herself to become. Her home, which had once been her pride and joy, now became a place to see criticism in every corner.

It was good enough for her, but not for Daniel. His advancement in life meant he deserved something grander—something which would reflect the successful man he had become. And she would flay herself by remembering all those times when he had tried to talk her into moving into something bigger, better, and, with this new way she had developed of looking at him, she began to understand why. No wonder he never brought any of his business colleagues home with him—he was most probably ashamed of the place!

Then, contrarily, she would be angry with him for not letting her into that other world he moved in. She might be guilty of being a silly blind fool who had barely changed in seven long years, but he had helped keep her that way by hiding her away like some guilty secret that did not fit his smart successful image!

Anger became resentment, and resentment a restlessness that made her quick-tempered and irritable—unpredictable to the point where she knew those around her trod warily, yet she couldn't seem to do anything about it.

What are you, Rachel? she asked herself one evening when—as had been perhaps inevitable after weeks of being home on the dot of six-thirty—Daniel was working late, and the restlessness grew worse because he wasn't there and she wanted him to be—needed him to be to feel any kind of peace with herself.

You can't blame Daniel for everything that has gone wrong, she told herself. You've been existing in oblivion. So wrapped up in your own cosy little world that you didn't even bother to wonder about the one he moves in beyond your sphere! You knew he went to business dinners a lot. You knew he had to move in certain circles if he was to keep his ear to the ground, but you never once wondered whether you should be moving there with him, listening with him—helping and supporting him!

You didn't even know the Harvey take-over had been wrapped up until Mandy told you! And the only reason you knew there *was* a thing called a Harvey take-over was because Daniel's mother had risen in his defence one night when you were bickering on about never seeing him. 'He's tied up with this Harvey take-over!' she'd said. 'Don't you realise how important it is that he wins this one?'

No, she hadn't, and no, she still didn't, because she had never bothered trying to find out! What did that make her in this marriage between two people that was nothing more than a house and a bed and three children they shared?

'I'm not even beautiful!' she sighed into the mirror one morning. Not in the classical sense of the word anyway. My figure is OK, I suppose, when you take into account that I've had three children. And my legs aren't that bad. But my face wouldn't stop traffic. It isn't the kind of face you would expect to see on the wife of a man like Daniel Masterson, is it? My eyes are too big, nose too small, mouth all cute and vulnerable-looking.

She scowled at her reflection in distaste.

And just look at my hair! she thought, lifting it up so that the long twisting strands fanned out on a crackle of golden static. I've been wearing my hair like this since I was Kate's age!

'Talk about Peter Pan!' she muttered in disgust. 'He has nothing on me!—even my choice of clothes is utterly juvenile!'

Then do something about it, an impatient-sounding voice inside her head challenged.

Why not? she mused, on a sudden new surge of restless defiance.

'I tell you what, Mike,' she turned to say to the baby

playing happily on the bedroom carpet, 'I'm going shopping for a whole new wardrobe of clothes! We'll see if Grandma will come and look after you. And if she won't, well—' her full bottom lip took on a mulish pout, just as Kate's did when set on some determined course '—we'll just go and dump you on your papa for the day—and let him stew in that for a change!'

But Daniel's mother was quite happy to mind the baby, which took the wind out of Rachel's sails somewhat. She'd quite liked the idea of marching into Daniel's ultra-modern office building and dumping his youngest child into his stunned arms! Mind you, she pondered as the taxi took her to London, it was one thing imagining herself doing something like that, but it was quite another actually carrying it out.

Underneath the defiance the timid Rachel still huddled, happy being just what she was and wishing she could stay like that.

And was it so wrong to be completely lacking in any personal ambition except to want to be a good wife and mother? she then demanded angrily of herself. She'd always loved her job. Loved being there for her children, having time to listen to them, play with them, or simply just enjoy them!

And Daniel. Daniel might stride like a lion through the cut-throat jungle of big business, but she knew how the tension would drain from his face and body when he came home to his ordinary family with their ordinary problems, waiting for him to sort them out.

He might come in through their front door at night looking grim and remote—wearing the face of a ruthless hunter, she realised now with clearer insight into the man himself—but within half an hour he would be stretched out on the floor with the twins, playing some really ordinary board game, or sitting cross-legged between the two in front of the television set, his mental processes dropped right down to their level while they battled against each other at one of Sammy's computer games—and there wouldn't be a sign of grimness or tension in him, only that relaxed boyish grin that was so like his son's, which said he had shrugged off the other world he moved in and sunk himself into the sheer relief from it all that his family offered him.

But now she wondered if that same process worked in reverse. She had never so much as considered it before but, when Daniel walked out of the house, did he shrug off the mantel of husband and father as easily? Was it a relief to get back into that other, more exciting world he moved in? Be the big man who wielded power over others and was treated as someone very special? And did the little woman and three small children at home fade into nothing once he was back in the sophisticated arena of sophisticated people with sophisticated intellects, who wore sophisticated clothes and could converse with him on his own sophisticated level?

Sophisticated, she repeated to herself for the umpteenth time. That was what Daniel had become—a matured and sophisticated man, while she had stagnated.

She hated herself for letting it happen. And she hated Daniel for forcing her to see her own faults, because that meant she had to shoulder some of the blame for what was happening to them.

Rachel was inexplicably relieved that Daniel's black BMW was not on the drive when her taxi dropped her off at the house well after six o'clock that evening.

She struggled up the drive with her arms so loaded with carrier bags and parcels that she had to ring the doorbell with her elbow.

'Good heavens!' Daniel's mother exclaimed when she opened the door, a look of complete disbelief on her face as Rachel staggered inside the house. 'And—good heavens again!' she repeated when she lifted stunned eyes from the tumble of packages Rachel dropped at their feet and looked—really looked—at Rachel instead.

'What do you think?' Rachel quizzed uncertainly.

The Rachel who had left the house only an hour after her husband that morning was not the one now waiting anxiously for her mother-in-law's opinion.

Gone was the long mass of pale blond hair. It had been cut, ruthlessly cut, and styled to fall in a fine silken bob on a level with her small chin. Her face had been expertly made-up to enhance those good features Rachel did not believe she had. Everything had been kept so cleverly natural that it was almost impossible to tell what the difference was about her eyes and mouth, only that suddenly they leapt out and hit you in a way Jenny found wholly disturbing.

But that wasn't all. Gone was the baby-blue woollen duffle coat and faded jeans Rachel had gone out in, and in their place was the most exquisitely tailored pure wool coat-dress in a soft and sensual mink colour which followed her slender figure from lightly padded shoulders to the delicate curve of her calf. It fastened on two rows of large brown saucer-type buttons down its revered front, and again in a single row of three along the deep cuffs at her wrists. Her new three-inch-high brown suede ankle boots and purse matched the buttons.

'I think,' Jenny Masterson murmured, eventually, 'that we had better have a stiff drink ready for my son when he gets home.'

Jenny couldn't know it, but she had given the most satisfying reply Rachel could have wished for. But that was because she was still running on full pistons of defiance, and the longer she had been out today the stronger that defiance had become.

The sitting-room door came flying open and Sammy's gasped 'Wow!' made Rachel grin like an idiot. But if she had worried a little bit about how the children were going to react to this new mother they'd got, then it was a worry wasted.

'What's in the parcels?' he demanded, dismissing the new Rachel as if she was no different from the one he was used to seeing. And within ten minutes the sitting-room floor was littered with half-open packages, and Kate was strutting around in a set of red beads that Rachel had bought on impulse—along with the set of building bricks for Michael, who was now engrossed in tearing up the cardboard box they came in, and a new computer game for Sam, who had already shot off upstairs to try it out—when Daniel walked in.

He stopped and stared. And, with that, the room seemed to come to a shuddering halt as Kate stopped strutting to view his reaction, and his mother stopped trying to tidy up some of the mess to eye him warily while Rachel, caught in the middle of coming to her feet, had to force her suddenly shaky limbs to finish the move, then stood staring at Daniel in a mixture of mutinous defiance and helpless appeal.

It was his mother who broke the spell, bustling forward to scoop Michael up from the carpet, then grab Kate's hand to hustle them all from the room.

'Children see and feel more than grown-ups give them credit for,' Jenny had told Rachel only a few days earlier. No more, just that candid one-liner, but it had been enough. Rachel received the message. The children had obviously been saying things to their grandmother they felt they could not say to their parents.

But at this moment Rachel was not thinking of her children; her attention was turned entirely on Daniel's perfectly inscrutable expression as he ran his narrowed gaze over her.

As she watched him in growing tension she saw a small smile twist his lips. It jolted her because she recognised it as the same smile he had used on entering the disco all those years ago when they first met—one she read as rueful and cynical—and it had the effect of pushing up her chin and adding a touch of challenge to her expression.

'Well, well,' he murmured eventually. 'Stage two has begun, I see.'

Stage two? Rachel frowned. What was he talking about?

'Going somewhere nice?' he asked before she could question him. 'You'll have to forgive me, Rachel, but if you did warn me that you'd made plans to go out tonight, they seem to have completely slipped my mind.'

Her frown deepened, and the way he clipped out the 'nice' was enough to make her bristle. He was a man who never let anything slip his mind! It was like a bank vault; nothing that went into it got out again without his say-so! He knew damned well she was not going anywhere, so what was he getting at with his cryptic 'stage twos', and 'going somewhere nice'?

And it was obvious he wasn't going to make a single remark about her new look—the rotter! Perhaps he didn't like it—perhaps he preferred the boringly plain other version who wasn't likely to cause him much trouble, the one who knew her place in his well-ordered life and never thought of stepping beyond it!

Or perhaps he wasn't so sure of this Rachel! she then mused on a growing sense of triumph. Perhaps the enquiry was really genuine and he was wondering if she was going out somewhere!

'And if I am considering going out, what would you do about it?' she demanded.

That smile tilted his mouth again and sent a trickle of angry frustration shooting down her spine. 'I would have to ask you who you are going with, I suppose,' he drawled, better at this game than she could ever be.

'So you could vet him—or her—to see if they're suitable company for your little wife?'

'Him?' He grabbed at that and threw it back sharply, sharply enough to make her sting in satisfaction. 'And just who is—he?' he demanded softly.

'I don't remember your having to inform me of every person you've ever gone out with,' she countered coolly.

His face tightened, grey eyes flashing a brief warning at her before he hooded them again. 'Humour me,' he requested. 'Give me a name—that's all—a name.'

This was a stupid conversation since she was going absolutely nowhere! she realised suddenly, and sighed, her shoulders slumping inside the soft mink wool. 'There isn't a name,' she muttered, angry at the easy way he had managed totally to deflate her exciting day. Her eyes glittered around the scattered parcels which had now lost all their pleasure. 'I'm on my way in, not out.' And one look at this room made it as clear as night followed day that she had just come in from a long day's shopping spree! Who was he trying to kid with that small frown that suggested he was only just noticing the mad clutter of boxes, bags and tissue-paper?

Daniel moved across the room to the nearest one—a long, flat box which had not yet been delved into by curious fingers—and Rachel took her chance while he was no longer blocking her exit, picked up her new brown suede bag and moved towards the sitting-room door, her mouth set in a thin line of disappointment.

'What's in this?'

She shrugged, feeling as petulant as Kate did when she did not get the response she had been anticipating. 'A suit,' she answered reluctantly.

'And this one?' He nudged another box with a highly polished shoe.

'Underwear.' She blushed uncomfortably, because the box was full to overflowing with the most expensive silk underwear Rachel had ever seen.

'And this?'

'A couple of new dresses!' Her eyes flashed resentfully at him. 'Why?' she demanded. 'You aren't going to read me a lecture on over-spending are you? It was you who gave me all those credit card things! One for every big store in London, I think!' She had a wallet stuffed with them. They had just taken up space in her purse until today, when she had learned the delights they could offer her.

He ignored that, his expression slightly guarded when he suggested casually enough, 'A dress worthy of dinner in one of London's most exclusive restaurants, with maybe a little dancing later?'

She had turned back to the door by this time, but the invitation had her spinning back to stare at him in blank incomprehension. 'Are you asking me out?' she queried, with such a blatant lack of guile that Daniel's smile became ruefully crooked.

'Yes.' He nodded, all dry mockery. And Rachel had a feeling that he found her lack of sophistication highly amusing. She flushed heatedly, wishing the world would just open up and swallow her rather than continue to put her through this purgatory. Nothing she could do, it seemed, would ever make her anything more than a silly, gauche fool! 'Yes, Rachel,' he repeated more gently, as though reading her discomfort and suddenly sorry for causing it. 'I am asking you if you would like to dine out with me tonight.'

'Oh.' Thoroughly disconcerted, and not sure how to answer him, she was very relieved when Sam came tumbling down the stairs at that moment, like a snowball out of control, to rumble right by her and leap like a jack-rabbit on to his father's chest.

'Hi!' he greeted, smiling into that face which was so like his own. 'Mum's got me this great new computer game,' he went on in an excited rush. 'Can I bring it down here and try it out on the big TV? It's a flight simulator and you have to take off and land a Tornado jet!'

'Why not?' Daniel agreed, smiling at his son while his eyes never left Rachel. 'If your grandmother doesn't mind, that is, since she will be staying here with you while I take your mother out to dinner.'

'You're taking Mum out?' The child sounded as surprised as Rachel had been, which made Daniel grimace. But Sam was already beaming his approval at Rachel. 'That's great!' he announced. 'Dad taking you out instead of you going on your own like last—'

'Sam.' The quiet warning from his father shut him up, and Rachel felt stiff and awkward.

'Maybe your mother doesn't want to baby-sit,' she said uncomfortably, knowing he had only asked her because he felt obliged to after seeing all the trouble she'd gone to to make herself different. 'She's been here all day as it is. It isn't fair to—'

'I don't mind,' another voice chipped in quietly from the hallway. Rachel turned to find his mother and Kate standing there, listening in as if there was no such thing as privacy in this house!

'That's not the point!' Rachel snapped. 'You've been put on quite enough for one day. I—'

'Take her somewhere nice,' Jenny said to her son over the top of Rachel's protests.

Rachel sighed impatiently because she was well aware that she was being thoroughly outmanoeuvred here. 'I haven't said I want to go out, as far as I recall!' she inserted crossly.

'Of course you want to go!' Jenny dismissed that argument. 'So just get upstairs with you—and take all those boxes with you!' she ordered. 'Kate—Sammy—help your mother upstairs with some of these,' she continued briskly, while Rachel heaved a small sigh of surrender because, unless she was prepared to tell all of them why she had no wish to go anywhere with Daniel, she really had no choice.

The children jumped eagerly to their grandmother's bidding, gathering up parcels and making for the door, leaving Rachel to bring the rest. She was just starting up the stairs when Jenny's voice drifted towards her, sounding cross and stern. 'If you ask me, Daniel, this evening out for both of you is well overdue! And it wouldn't go amiss if you began involving her in your business socialising too!'

Pausing on the stairs, Rachel waited curiously to hear Daniel's reply to that stern scold, but his voice was pitched too low for her to catch the words.

But Jenny could be heard plainly. 'Rubbish!' she snapped. 'How do you know she'll hate it when you've never given her the chance to find out for herself? The trouble with you, Daniel, is you've kept her so wrapped up in cotton wool that she's never been allowed to discover what she wants out of life!'

Was that what Jenny really thought? Rachel mused curiously. She'd always thought she knew exactly what she wanted out of life—to be a wife and mother. That was all.

Nothing fancy. Nothing ambitious or over-exciting. Just a wife to the man she loved and a mother to the children she adored.

Was there something wrong with that?

'And I'll have my say about something else, while I'm about it,' Jenny continued brusquely. 'I don't know what has been happening here to break that poor child's heart, but I know her blessed eyes have been opened to something nasty—and I know where the blame for that lies too!'

Rachel felt her heart sink, that horrible feeling of desolation washing over her as it always did when she was reminded of Mandy's call.

Lights really do go out when your world caves in, she observed sadly.

'Take my advice, son,' Jenny was saying, 'and tread very carefully from now on. Because if Rachel ever...'

Rachel ran. She didn't want to know what would happen if Rachel ever! What was happening right now to Rachel was more than enough to contend with without worrying about what would happen if Rachel ever...!

CHAPTER SIX

IF RACHEL ever—what? she found herself wondering later, while she hovered in Michael's small bathroom waiting for Daniel to finish in their bedroom so that she could sneak in there and get ready without having to come face to face with him again.

If Rachel ever found out about his other women? Well, Rachel had already done that.

If Rachel ever decided to grow up? she then pondered cynically, catching a glimpse of her new self in the bathroom mirror and almost doing a double-take because it was like looking at a total stranger!

And just look at you! she told that reflection. Hiding away in here when you don't even need to use the bathroom! You daren't bath in case the steam ruins your new hairstyle. You daren't wash because you aren't confident enough to re-do your clever make-up. Daniel is taking you out—but only because of some reason of his own which has to hinge on his guilty conscience! And he's expecting to take out that other person he met downstairs—the same one you're staring at right now—when really she's just an illusion! A disguise the real Rachel is trying to hide behind!

She heard a door open and close, then Daniel's distinctive tread as he made his way back down the stairs. With a deep breath and a harried glance at the woman in the mirror, she let herself out of her hiding place. Over her arm lay one of the new dresses she had bought that day, and she hung it on the wardrobe door, then stood back to harry herself over whether she dared wear it or not.

It was a rather disturbingly sexy thing, made of a dark ruby lace lined in fine black silk. It had a heart-shaped bodice held up by two rather flimsy-looking bootlace straps, and the delicate fabric clung almost lovingly in sensual lacy scollops across the creamy slope of her breasts. It left her arms and shoulders bare—and the best part of her back, she recalled, giving the dress a twitch with her hand to remind herself just how low it dipped at the back. The assistant had seen her uncertain expression when Rachel had realised just how much of her skin it revealed, and had rushed off to come back with a black velvet bolero with long fitted sleeves, a small stand-up collar and two curving front panels, which left the seductive dip of ruby lace between her breasts tantalisingly exposed.

So, did she wear it? she wondered pensively. Or did she revert to the black dress hanging in the wardrobe that she usually wore when she went out with Daniel?

Kate slipped into the bedroom, looking all rosy pink and smelling of talcum powder. She came to stand beside Rachel, her blue eyes widening on the new dress.

'Is that what you're going to wear?' she asked in soft awe.

'I don't know,' Rachel answered uncertainly. 'Maybe— maybe I should just fall back on my black dress...' Her hand went to draw the other dress from the wardrobe when Kate stopped her.

'But you can't wear that!' she exclaimed, sounding horrified. 'Daddy is all dressed up in his penguin suit and bow tie! He looks fantastic!'

Rachel's lips twitched; obviously Kate's fantastic daddy deserved something better than the black dress.

'That old black thing is boring, anyway,' her daughter added.

Boring, Rachel repeated to herself. Now there's a word

she had become very familiar with over the last few weeks. 'Then the red it is,' she drily agreed. The old Rachel was boring; this new one was determined not to be! 'Now you go and help Grandma with Michael while I get myself ready.' She dropped a kiss on her daughter's cheek then watched her scamper off—eager, it seemed to Rachel, to be as much help as she could to see her parents go out and enjoy themselves.

Well…she thought a trifle breathlessly as she paused outside the sitting-room door. She had been suitably drooled over by all those in the kitchen playing snap. All she had to do now was steady her stuttering heart and go and face the real expert!

Kate was right, she observed as she slipped quietly into the room, Daniel did look fantastic in his black dinner-jacket. But it was more than just the superb cut of the cloth. It was the man inside it that made all the difference. There was an air of maturity and sophistication about him which only seemed to increase that innate sex-appeal he had always possessed. He was over by the drinks tray, his face turned away from her as he poured himself a simple tonic water. He hadn't realised she'd come into the room yet, and Rachel was glad because it gave her a few moments to steady the effect he had on her senses. His thick dark hair was as neat and semi-casual as it always was, neither too short nor too long, fashionable or old-fashioned. But then, that spoke a lot about his character. Daniel had always stamped his impact on people with a clever balance between the conventional and the unconventional. A man of super-confidence—underplayed. And intimidating for it, because there was so much of the real person he liked to keep hidden.

He was intimidating her now as she stood there nervously fingering the lip of her black velvet bolero. He had never used to make her feel like this—in fact, she had never used to think of Daniel as anything but the man she loved. And it was yet another first she had to contend with, that she could actually feel overawed by a man she had lived and slept with for seven years of her life.

He was a stranger to her, she realised with a painful start. A stranger living beneath an umbrella of close intimacy. Had it always been like that? she wondered. Then she went cold inside as the answer came back to her, clear and cruel in its honesty. Yes, it had always been like that. Daniel was the stranger she had loved blindly, married blindly, and lived with blindly for seven whole years.

Was he aware that she didn't know him, really know him, for the man he was out there beyond these cloistered walls? And if he did know, did it matter to him much? Or had he been quite content to live the dual life of family man and dynamic tycoon where one role did not intrude on the other?

He turned then and saw her standing there, and her heart gave another painful twist as she watched him narrow his eyes so that she could not read their expression as he ran them slowly over her.

He hides away from me, she realised. He does it all the time. Even now, as he ran his gaze from the top of her gleaming new hairstyle and her perfectly made-up face which did so much to enhance all those beautiful features even Rachel herself was not aware she possessed, he revealed nothing of himself. The dress was different, far more sophisticated than anything she had ever worn before. It accentuated her slender figure, the long graceful line of her legs. Daniel took it all in without showing a single hint of what he was thinking behind his urbane mask.

Then, without any warning, his lashes flickered, and

there was a flash of emotion before he had severely dismissed it again.

Hurt. It startled her because she was sure she saw hurt in that expression then! But why should he be hurting because his wife was standing here dressed up to go out with him?

Or maybe it wasn't hurt, but guilty conscience which caused that spasm. What was it his mother had said? 'You've kept her so wrapped up in cotton wool.' And that must have hit him on the raw, just as looking at her standing here like this, different, yet still the same Rachel inside, was hitting his conscience, because he must know she would never have gone to these extremes to make herself different if he had not made her feel so damned uncertain of the person she had always believed herself to be!

'Drink before we go?' he asked.

He wasn't going to comment. She felt like a balloon slowly deflating from a central prick with a pin. 'No—thank you,' she refused, damning her voice for sounding husky. 'Did...did you manage to reserve a table somewhere?'

His twisted smile seemed to mock her for some reason. 'I managed,' he said. 'Shall we go then?'

Oh, let's not bother! Rachel thought with silent resentment as she turned to walk out of the sitting-room door.

She sat stiffly beside him, watching his long fingers control the car as the BMW accelerated towards London. She rarely rode in this car because when they went out together it was usually as a family, and since it was her white Escort which had been fitted out with all the correct safety gear to take the children, that was the one they usually used. So she felt strange riding in the BMW—strange with everything, she acknowledged heavily, even herself.

'Where are we going?' she asked with little enthusiasm.

She felt his glance brush her and looked round at him in time to see his jaw tighten as he turned back to the road. He named a club-cum-restaurant that made her skin prickle with alarm. It was one of those well-known places which the rich and famous generally frequented. She'd always believed you needed a celebrity status to get into places like it. The fact that Daniel was tossing off the name as though it were nothing increased her mood of discomfort.

'The food's good,' he was saying casually. 'Good enough to tempt even the frailest appetites…'

Was that meant for her? It could have been, she conceded. She was well aware that her appetite had been sadly missing recently. But then food was a problem to swallow when you lived with a permanent lump in your throat.

'You've been there before, then,' she surmised.

'Once or twice.'

With Lydia? She could not stop the thought from coming and, once there, it left her quiet and even more subdued for the rest of the journey.

If Daniel noticed he didn't bother remarking on it, his own mood not much better than her own as he guided her into the foyer, where clever lighting enhanced the luxury of their surroundings.

'Good evening, Mr Masterson.' A short rotund man with a bald head and dark French eyes appeared like magic in front of them. He bowed politely to Rachel, who smiled jerkily in return.

'Good evening, Claude,' Daniel was saying in a familiar way which made Rachel grimace. 'Good of you to fit us in at such short notice.'

Claude gave a typically European shrug. 'You know how it is sir. Some people you always have room for. This way, please…'

Daniel's hand came to her waist, his fingers settling in

an intimate curve of her ribcage as he propelled her forwards. Trying not to look awed by the elegance of her surroundings, she looked around her as Claude took them through to a restaurant that was nothing like any restaurant she had ever been in before.

On the other occasions when Daniel had taken her out it had usually been to one of the local places, Indian or Chinese or Italian, where he could wear a pair of his casual trousers and a polo shirt under his sports jacket, and she could wear something equally casual. They would lounge in their seats and share a meal and a bottle of wine with the relaxed intimacy of two people who felt comfortable in each other's company. But here Rachel could not imagine daring to lounge in her seat. Just as she couldn't imagine Daniel pinching a prawn off her plate if the mood took him, or herself leaning across the table to feed one to him, because she knew his insatiable love of prawns meant he would suck it greedily from her fingers.

The mood here did not encourage that kind of relaxed intimacy. In fact, she realised as the awe wore off to be replaced with something closely resembling contempt, she thought the place rather lacked atmosphere of any kind but the We-eat-here-because-it-is-fashionable-to-eat-here kind.

'You don't like it.' She glanced up to find Daniel watching her expression.

'It all looks very—nice,' she replied.

'Nice,' Daniel huffed out sardonically. 'This happens to be one of the finest restaurants in London, and you call it—nice.'

'I'm sorry.' She looked at him. 'Am I supposed to be suitably impressed?'

'No.' That nerve twitched in his jaw.

'Or maybe I'm supposed to be impressed with your ability to get in here at short notice?' she suggested. 'Be careful, Daniel,' she drawled, 'or I might even begin to suspect that you're trying to impress me.'

'And that is just too ridiculous to contemplate, is it?'

She thought about that, her gaze drifting among the other tables where people sat in their elegant clothes with their elegant faces wearing elegant expressions. Then she looked back at Daniel.

'Frankly, yes,' she replied, her mouth taking on a self-derisive slant. 'I thought we both knew that you've never had to do anything to impress me.'

He sighed impatiently. 'Rachel. I didn't bring you here to argue with you. I only wanted to—'

'Give me a special treat?' she suggested sardonically.

'No!' he denied. 'I wanted to please you—please you!' he repeated with a bitter-soft ferocity.

'By showing how your other half lives?' she mocked.

'My other half?' He looked genuinely nonplussed. 'What the hell is that supposed to mean?'

'The other you I know nothing about,' she shrugged, adding heavily to herself, The Daniel who's grown stronger while the other one has been slowly fading away before my very eyes without my noticing it. 'The one who feels perfectly at ease in places like this.'

His grey eyes flashed her an impatient look. 'Would you rather we had gone to the local Chinese dressed like this?' he derided. 'You went to a lot of trouble today to create your new image, Rachel. This—' his gaze flicked briefly around their surroundings '—suits the new image. It's up to you to decide whether you prefer it or not.'

Not, she thought, then grimaced when her heart gave a dull thump in acknowledgement of what that answer meant. This was not her, dressed for the part or not. But it was so obviously Daniel that she wanted to weep. Had they anything in common left worth hanging on to?

'And do you prefer it?' she asked him curiously. 'The new image?' she enlightened his puzzled frown.

He sat back in his seat, his eyes wearing an odd expression as they ran over her. 'I like the new hairstyle,' he admitted after a moment, 'but I'm not sure I like your reasons for doing it. I like the dress,' he went on, before she could respond. 'It's beautiful—as you probably well know—but I don't like what it does to the woman I—'

A waiter appeared at her side, effectively cutting Daniel off mid-word as he placed a glass of something cool and clear in front of Rachel then offered the same to Daniel. 'Your menus, sir,' he murmured, opening the dark green leather-backed menus and presenting them with one each.

'Thank you,' Daniel said, abruptly dismissing the man with a curt flick of a finger. The waiter bowed politely, then left them.

'You were very short with him,' Rachel censured. 'What did he do to make you behave so rudely?'

'He interrupted me while I was trying to compliment you.'

She sent him a deriding look. 'If you call those compliments, Daniel, then I'm certainly not impressed with your style!'

He grimaced ruefully. 'All right,' he conceded, 'so I'm finding it difficult to come to terms with the new you. Rachel—' he leaned forward suddenly, his gaze urgent as he took hold of one of her hands '—you're beautiful, you don't need me to tell you that—'

Don't I? she questioned wryly.

'But don't—please don't lose the lovely person you were before in your effort to prove something to me!'

'I didn't do this for you, Daniel,' she informed him coldly. 'I did it for myself. It was time, after all,' she added bleakly, 'that I grew up.'

'Oh, no, darling,' he murmured thickly, 'you're so wrong! I—'

'Well, Daniel Masterson, as I live and breathe!' a smoothly sardonic voice drawled.

'Damn!' Daniel muttered, his grip tightening on Rachel's hand before he let go of her abruptly, schooled his expression into a fascinatingly bland mask, then looked up into the face of their intruder.

'Zac,' he acknowledged, coming smoothly to his feet. 'I thought you were in the States.'

He stepped from behind their table to shake the other man's hand, and Rachel glanced up to find herself gazing into the attractive face of a man around Daniel's age. He was rake-thin and blond, with a pair of bright green eyes that appeared sharp enough to cut armour-plating if he wanted them to.

'Been back several weeks now,' he replied. 'It's you who seem to have been out of circulation recently...' His glance swept curiously down towards Rachel—then darkened with pure male interest. 'Could this beautiful creature be the reason why?' he mused softly. Then, boldly to Daniel, 'So what happened to the lovely L—?'

'My wife,' Daniel cut in, editing out whatever the other man had been going to say—but not before Rachel had added the last word for herself. 'Rachel.' With what seemed to her a very reluctant move, he shifted to one side to place her in full view of the newcomer. 'This is Zac Callum. We use the same legal firm,' he concluded tautly.

Zac Callum threw Daniel a sharply speculative look. 'Don't we just?' Rachel thought she heard him murmur beneath his breath as he stepped by Daniel's stiff frame to hold out his hand to her.

But she was too busy repeating his name to herself to find time to wonder what that soft remark could mean, because the name she knew. He was the political cartoonist for the *Sunday Globe*, and cruelly witty he was too. He had an unerring ability to latch on to people's weak points and use them to turn even the most prominent person into a laughing stock, which also made him quite a TV celebrity. He tended to turn up on quiz shows and the like, adding a bit of wicked spice to the proceedings.

'No wonder Daniel has been noticeable for his absence over the last few weeks,' he murmured as Rachel placed her hand in his. Long, incredibly slender fingers closed over hers. 'A wife,' he added softly. 'Your taste has certainly improved, Daniel.'

He means Lydia, Rachel thought wretchedly. 'Thank you,' she said, answering for Daniel. He looked so tense that she had a suspicion he wouldn't be able to speak even if he wanted to. 'I—I've heard of you, Mr Callum,' she told him shyly. 'I enjoy your work.'

'A fan?' His eyes began to glint with humour. 'Tell me more…' Gripping the back of a vacant chair, he went to pull it out from beneath the table.

'Zac, darling—aren't you forgetting something?' a wry voice intruded.

Pulling a rueful face exclusively for Rachel's benefit, he straightened, then turned towards the woman standing just behind him. 'Sorry,' he apologised. 'But you must understand, this is a moment to be savoured. This man, of all men, surrendering to the wedded trap.' His sigh was explicit, as was the taunting expression he turned on Daniel. 'Claire.' Placing a hand around his companion's slender waist, he drew her forward. 'This is Daniel Masterson of whom you no doubt have already heard.'

'Who hasn't?' she said drily. 'We all waited with bated breath for the outcome of the Harvey bid.'

The Harvey bid. Rachel lowered her eyes, wondering if

she was the only person in the world who didn't know just how important the Harvey thing had been.

'Nice to meet you,' Claire was saying, while Daniel only acknowledged her with a slight impression of a smile. His hard gaze was fixed on Zac Callum, who was still eyeing Rachel with undiluted interest.

'We would ask you to join us, but we've already ordered,' Daniel lied. 'And…' He left the rest unsaid, but it was obvious to all of them Daniel did not want them intruding.

'Don't worry.' Zac laughed—a pleasant, huskily teasing sound. 'We have no wish to gate-crash on newlyweds.'

At last Daniel opened his mouth to contest the mistake— then caught Rachel's gaze and was silenced.

Don't, her eyes pleaded with him. Don't tell them the truth! He knows about Lydia. Don't put me up for ridicule by telling them you've had a wife for seven years and children for six when he obviously knows about your mistress!

Grimly he looked down and away, his mouth thinning even more in angry frustration with the whole unwanted scene.

Which only made her feel worse, so out of her depth here that she wanted to run away and hide—hide in choking humiliation.

Then Daniel did a strange thing. He reached out for her, capturing her chin with a hand as he suddenly bent his own dark head towards her. And there, among London's best and most sophisticated, he kissed her, hot and possessively. And when he released her surprised mouth his eyes were so darkened by pain that it brought tears springing into Rachel's own.

'The honeymoon is obviously not over,' mocked Zac Callum. 'Come on, Claire. I think we should leave these two love-birds alone.'

'What do you want to eat?'

Miles away, feeling hot and flustered by Daniel's unexpected kiss, and unbearably moved by that revealing expression in his eyes, Rachel had to force herself to concentrate on what he had said. He was back in his seat, guarded eyes watching her intently.

'I...' She looked down at the menu in front of her, the list of dishes blurring into illegibility. 'I...' Her heart was stammering in her breast, the nervous tip of her pink tongue desperate to flick around lips still burning from his kiss. 'You order for me,' she invited in the end, tossing the menu aside because it was no use her trying to make sense of it feeling as she did.

Grimly he made a small gesture that brought the waiter scuttling over, then ordered in a curt clipped voice that had the waiter nodding nervously before scuttling away again as if the tension at the table was too much to stand near for long.

Had the waiter seen Daniel kiss her? Had the whole room? Cheeks heating, Rachel cast a furtive glance around her to find everyone seemingly engrossed in their own interests rather than theirs. Knotting her hands together beneath the cover of the oyster-pink tablecloth, she made herself speak normally.

'How do you know Zac Callum?' she asked.

He gave an indifferent shrug. 'He inherited a couple of small companies from his father,' he explained. 'He didn't want them, so he sold them to me.'

'I like his work,' she remarked. 'It was a medium I was rather good at myself, so I find I can appreciate the gift he has.'

'Appreciate his charm, too, did you?' Daniel clipped out tightly.

Rachel's eyes widened, surprised by the unveiled green-eyed jealousy she heard in his tone.

Daniel—jealous of another man looking at her? The mind boggled on the concept. 'Is that why you kissed me like that?' she demanded.

A sudden blindingly bitter look shot across his gaze. 'He was eyeing you up like a tasty new dish on the damned menu,' he gritted. 'I wanted there to be no mistake about who you belonged to.'

Belonged? She belonged to Daniel, but Daniel apparently did not belong to her, if Lydia was a gauge in belonging. 'Does anyone in this other world you move in know about me and the children?' she asked heavily then.

He took exception to her reference to his other world, but bit the bullet on it. 'My private life is none of their business,' he said brusquely. 'I mix with them purely for business' sake, that's all. Now can we drop the subject?' he snapped. 'Unless of course you found Zac Callum's charm more appealing than my company, in which case I'll call him back if you like, and you can both flatter each other's egos a little bit more!'

Oh, he was jealous! The idea certainly gave her flagging ego an enormous boost. 'Well, at least he didn't snap his dining companion's head off every time she opened her mouth,' she taunted sweetly, watching with a growing sense of pleased triumph as dark colour slid across his cheeks at the rebuke.

Their first course arrived then, thankfully, because sitting here in public with him like this, when really all they both seemed to want to do was snap out taunts at each other, made eating the better option.

He'd ordered her a light salmon mousse that made her mouth water when she had believed she wouldn't be able to eat a single morsel of food. And she was halfway through when Daniel reached across the table and touched her gently on the back of her hand.

'Rachel,' he murmured huskily, bringing her wary gaze up to clash with his. 'Can we at least try to make this a pleasant evening for us both?' he pleaded. 'I don't want to fight with you. I want—'

'Daniel—how nice to see you!'

His face darkened with irritation, and Rachel herself felt a stab of disappointment at the new interruption because she had been allowing herself the rare pleasure of drowning in the smoky urgency of his beautiful eyes.

This time he didn't get up to greet the middle-aged couple who had stopped by their table. Nor did he introduce her. He just made all the right polite noises, but in a way that had them quickly moving on.

'Now you know why I don't like bringing you to places like this,' he grimaced. 'We are destined to be interrupted like this all evening.'

'And what's wrong with that?' she asked, bristling because she saw his impatience as reluctance to acknowledge her here for what she was to him.

'Because when I take you out, I like to have you to myself!' he said, and that look was back in his eyes, that darkly smouldering, intensely possessive one that turned her stomach inside out and made eating anything else a near-impossibility.

But he was right. They were interrupted no less than three more times during the course of their meal, and in the end Daniel sighed and reached across the table for her hand to draw her with him as he stood up.

'Come on,' he said. 'We may as well go through to the club and dance. At least while we're dancing people will be reluctant to interrupt.'

Keeping hold of her hand, he threaded his way through

the tables towards a pair of closed doors that swung open at the touch of his free hand. It was darker in here; from the entrance she could just see through the gloom to the opposite side of the room, which had its own bar and a small raised stage where a group of musicians sat playing slow, easy jazz.

Daniel drew her on to the dance-floor and turned her into his arms. Instantly she was assailed by a weird feeling of nervous uncertainty—as if he were a stranger, the kind of tall, dark stranger that appealed to her senses and made her excruciatingly aware of herself as a woman.

This is Daniel, she reminded herself fiercely as he began to sway with her to the music. No stranger, but the man you've been married to for seven years.

But this Daniel was a stranger to her, she acknowledged heavily. And not only because she was here with him in his other world, so to speak. They had become strangers weeks ago—estranged while still living together as man and wife.

A sigh broke from her. The sadness in it must have reached Daniel, because the hand covering hers where it lay against the smooth lapel of his dinner-jacket squeezed, and his other moved on her waist, sliding up and beneath her black bolero with the intention of pressing her closer— then stopped, a sudden breathless stillness assailing both of them as his fingers made surprised contact with warm bare flesh.

She'd forgotten the backless design of the dress until that moment, had been uptight about too many other things to care about something she'd had no intention of revealing. But she remembered now and had to close her eyes as a wild wave of sensation rippled right through her.

She tried to fight it, moving her head in an effort to take in air that was not filled with the musky sensual smell of him emanating up from his warm throat. But he stopped her, the hand holding hers lifting to curve her nape, pressing her back against him.

'*Déjà vu*,' Daniel whispered, and she gasped out an unsteady breath when she realised what he meant.

The first time they'd ever danced together she'd been wearing a little cropped T-shirt that he'd slipped his fingers beneath. This time it was a velvet bolero, more elegant, more sophisticated, but her reaction was the same.

Hot and drenching, a sexual awareness that sizzled like liquid on burning coals. Her heart hammered in response, and as she stiffened on a fizz of sensation his fingertips began to graze lightly along her spine.

No, she told herself breathlessly. Don't let him do this to you!

But the fine hairs covering her body began to tingle in pleasurable response to his caress, forcing her eyes to close and her spine to move into a supple arch that sent the sensitive tips of her breasts brushing against the heated wall of his chest. She felt Daniel's body tighten against her, harden, begin to throb with a need older than time itself, and let out a shakily helpless sigh.

His dark head lowered to nuzzle her throat. 'It hasn't changed one iota, has it?' he breathed. 'We still have this amazing effect on each other.'

He was, oh, so right. And on a final sigh that came from deep, deep inside her, she surrendered to it all, letting herself do what she was desperate to do, and stretched up to brush her mouth softly against his.

It was the first time in long weeks that she had made a voluntary move towards him, and he acknowledged it with a rasping intake of air, his lean body shuddering as he released the air again.

'Let's go home,' he said hoarsely. 'This isn't what I want to be doing with you.'

'I…' All right, she was about to concede, feeling as if she had nothing left to fight him with. But then another acidly mocking, shudderingly familiar voice intruded, and everything within her seemed to shatter into a thousand broken pieces.

'Well, if it isn't Don Juan himself. And with a brand-new conquest too…'

CHAPTER SEVEN

RACHEL closed her eyes, a dark wave of recognition making her blonde head drop wearily on to Daniel's shoulder while he stiffened like a board.

'You do know he's married, don't you, dear?' the cruel voice taunted.

Obviously Mandy had not recognised the new Rachel in the woman Daniel was holding in his arms.

'For seven long years, no less,' she went on regardless. 'To a pretty, if insipid, little thing, who will be sitting at home at this very moment, taking care of their three sweet children while her darling husband plays lover to any woman who will have him.'

'Oh, not just anyone, Amanda,' Daniel countered coldly. 'I always found it very easy to turn you down, after all.'

Mandy wanted Daniel? Lifting her face, Rachel stared into his harshly cynical eyes and felt something else rend apart inside her as yet another veil was ripped from her blind, trusting eyes. Daniel watched it happen with a grim clenching of his jaw.

Daniel and Mandy did not get on; she had always accepted that as one of those things, without bothering to question why they were so hostile towards each other. Well, now she knew, and she felt sick with the knowledge.

'Man must always beware of a woman scorned, Daniel,' Mandy cautioned sagely. 'It is one of our most—destructive little weapons, after all.'

'And you used it so well, didn't you?' Daniel drawled. 'Aiming directly at the weakest point.'

'How is Rachel, by the way?' she drawled. 'Has the poor thing any idea how quickly you've found a replacement for the ousted Lydia?'

Enough. Rachel had heard enough. Twisting within the constricting grasp of Daniel's arms, she turned to look at her once-best friend, watching with a complete lack of expression as all the colour left Mandy's face; without saying a word, Mandy spun gracefully on her heel and walked away.

The mood was shot, the evening a disaster. Neither spoke as they left the club and walked the short distance to where Daniel had parked the car.

Then, 'How long?' she asked, once he'd slid the car into the steady stream of traffic leaving London.

'Years,' he shrugged, not even trying to misunderstand her.

'Did you ever take her up on it?'

As she watched him she saw his fingers take a white-knuckled grip on the steering wheel, his mouth tightening because the question offended his dignity, but he had to accept her right to ask it. 'No,' he answered flatly. 'Never even considered it.'

'Why not?'

'She leaves me cold,' he replied dismissively.

And it was a dismissal, one Rachel had to believe simply by the sheer lack of feeling with which he said it.

'Then why didn't you tell me what she was trying to do?'

'And ruin your faith in someone you cared a great deal for?' He sent her a sombre glance. 'I never hid the fact that I thoroughly disliked her, Rachel,' he reminded her grimly.

'But you never went out of your way to discourage the friendship either,' she pointed out. 'One word—one word, Daniel,' she emphasised tightly, 'that she was only using me to get to you, and tonight's little scene could have been avoided.'

'Knowing how deeply the truth would hurt you?' His expression was harsh in the dim light inside the car. 'I would have had to be some kind of heel to do that to you, Rachel.'

'True,' she conceded, and left that single word hanging in the air between them, knowing he had read the other meaning it offered—and knowing he had no defence against it.

She entered the house first, making directly for the stairs without bothering to go in and speak to Jenny. 'I have a headache,' she mumbled, which was not exactly a lie. There were a lot of different bits aching inside her, her head only one of them. 'Please apologise to your mother for me.'

She was not asleep when Daniel eventually came to bed after taking his mother home. But she pretended to be, while intensely aware of every move he made around the quiet room as he prepared for bed. He came into it naked as he always did, lying on his back with his head supported on his arms, staring at the darkened ceiling while she lay very still beside him, wishing with all her aching heart that fate would just wave a hand across them and dismiss the last few weeks as if they had not happened.

But of course fate was not that kind or that forgiving, and they lay there like that for ages, the tension so thick in the darkened room that Rachel began to feel suffocated by it. Then Daniel let out a sigh and reached for her. She went unresistingly into his arms, needing what he was going to offer with probably as much desperation as he did. And their loving took on a silent frenzy which was almost as unbearable as the tense silence had been.

Lydia came to visit her again that night, stiffening her passion-racked body just at the point where she'd begun to believe she was going to gain release form her pent-up desires at last. Daniel felt the change in her, and went very still while he watched her fight the devils which were haunting her.

And she did fight, eyes closed over wretched tears, kiss-softened mouth quivering, her fingers biting into his muscle-locked shoulders.

Another obstacle climbed, she thought, with no sense of triumph when, for once, she managed to thrust Lydia away. And, on a shaky sigh, she pulled Daniel's mouth down to hers.

'Rachel,' he whispered as he entered her. Just, 'Rachel,' over and over again in a raw shaken way which said he had understood the battle she had just fought and won, and knew too that she had done it for his sake. For him.

Yet though they climbed together, and although their bodies throbbed to a mutual drum-beat of growing fulfilment, when it came to it Daniel leaped alone, leaving her feeling lost and empty. A failure in so many ways she did not dare count them.

Daniel became very busy—another take-over deal—and he had to spend nights away from home in negotiation with a small engineering company near Huddersfield. Rachel accepted his word with a tight-lipped refusal to comment, which sent him off tense-faced with angry frustration while she sat at home and tormented herself with suspicions she knew were unfair even while she allowed them free rein in her wretched aching soul. That Daniel in turn refused to comment on what he knew she was thinking told her that he had decided not to justify his every move to her. He was, in short, demanding that she trust him. But she couldn't, which only helped to pile the strain on their marriage. And life became hardly bearable over the next few weeks.

Then one afternoon she happened to be glancing through the local paper that dropped through her letter-box once a week, and saw something there that set her pulses humming.

Zac Callum was giving a talk about his work at the local college of art that evening, and anyone who was interested was invited to go along.

Daniel was away. But if she got his mother in to baby-sit, then it wouldn't hurt anyone if she went along, would it?

But, deep down, she knew she was only going out of a rebellious need to hit Daniel on the raw.

His own fault, she defended her reasoning as she guided her white Escort into a vacant parking slot outside the centre. He shouldn't have let her see that he could be jealous of someone like Zac Callum. It was only knowing that which had given her the incentive to come at all!

Slipping into the small assembly hall where the talk was going to be held, she took a seat close to the back, not expecting Zac to notice her or, even if he did, to recognise her. They had met only briefly, after all.

Yet he did notice her—and recognised her instantly. He walked on to the raised podium, glanced smilingly around the three-quarters-full room, saw her, paused, focused on her again, then made her blush by widening his smile so that everyone present turned to see whom he was personally acknowledging.

Her answering smile was shy and self-conscious, and she sank herself deeper into her pale blue duffle coat with a wish to fade away completely.

But once he began talking she started to relax again, finding herself caught up in the clever, quick, witty way he explained how he homed in on the weaknesses of his victims. He was relaxed and generous with his smiles, easy to laugh with, a clever entertainer as well as a good speaker.

Several times he caught her laughing with everyone else and winked at her, his familiarity giving a boost to an ego that had been sadly flagging over the last few weeks.

Afterwards he came straight to her, lightly fielding any remarks made to him as he made his way down the aisle to where she was standing preparing to leave.

'Rachel—' his warm fingers made a light clasp around her own '—how nice of you to come.'

'I'm glad I did.' She smiled, feeling stupidly shy and self-conscious again. 'You made it all sound so interesting.'

'Do you attend classes at this college?'

Her eyes widened. 'No!' she denied, flushing a little because it had never occurred to her that he would make such an assumption. But then she realised how she must look tonight in faded jeans and a casual duffle coat, her face completely free of make-up.

Nothing like the woman he had met as the wife of the dynamic Daniel Masterson, anyway. And probably more like a student.

'We live not far from here,' she explained. 'I read about tonight in the local newspaper and decided to come along on impulse.'

'By yourself?'

'Yes.' The flush deepened, why, she wasn't sure, since this man could have no idea that this was an unusual diversion for the stay-at-home Rachel to make. 'Daniel is away on business.'

'Ah.' As if that seemed to say it all, he sent her a strange look. 'Interested in politics?'

She shook her pale head. 'Art,' she corrected. 'Caricature, anyway. I used to have quite a flair for it myself, believe it or not,' she shyly admitted, 'before being a wife and mother took up most of my—time.'

Oh, damn. Her heart sank to her feet when she realised what she had just said. Zac Callum believed her and Daniel to be newly-weds; now he was frowning at her in confusion, and her teeth bit guiltily down on her full bottom lip at being caught out in the lie.

Luckily they were interrupted by someone who wanted to ask Zac questions. Deciding to take her chance and slip away while he was busy, and before she could drop herself and Daniel further in it, Rachel pushed her hands into her duffle coat pockets and turned to leave. But his hand coming out to catch her arm stopped her.

'Don't go,' he said. 'I need to say goodbye to the people who organised this, but if you'll wait for me, I would love your company for a drink in the pub I saw over the road.'

She hesitated as something close to temptation fizzed up inside her. Having a drink, in a pub, with a man who wasn't Daniel, constituted crossing that invisible line drawn by marriage. Or did it? she then asked herself defiantly. People did it all the time! Daniel did it all the time! The modern-day line was surely drawn much further down the page on morality. What harm could it do to anyone if she did accept? What business was it of anyone's if she did accept?

Daniel's business, she answered her own question. But ignored it. And ignored too the deep-seated knowledge that it was defiance making her ignore it. She liked Zac, she defended the temptation. She was interested in what he did.

'Thank you,' she heard herself accept. 'That would be nice.'

Funnily enough, he hesitated now, that shrewd speculative look she remembered from the first time she met him entering his eyes again.

Then he nodded and let go of her arm. 'Five minutes,'

he promised, and walked away, leaving her standing there doing battle with whatever was niggling at her conscience.

Still, she enjoyed the hour they spent in the pub. The place was crowded because more than half the people who had been to the talk had crossed the road into it, and she and Zac stood leaning against two bar-stools with a glass of lager each.

It was nice, she decided, being here like this, being at ease and talked to as a reasonably intelligent human being rather than as a housewife or mother. She liked his relaxed manner, and the way he listened intently when—shyly at first, then with more enthusiasm when he didn't immediately shoot her down—she put her own ideas forward, surprising herself by what she had retained from her school days.

Daniel's name did not come into things until they were just about to part company, when Zac asked quietly, 'How long have you and Daniel been married, Rachel?'

She sighed, feeling the pleasure of the evening seep out of her. 'Seven years,' she answered, then, with a defiant lift of her small chin, 'We have three children. Two boys and a girl. And no, he doesn't keep me barefoot and pregnant. Sammy and Kate are twins.'

He smiled at the quip, but not with any humour. 'I think I owe you an apology for the first time we met,' he said.

He meant his references to Daniel's other women. Rachel felt an ache clench at her chest, but shrugged it and his apology away. 'No, you don't,' she answered. 'You were just being open and honest. It was Daniel and I who were being deceitful. Goodnight, Zac,' she added, before he could say anything else. She didn't want to talk about that night. She didn't want to know what else must be running through his mind right now. 'I enjoyed tonight very much. Thank you.'

Turning away, she went to unlock her car door when his voice stalled her. 'Listen,' he said. 'I'm thinking of doing a twelve-week course on Caricature here at this college one evening a week. Would you be interested in coming along to it?'

Would she? Rachel took her time turning back to face him, suspicious—well, half-suspicious—that he'd just thought of that on the spur of the moment.

Which meant—what exactly?

'I don't know,' she therefore answered warily. 'Is there enough interest here to make it worth your while?'

His cynical smile mocked her naïveté. He was, after all, a celebrity. People didn't need to be interested in what he did. Who he was would be enough to have them flocking to his class.

'You would enjoy it, Rachel,' he added softly when she said nothing. 'I can certainly promise you that.'

A small fizz of sensation erupted low down in her stomach, warning her that there was more to his promise than he was actually saying.

He was attracted to her. He had, in fact, made no effort to hide it.

The thing was, did she want to encourage something she knew had the potential to become very dangerous?

No, she answered herself flatly. Her life was complicated enough at the present without further complicating it with a man of Zac Callum's ilk.

Which was a shame, really, because if the man himself didn't appeal, the idea of taking up a sketch-pad and pencil again did.

'Let me know what you decide,' she prevaricated in the end, 'and I'll think about it.'

'Zac Callum teaching at a local art college?' Daniel was scornful to say the least. 'Why should he be bothered with small fry like that?'

'Maybe because he cares,' Rachel said, offended on Zac's behalf by Daniel's deriding tone.

He wasn't pleased that she'd gone out that night without his knowledge, but discovering that it was none other than Zac Callum who had tempted her out had turned him into a rather intriguingly surly brute!

'How did you know he was giving a talk?' he demanded.

'Local *Gazette*,' she replied. 'Have you eaten?' she asked, diplomatically changing the subject. 'Or do you want me to get you something?'

'No! I want to talk about you going out with Zac Callum!' he barked at her.

'I didn't go out with him!' she denied. 'I went to listen to him!' There was an ocean of difference between that and what Daniel was implying. 'What the hell are you trying to say, Daniel?' she demanded, beginning to lose patience. 'That we arranged some kind of elaborate set-up just so we could meet each other?'

The sudden flash of dark heat in his cheeks told her that that was exactly what he was thinking. 'He's capable of it,' he grunted. 'He fancied you from the first moment he laid eyes on you!'

My God, she thought, as an angry sense of elation whistled through her blood, the invincible Daniel Masterson was frightened that his little wife was considering taking on another man!

'It's you who is the untrustworthy person in this marriage, Daniel,' she reminded him bluntly. 'Not me.'

'But you could be out for revenge.'

'And you could be getting paranoid inside your guilty conscience,' she threw back. 'Don't tar me with the same brush as yourself.' And once again she deliberately ignored that little voice that was telling her she wasn't being entirely truthful.

'I wasn't doing that,' he sighed, going over to pour himself a stiff drink.

'Then what were you doing?' she snapped.

'Actually—' on another sigh, he shook his dark head wearily '—actually, I don't know what I'm doing,' he confessed. 'Are you going to take the course?'

'Are you going to play the domineering husband by telling me I can't if I decide I want to?' she countered, small chin coming up.

'Will you listen to me if I do try to talk you out of it?' he parried drily.

'No.'

He shrugged. 'Then it isn't worth my trying, is it?' he said, and walked out of the room, leaving her sitting there feeling angry and frustrated and a hundred other things that revolved almost entirely around one emotion. Hurt. Whether she fought with him or made love with him or simply ignored his very existence, she still hurt like a love-lost child whenever he walked away from her.

The trouble with you, Rachel, is you've gone so long living for him, you have no idea how to live for yourself!

Which was why she decided to go on the course when Zac rang to tell her it was all set up.

Daniel didn't say a word—not a single word. But, good grief, she knew his opinion by the time she left the house for her first class a couple of weeks later. And when she came back he didn't wait for the darkness to shroud their marriage-bed before he reached for her. He grabbed her hand almost as soon as she walked through the door and hauled her up to bed, staking claim over her senses in a way that left them both bitterly frustrated, because even while she went eagerly with him through the blistering avenues of sensuality, he still reached heaven alone.

Which, in the end, satisfied neither of them.

But at least her flair for caricature blossomed through the ensuing weeks. And even Daniel had to smile at the fun she made of them all with her pencil.

Zac was quietly encouraging. It helped that he never made any personal reference during the classes themselves but later, when they all retired to the pub across the road for a drink before going home, he would always make sure he sat next to her, his interest in her more than clear then. She tried to ignore it most of the time, wanting to learn all he had to teach her about drawing and frightened that, if he came on too strong with her, she would have to give it all up.

December loomed on the horizon: Rachel became engrossed in Christmas preparations. Shopping, planning, mad bursts of cooking and baking that filled the freezer to its limits and made everyone's mouth water as the different rich and spicy smells permeated the house.

Daniel became even busier—and more preoccupied. His one real concession to Rachel's restless need to be seen as an individual in her own right was to take her out on a regular basis. They went to the theatre, the cinema, to clubs and restaurants. Her wardrobe, by necessity, became filled with yet more elegant clothes, although she'd soon returned to wearing her casual stuff for the more mundane areas of her life. But she kept the new hairstyle because she liked it, and she found it easier to manage than the long, thick swath she used to have.

But the strain their marriage was putting on her began to tell in other ways. She tired easily, became fractious over the silliest things, and would burst into fits of weeping for no apparent reason, which troubled her family and made them yearn for the other sunnier Rachel they used to know.

Growing pains, she ruefully diagnosed her problem, after one such uncalled-for outburst had the children creeping around her warily and Daniel studying her through those hooded eyes which rarely looked directly at her these days.

Her car wouldn't start one evening when she was about to go to her evening class. Daniel was in Huddersfield and not expected back until very late that night. Jenny was baby-sitting. It was sleeting heavily outside, and Rachel looked reluctantly towards the house she had just left, knowing she should go back inside and call a taxi but oddly unwilling to do so now she had escaped.

Escaped! It hit her, then, that she was beginning to see her home as some kind of emotional prison.

On a heavy sigh, she pulled her warm coat up around her ears and walked off down the drive to catch the bus.

She arrived at the centre soaked through to her skin, her hair plastered to her head and her face white with cold. The rotten weather had found its way right through to her clothes beneath and, on a mass cry of concern, the class set about helping her to get dry. Someone began rubbing at her hair with a paper towel while someone else pulled off her boots and wet woollen socks.

'Socks!' someone cried in mock horror. 'The lady wears men's woolly socks inside her dainty boots!'

Everyone laughed, and so did Rachel, light-hearted and suddenly feeling set free from something she had been dragging around with her for weeks now. Her blouse was wet, and Zac pulled off his own black woollen sweater for her to use. She took off her blouse and put it on while the other women in the class shielded her from interested male eyes.

By the time they had all finished with her her wet clothes

lay across the warm radiators drying, and she was dressed in nothing more than her underwear beneath Zac's big sweater which came down to her knees.

But her clothes were still very damp when it was time to leave, and swapping the warm sweater for her damp shirt and jeans gave her no pleasure. When Zac offered to give her a lift straight home, instead of going with the rest of them to the local pub, Rachel read the expression in his eyes but accepted anyway, stubbornly ignoring what the warning bells going off in her head were telling her.

He drove a new model Porsche which gripped the icy wet road like glue and surged off with a growling show of power. 'Mmm,' she murmured luxuriously as the car's heater began to warm her cold legs.

Zac glanced at her and smiled. She had her eyes closed, a contented smile playing about her mouth. 'Better?' he asked.

'Mmm,' she murmured again. 'Sorry you had to miss your pint.'

'No bother,' he dismissed, then added softly, 'I'd rather be here with you.'

Rachel's eyes flicked open, a warning *frisson* skipping down her spine. 'Next left,' she directed.

Dutifully, he made the turn. 'What does Daniel think of your being with me every Wednesday night?' he enquired smoothly then.

Rachel shrugged. She didn't want to talk about Daniel—she didn't to hoist up her guard either. 'He's very encouraging,' she said, then grimaced at the lie. Daniel hated it and, because he hated it, she rubbed his nose in it. He rarely saw her without a sketch-pad in her hands these days—reminding him of who had helped her rediscover her love of drawing.

'Yet you never draw him, do you?' Zac prodded quietly.

'You poke fun at every other member of your family, but never him.'

'He isn't a good subject,' she said. 'Go right at the next junction.'

'Daniel?' His tone was filled with mockery. 'I would have thought him an ideal subject, being the hard-hitting, ruthless devil he is at work and the ordinary family man he is at home. Real scope for humour there by mixing the two, I would say.'

But Rachel didn't agree. She saw nothing funny in Daniel any more. Once, maybe, she would have delighted in drawing him in cartoon form. But not any more. 'Then maybe I'll have a go one day,' she said lightly, knowing she would not. 'This is it,' she told him. 'The white rendered one with the black BMW parked outside.'

So Daniel was home. She shivered slightly, but not with the cold.

Zac drew the car to a halt at the bottom of the drive. The engine died, and they both sat there listening to the rain thunder against the glass. He turned in his seat to look at her, and Rachel made herself return the look.

'Well—thank you for the lift,' she said, without making a single move to get out of the car. She felt trapped, by Zac's expression, by the warmth inside the car, by her own breathlessness caused by the darkened look in his eyes.

'My pleasure,' he said, but absently. His mind was elsewhere, searching her face for something she wasn't sure whether she was showing him or not. Then she found she was, because he leaned across the gap separating them and kissed her gently on the mouth. She didn't respond, but nor did she pull away. Her heart gave a small leap, then began thundering in her breast, but she wasn't certain whether that was because she was playing with fire here, or because she was genuinely attracted to him.

His hand covered her cheek, long artistic fingers running into her hair, and as the kiss continued he moved his thumb until it rested against the corner of her mouth and began stroking gently, urging it to respond.

But even as he did so she was pulling away, suddenly very sure that this was not what she wanted to do. He let her go, sitting back to study her through lazy, glittering eyes.

'I'm sorry,' she mumbled awkwardly—why, she wasn't sure.

'What for?'

She didn't answer—couldn't. All she wanted to do now was to get out of this car. And her hand fumbled for the door-catch again, trembling in its urgency to get away.

'You wanted me to kiss you, Rachel,' Zac murmured softly. 'Whatever else is going through your mind right now, remember you wanted it as much as I did.'

He was right, and her cheeks flushed with guilt. She had wanted him to kiss her—had wanted to know what it was like to feel another man's lips besides Daniel's against her own.

But now she just felt foolish, and angry with herself for allowing it to happen, because it had encouraged Zac to think there might be a place for him in her life, when there never could be. Daniel was everything she wanted, damn him. Damn him to hell.

It was only as she ran through the driving rain towards the house that she wondered suddenly if Daniel had heard them arrive. She sent a sharp glance at the curtained windows, but there was no revealing twitching of velvet. He hadn't seen her kissing Zac, she decided with relief. He would be expecting her to come home by bus, so even if he'd heard the car, he would not have associated the deep sound of Zac's Porsche with her arrival home.

He wasn't in the sitting-room. The study door was ajar and she glanced in but there was no sign of him there either. She found him in the kitchen.

'You're back earlier than I expected,' she remarked casually as she entered. He had his back to her as he waited for the kettle to boil. And he looked nice in a simple black sweatshirt and casual jeans.

'I let my mother go home,' he told her, ignoring her remark. His hand was shaking a little as he poured the boiling water on to the tea-bags. 'She was concerned about you when she saw your car was still on the drive and you were nowhere to be found. You could have let her know that you weren't taking your own car.'

'It wouldn't start,' she explained. 'So I caught the bus. I'm sorry,' she added belatedly. 'I didn't think it would worry Jenny. I'll apologise to her tomorrow…'

Silence. He still hadn't looked at her, his whole attention seemingly fixed on the tea-tray he was preparing. It suddenly hit her that Daniel was blindingly angry about something. It showed in the cording of the muscles in his neck, in the way his every movement was being severely controlled as he moved about the kitchen without so much as glancing her way.

Had he seen? Letting out a nervous little laugh, she said, 'I'm soaking wet through!' Trying to sound normal and failing miserably, guilt was staining her cheeks red. And she knew that if Daniel did bother to look at her he would know in an instant that she had been up to no good. 'I think I'll go and have a hot bath,' she decided nervously. Then, belatedly, 'H-Have you eaten? Can I get you anything before I—'

'*No*!' he barked out so violently that Rachel jumped.

Chewing pensively on her lower lip, she watched him make an effort to control himself, his shoulders heaving on a long intake of air as he lifted his face from its contemplation of the teapot to stare at the slatted blinds covering the kitchen window.

'No,' he repeated more levelly. 'I've already eaten. Thank you.'

'Then I'll…' She floundered to a halt, staring helplessly at the uncommunicative length of his rigid back—then fled.

He had seen, she accepted uneasily as she watched the water fill the bath, and felt a skitter of alarm chase down her spine, but could not make up her mind whether it was caused by fear, guilt or just the sheer thrill of getting her own back if only in a small way.

She went to bed feeling tense with nervous anticipation, a driving defiance, and ready to do battle when Daniel eventually joined her.

But he didn't join her. Daniel did not come to bed at all that night.

CHAPTER EIGHT

THE next few weeks were horrible. Daniel turned into a grim-faced uncommunicative stranger, and their nights were cold, dark places where he did not so much as touch her. The children became fractious—excited about the coming Christmas, Rachel blamed, but really she knew that it was her and Daniel's fault. The strain in their marriage was affecting the children almost as badly as it was affecting them.

The trouble was that she didn't know what to do about it, short of going to Daniel and making a full confession of what had gone on between herself and Zac, before humbly asking for his forgiveness, and she couldn't do that. It smacked too much of caring what he thought or felt, and she was determined not to care—outwardly anyway.

Then one day Rachel was sick. She spent the whole day wandering aimlessly around the house, feeling dull-witted and weak-tummied, and the twins had to pick that same evening after school to play noisily about the house until her head was thumping like a sledge-hammer, and she was plainly relieved when Daniel walked through the front door so that she could pass responsibility over to him and drag herself off to bed.

'Why didn't you call me?' he rebuked as he watched her slog her way up the stairs. 'I would have come home straight away if you'd only let me know you didn't feel well!'

She just shrugged an obscure reply and continued on. It had not even entered her head to call him. In fact, she realised as she crawled beneath the duvet, she had never rung him at work—not in all the years since they married. Daniel called home often enough, but she'd never bothered to call him. And again she was struck by that invisible barrier they'd managed to erect between Daniel the husband and father and Daniel the high-powered businessman. And she could not bring to mind one single time when she had voluntarily crossed that barrier.

Well, whatever he was at this moment, she noted as she settled with relief into the blessed darkness, he had effectively quietened the children, and within seconds she had fallen into a blissful sleep which remained that way because not a single sound in the house was allowed to disturb her.

She came awake long hours later to find it was already morning and that Daniel was standing over her. 'I thought you might want this…' He was standing with a mug of something hot in his hand. As he spoke, he put it down on the bedside table. 'How are you feeling this morning?' he enquired coolly.

'Better,' she said, though she was very careful not to jolt her tender stomach as she levered her way up the pillows, then pushed her hair away from her pale face before reaching for the mug. 'Thank you,' she murmured.

Daniel hovered, studying her grimly. 'I can take the day off,' he offered. 'Work from home if you want.'

Rachel shook her head. 'It's not necessary,' she assured him. 'I'll probably feel a bit weak today, but I can manage OK.'

'Still…' It was odd, but she got the distinct impression he was struggling with something. 'You'd better not plan on going to your class tonight—not while you're feeling so under the weather…'

The mug of tea was hot. She blew absently at the steam.

'We've planned a Christmas party tonight,' she informed him as lightly as she could manage. 'Zac is taking us all out to a club after class. I don't want to miss it.'

Her tone smacked of the usual defiance, and from the corner of her vision she saw his jaw twitch revealingly. He was trying hard not to make the cutting remark she just knew was hanging on the end of his tongue. It was horrible; even while she wanted to taunt him, it was horrible.

'We'll see how you feel later,' was all he eventually replied, then turned to leave.

And suddenly she felt an aching need to make him stay! 'M-My parents are coming down for Christmas as usual,' she rushed out, watching him halt stiffly by the bedroom door. 'But we have a problem this year...' He didn't look at her, just waited for her to say what the problem was with his back placed firmly towards her. 'Last year we didn't have Michael taking up the spare bedroom. Now I don't know how we're going to put them up for two nights—I just can't imagine my father jammed between two chairs in your study while my mother hogs the sofa in the sitting-room!' She'd meant it as a joke but, as Daniel turned to look at her, she saw he was not smiling and felt her heart sink even deeper into that cold, bleak place where it existed these days.

'So what do you want me to do about it?' he demanded. 'I've lost count of the times I've tried to get you to move to something bigger than this house. But you would never so much as discuss it. Well, now you're stuck with a problem that you will just have to solve on your own, because I'm damned if I'm having anything to do with it!'

Rachel stared at him in angry amazement as he just turned and slammed out of the room.

She went to her evening class that night. Not because she felt well enough to go—because she didn't. And not because she wanted to go—which she didn't. But because she felt so angry with Daniel that she refused to give him the satisfaction he would feel if she stayed at home instead!

But she did not enjoy it. Her mind was preoccupied with a million and one things she could be doing at home, and her stomach refused to settle down. She was tired, tense and pale. And, on top of all that, Zac spent the whole time watching her through dark, disturbing eyes.

OK, so it was the first time since he first met her that he'd seen her in anything but jeans, and she had to acknowledge that he looked rather dishy himself in a dark silk lounge suit and creamy shirt. She was wearing a little black dress she had bought on that first bout of restlessness that had sent her up to London to create her new image. It was off-the-shoulder, short and figure-hugging, and she received several teasingly provocative comments from some of the other men when they saw her.

But the way Zac was looking at her made her feel distinctly uncomfortable. And his eyes kept on telling her that he was remembering that kiss they'd started in his car, whereas Rachel had spent the last few weeks trying to dismiss it from her mind. Which wasn't difficult—it was the guilt that was the hardest to dismiss, not the kiss.

They were going on to a local nightclub later. It was in actual fact an old cinema converted into a club. They'd booked a table in the mezzanine restaurant that looked down on the old stalls area, which was now a disco dancefloor with laser lights and throbbing disco music played so loud that it was virtually impossible to speak. Any other time she would have thoroughly enjoyed the whole thing. The places Daniel took her to were more sophisticated and sedate, the restaurants quiet, the music easy-listening, middle-of-the-road stuff. And until this last bust-up with him she had been quite looking forward simply to letting her hair down and discoing the night away.

As it was, her stomach would not let her enjoy the meal she'd ordered, and the music grated on her thumping head. Zac had pulled his chair up close to hers and was insisting on monopolising her attention with soft conversation that forced her to lean towards him to catch what he was saying, and brought her into too intimate contact with his body.

Then he began touching her—nothing too heavy, just light brushes of his long fingers against her arm, her shoulder, her cheek and her hair. But she became so uptight with the situation, and felt so helpless to know what to do about it without causing a scene in front of the others, that she was glad when he suddenly asked her to dance.

At least dancing meant no body contact—not the kind of dancing they did here anyway—so she let him lead her down the stairs on to the dance-floor, then almost groaned when, determinedly, he pulled her into his arms.

'No, Zac,' she objected, trying to move away from him.

'Don't be stupid, Rachel,' he drawled. 'It's only a dance.'

No, it wasn't, and he knew it. After weeks of playing it relatively cool, he had decided to make his move on her. And if she didn't put a stop to him now, then she really would be guilty of betraying Daniel.

'No,' she repeated firmly, slapped his hands away and turned to walk off the floor.

She shouldn't have come. She had known she shouldn't have come after that kiss they'd shared in his car. She'd known from the moment their eyes clashed across the lecture hall weeks ago that she should not have anything to do with Zac.

He wanted her and she did not want him.

She wanted Daniel. Only Daniel. And that hurt so much that it made her want to weep inside.

She sensed Zac behind her as she made her way to the main foyer, but refused to look back at him as she moved grimly for the line of phone booths and began ringing the several different taxi companies whose telephone numbers were scrawled all over the pay-phone backboard.

But to no avail. It was Christmas, and anyone with any sense had booked their ride home before even coming out.

In sheer desperation she rang home, her stomach flipping wistfully when Daniel's deep voice came impatiently down the line.

'It's me,' she murmured huskily.

There was a long pause on the other end, where all she could hear was Daniel's steady breathing whispering in her ear. 'What's the matter?' he asked at last.

'I—can't get home,' she confessed. 'I've tried all the taxi firms and they're all booked out... What shall I do?'

Just like that. As easily as that she had fallen back into her old Rachel role. Any problem, refer it to Daniel. He would deal with it. He would sort it out. And all she had to do was stand back and wait for a solution to come via the man who had never let her down yet. Not in this way anyway.

There followed another silence, and Rachel lowered her head, hugging the dark grey plastic receiver to her ear, as though by doing so she was hugging tightly to Daniel himself.

'Won't your—Romeo bring you?' he taunted eventually.

'He's not my Romeo!' she denied. 'And—anyway,' she added, 'I...' No, she changed her mind about what she had been going to say, not wanting to give Daniel the pleasure of hearing that she did not want Zac anywhere near her. 'I can't drag him away from a good party so early just because I've had enough—can't you come for me, Daniel?' she pleaded softly.

'What about the children?' he came back sarcastically. 'Am I supposed to leave them here on their own while I come out to get you?'

'Oh.' She felt foolish again. She hadn't considered that problem. All she had done was realise she was in a mess and ring the man who always put things right for her.

'Now she wishes she had taken my advice and employed a nanny!' he mocked her acidly.

'I'll get Zac to bring me,' she hit right back. The nanny thing was an old point of friction between them. Daniel wanted a bigger house, a housekeeper to take care of it, a nanny to take care of the children. What Rachel would like to know was what was left for her to do if he made her redundant in just about every part she played in his life.

'I'll call my mother, get her over here to sit while I come and get you.' Daniel changed tack like a sailor, his voice like a rattlesnake waving its tail in warning. 'I'll have to get her out of bed, I suppose, and she won't like it—for which I don't blame her. But I'll—'

'Oh—no,' Rachel drawled in angry refusal. 'I wouldn't like to think that I had inconvenienced you all to that extent. Zac will do it just as easily!' And she slammed down the phone before Daniel could come back with a reply.

'No luck?' She turned to find Zac leaning against the wall, not three feet away from her, his eyes flickering curiously over her angry red cheeks. She had no idea how much of her conversation with Daniel he had overheard, and at that precise moment didn't care.

'No,' she clipped. 'I'll just have to call one of the taxi firms back and book the next car they have free.' Her shrug told him she was already resigning herself to a long wait.

'I'll take you,' he offered. Rachel stared at him dubiously. She did not feel like half an hour more of his company. But then neither did she feel like hanging around here for the hour or so the taxi companies had said she would have to wait. Zac made the decision for her, reaching out to take hold of her wrist. 'Come on,' he said quietly. 'I'll take you—I'll take you, Rachel.'

His green eyes mocked her foolishness. And, tired, fed up and feeling more than a little depressed by the constant emotional battle she seemed to be having with everyone around her, including herself, she gave in.

They went together to retrieve her coat, then braved the biting December wind outside to scramble inside the bright red Porsche. Then they were driving out of the club's car park and on to the main road while she huddled into her thick woollen coat, watching emptily as the salt-stained road slid slickly beneath them.

'Why do you put up with him when he's such a selfish bastard?' Zac bit out suddenly.

'Aren't all men?' she countered tartly.

'Not like Daniel,' he muttered. 'I still find it hard to believe that he's married to someone like you.' He glanced at her. 'The Lydia Marsdens of this world suit him much better, you know.'

It was a ruthless thrust and hit home painfully, draining her lungs and blanching her face, because she couldn't even argue the point with him. Lydia Marsden *was* probably more suited to Daniel—not that she'd ever seen the woman to judge—not that she ever wanted to see her.

Lydia Marsden was the faceless ghost who visited her in the night. That wretched haunting was more than enough to deal with.

'And Mandy Sales,' he added tauntingly. 'That was quite a revealing confrontation you all had on the dance-floor that night, wasn't it?'

'You overheard?' Rachel gasped.

'Half the room overheard it, darling,' he drawled. 'And stood in stunned amazement as it all began to sink in. Daniel Masterson—' his smile was drily mocking '—whiz-kid of the new-age tycoons, had a little wife and three children tucked away nobody seemed to know about— I bet that news, when it got out, hit Lydia right where it hurts the most. She was after marrying him, you know. Daniel was the ideal choice for an up-and-coming corporate lawyer like her.'

So Lydia was a lawyer, not Daniel's secretary, as she had assumed. The news jolted her. Compete with that if you can, she mocked herself bitterly. It was one thing believing you were fighting an ordinary secretary for your husband's attention—but some female hot-shot lawyer?

As if thinking along similar lines, Zac murmured curiously, 'If you've been married for seven years, then that means you caught him before Daniel made his meteoric elevation into the killing-fields of finance. So what does that make you, Rachel?' he asked. 'A hanger-on from his reckless youth?'

Insults were insults and, in Rachel's mind, some were probably deserved. But that last remark had aimed to cut— and cut it had, if only because it pierced directly at the truth she was beginning to believe for herself.

'I think you'd better shut up and stop this car so I can get out before you say something I'll take real exception to,' she snapped.

To her consternation he did exactly that, pulling the car into the kerb and stopping with a jerk before turning to glare angrily at her. 'Well, I've already taken exception,' he muttered, 'to the way you've been playing me along all these weeks. My God!' he grated before she could say anything. 'I never stood a chance with you, did I?'

'No,' she answered honestly.

'Then why the hell didn't you stop me before we got in this deep?'

'This deep—what deep?' She turned to challenge him with a deriding look. 'We haven't done anything but share a fumbled kiss on a rainy night!'

'We were sharing more than that, Rachel, and you know it,' he scathed her derision. 'But it was all just a game with you, wasn't it? You saw I fancied you and thought you would play me along for a while. What was it?' he demanded bitterly. 'Did your ego need a bit of a lift? Has it begun to get to you at last that he gets a bigger kick out of bedding his legal adviser than he does his wife?'

She hit him then, her hand striking at his cheek while her own face went white with pain. Then she made a grab for the door-handle, her other hand fumbling to unfasten her seatbelt so that she could get away. But Zac grabbed her arm, his fingers biting. 'Oh, no,' he muttered. 'You don't get away with that so easily.'

With a tug he pulled her against him, and his mouth came down on top of hers. It was an intrusion—a vile rape of her unresponsive mouth. And by the time he let her go again she was choking on the taste of him.

Then thankfully she was out of the car, slamming the door shut in his hard angry face.

He didn't hang around. He fired the car engine into life, then was driving off on a screech of tyres, leaving her standing there in the biting cold wind, watching his red taillights disappear from view.

She dragged a hand across her mouth, grimacing when she felt the telling sting which said he had managed to cut her inner lip. Damn him! she thought, wishing herself back in that old fairy-tale world she used to exist in, where nothing nasty happened. Damn Mandy for waking her up out of it! she added bitterly as she began the walk home. Damn Daniel for his infidelity and damn Lydia for giving in to his expert seduction! But most of all—damn herself!

She wasn't too far away from home, she noted thankfully, but her feet were killing her by the time she hobbled through the front door, and she kicked the offending high heels off as soon as she'd closed the door behind her. It was warm inside, after the biting cold night air.

One o'clock, she noticed testily as she climbed the stairs. She felt utterly done in; depression sat on the top of her head with a vengeance and the ugly scene with Zac echoed over and over in her mind. She didn't bother trying to look for Daniel. He could be in hell for all she cared. And anyway, she was in no mood for yet another row tonight. He obviously agreed that they'd done enough of that on the phone because he hadn't bothered meeting her with the proverbial whip at the front door as she came in.

But she was wrong if she thought he was going to ignore her completely. She had only managed to strip off her dress and pull on her dressing-gown when he entered the bedroom, her discarded shoes dangling from his fingers.

'You forgot these.' He dropped them by the closed bedroom door.

'I didn't forget them,' she snapped. 'I just left them where they came off.' She was sitting on the edge of the bed, massaging her aching toes, her head lowered so that the soft cloud of her hair hid her face from view.

'He didn't bring you all the way home,' he remarked with suspicious levity.

Been spying through cracks in the curtains again? she wondered bitterly. 'Maybe he didn't bring me at all,' was all she said.

'You haven't had time to walk all that way.'

I've walked far enough! she thought, studying her poor aching feet.

'Have a lovers' tiff, did you?' He was getting nasty; she could hear the level of control dropping with each word.

'Something like that,' she shrugged, getting off the bed and walking towards the bathroom. Let him think what he liked! she thought mutinously. Let him think what he damned well liked.

His hands grasping hold of her upper arms brought her spinning round to face him. He wasn't just angry, she noted on a small bubble of alarm, he was furious—tense with it, pulsing with it, eyes like silver beacons.

'And what was this—tiff about?' he demanded tightly. 'Wouldn't you go back to his place with him? Is that it? What's the matter, Rachel—weren't you in the mood?'

Her own eyes flashed, bitterness and a downright disgust with men in general tonight making her retaliate in kind. 'But how do you know I haven't been at his place all evening?' she taunted. 'I could have rung you just as easily from there, you know. How are you to know the difference?'

He went white, his fingers biting painfully into her flesh, hard eyes flashing over her face as if he were looking for evidence to prove what she was suggesting could be true. 'Your lip,' he growled. 'He bruised your lip!'

'And you're bruising my arms!' she cried. 'Will you let go?' She tried to pull away but he just increased his grip until she winced.

'How could you?' he bit out hoarsely. 'How could you do it, Rachel? How could you?'

It was all beginning to boil. It had been threatening to do it for long enough, and at last the full force of their pent-up emotions was beginning to bubble to the surface.

'I tell you what, Daniel,' she flashed, 'let's exchange

notes since you're so damned interested! You tell me how it was with Lydia and I'll tell you how it was with Zac!'

'God, stop it!' He closed his eyes, pain raking across his features, and Rachel felt tears of utter wretchedness burn at the back of her eyes. For the second time that night she hit out at a man, hitting him with both her fists until Daniel let her go.

'You disgust me, do you know that?' she whispered bitterly, and flung herself into the bathroom, her fingers trembling as she slid home the small bolt which was never used.

When she came out again, calmer but by no means under control, she found Daniel sitting on the bed with his head buried in his hands. It hurt to see him like that. But, there again, everything hurt these days. She couldn't remember a time when she had last felt like laughing in this house.

'I want to go to bed,' she said, refusing point-blank to give in to those weaker feelings his defeated pose raked her with.

He didn't move, and after a long taut minute while she stood there, hovering between a bitter desire to hit him again and a weak need to run over there and hold him, simply hold him because he was hurting and she loved him—damn her!—loved him no matter what he said or did to her—she felt something go snap inside her, and on a groan that was a wretched cry of frustration she dropped down on her knees in front of him, her hands going up to grasp his wrists angrily, pulling them away from his face.

'Do you really want to know what happened tonight?' she demanded shrilly. 'He came on to me but I repulsed him, so he paid me back by taunting me with Lydia!' The hurt shot across her eyes and Daniel closed his to shut it out. 'Lydia,' she repeated thickly. 'The high-powered lawyer who is far more Daniel Masterson's type than pathetic little Rachel is!'

'That's not true,' he whispered tensely.

'No?' Tears spread across her eyes, the torture of it all making her heart muscles tremble. 'Well, I think it's true,' she asserted thickly. 'We've grown apart, Daniel! You going one way while I've stayed still, and I think the Lydia Marsdens of this world are far more your type now!'

To her surprise, he laughed, deridingly shaking his dark head as if he couldn't believe she'd actually said that. 'Does it look as though I've grown apart from you?' he demanded tightly. 'Am I straining at the leash to get away? Are my suitcases packed and standing by the door? Hard ruthless bastard that I am, Rachel, don't you think I'm quite capable of walking away from you if I decided it was what I wanted to do?' She had no idea how it happened, but suddenly it was Daniel gripping her wrists, not the other way around.

She shook her head. 'Lydia,' she murmured. 'She's—'

'To hell with bloody Lydia,' he dismissed scathingly. 'This is not about her. This is about you and me and whether we can still stand the sight of each other!'

'Guilty conscience, then!' she sighed. 'You stay because of your damned guilty conscience!'

'Well, I certainly have one of those!' he bitterly agreed. 'But don't be foolish enough to grant me concessions where none are due,' he warned. 'I am no one's martyr, Rachel. If I believed this marriage of ours a waste of time, I would have walked out long ago. Be sure of it. This is the nineteen-nineties after all,' he added cynically. 'Marriages break up all the time. No,' he murmured roughly, 'this is why I stay.' He pulled her towards him to kiss her hard. 'I want you,' he growled. 'I can't honestly get enough of you! Even after seven years I can still get hot in the groin just looking at you! My God!' he added harshly. 'I can't even stop myself from taking you when I know I can no longer satisfy you.'

He shook his dark head in self-disgust. 'But that doesn't explain why you haven't thrown me out,' he went on grimly. 'How can you, Rachel, having had me hurt you, break your trust, make your life a misery? Why?' He gave her wrists a hard shake. 'Why haven't you told me to get out?'

'I...' No. She shook her head, refusing to answer, because the answer was so utterly degrading to her already humiliated soul.

'Then would you *like* to call it a day?' He altered the challenge slightly. 'And have me out of your life?'

Her body jerked in reaction, a harsh stab of pain cutting right through her. 'No,' she whispered, feeling the weighted beginning of tears build in her chest.

'Why not?' he persisted ruthlessly. 'How do you stand having me living in the same house with you—sleeping in the same bed as you—touching you—holding you—how do you stand it, Rachel? How—how—how?'

Because I love you, you rotten bastard! she thought, and let the tears break free on a helpless sob.

Daniel sighed, the sound coming from some deeply wretched part of him, and the next thing she knew he had freed her captured wrists to wrap his arms around her and he was falling back, taking her with him, his body covering her, curling around her and holding her, holding her so tight and so close she could barely breathe.

'Does this feel as though we've grown apart?' he demanded sensually.

'No.' This felt wonderful, the only place in the world she wanted to be.

'Then shut up about us growing apart,' he said thickly, then kissed her, long and fiercely, giving her no chance to think, no chance to recover, but just governing her every thought and feeling until she began to sink languidly into the warm morass of his loving.

'Did you let that bastard touch you, Rachel?' The rough-voiced enquiry brought her swimming protestingly up from the wonderful place she had sunk to.

Her eyes flicked open, furious blue staring into tortured grey, searching, half refusing to believe that he had actually asked her that question.

But he had. 'Did you?' he persisted when she said nothing. 'I want to know—I *need* to know! God,' he choked, '*I have to know*!'

She stared at him for a moment longer, then bared her angry teeth to say, 'Go to hell.'

He did, it seemed, she realised later, go straight to hell, but he made sure he took her with him. It happened with an angry passion that had him wrenching open her robe then releasing himself from his own clothes so he could thrust inside her with such appalling ruthlessness that she didn't think she took a single breath until it was all over.

Then she rolled away on to her own side of the bed and Daniel went into the bathroom and shut the door.

He stayed in there a long time. Long enough to let her crawl beneath the duvet and be asleep by the time he came back.

The next evening, the telephone began ringing just as she was clearing away the children's evening meal. She walked towards the hall extension and picked it up, frowning in annoyance because the children had the TV on too loud.

'Rachel Masterson,' she murmured absently into the receiver, stretching the telephone cable to its limits in her effort to reach the sitting-room door so that she could pull it to.

There was a pause on the other end of the line, then a cool voice asked to speak to Daniel.

'I'm afraid he isn't home yet,' she answered. 'Can I take a message or get him to call you back?'

Another pause while the caller deliberated with herself, and Rachel looked distractedly at the time. She had a pair of steaks under the grill; if the woman didn't hurry up, she—

'This is Lydia Marsden,' the cool voice explained, and Rachel went absolutely still.

CHAPTER NINE

RACHEL was still staring at the telephone where she had placed it very carefully back on its rest when Daniel came home a few moments later. He saw her as soon as he got in the door—and stopped dead in his tracks.

'What is it?' he asked sharply, seeing at a glance that she was suffering some kind of shock.

Her hand lifted to her cheek, ice-cold fingers resting on equally cold flesh. 'Lydia just called,' she told him blankly. 'She wants you to call her back.'

As she continued to stare at him, wondering if she was just going to faint quietly away or go the whole hog and fall apart at the very seams, she saw Daniel's face suffuse with hot colour, watched his chest lift and fall on a single throbbing breath as emotion, the like of which she had never seen him display before, threatened to explode right over her bemused head.

His mouth tightened and lost all vestige of colour, his nostrils flaring like a wild animal threatening attack. He dropped his briefcase to the floor, sucking in another breath through teeth so tightly clenched that the air whistled as it was pulled into his heaving lungs.

Then he moved to a paralysed Rachel, taking hold of her to move her bodily out of the way so that he could get to his study. The door slammed shut behind him. Rachel stood staring at it, wondering just what had taken place here in her hallway—besides the holocaust happening inside herself, that was.

The mere mention of Lydia's name could bring on a

133

reaction like that? Have him bodily shifting her aside like that?

She choked on a strangled sob, then quite ruthlessly controlled herself, refusing to give in to what was going on inside her.

Lydia had called, and Daniel had run like a man possessed!

She was nursing Michael in the sitting-room when Daniel came looking for her. He looked pale, and, although most of that terrible emotion had diminished, she could still see the residue glimmering in his eyes. Kate ran to him for her customary hug but only received a token stroke of her golden head. Sam waved a leg—he was stretched out in front of the TV, engrossed in an old black and white movie. Michael was tired, and only fit to give his father a concessionary glance before sinking himself back into the pleasure of being held in his mother's arms.

Daniel was looking fixedly at Rachel. 'I apologise,' he said roughly. 'She's been told never to ring here.'

'It doesn't matter.'

'Of course it bloody matters!' he barked, and in unison the children turned to stare at him in surprise. He ran an impatient hand through his hair, sighing in an effort to control himself. 'Sammy—Kate. Play with Michael for a moment while I talk to your mother.'

Without waiting for any arguments, he plucked a complaining Michael out of Rachel's arms and sat him between Sam's legs on the floor, gathered together a selection of toys around them, then smiled at all three in what Rachel assumed to be an attempt at reassurance since they were all staring warily at him.

Then he turned and grasped Rachel's hand, pulling her to her feet and through to his study, only letting go of her when they were safely shut behind the closed door.

'She's been told never to call here,' he repeated tautly. 'She was told to get the damned cleaner to call me if it was that urgent! But never to do it herself!'

'As I said, it doesn't matter.'

'But it does matter!' he exploded with rasping ferocity. 'She hurt you just now—and I was determined that was not going to happen!'

'Then you should have...' She bit back the accusing words wanting to tumble from her lips and, with a small shrug, moved jerkily to his desk, finding his scattered papers in sudden need of tidying. 'How is it that she still works for you?' she questioned tightly. 'If you say it's over.' It had been a bitter blow that, finding out that Lydia still worked for him.

'She doesn't work for me,' he said tightly. 'She works for the firm of lawyers I employ,' he explained at her puzzled look. 'I had all my business transferred to one of her partners weeks ago.'

She didn't believe him. She could still see the expression on his face when she had told him Lydia rang. She could still feel the way he had moved her roughly to one side.

She shuddered. 'Then what is she doing calling here?' she asked.

Daniel took in a short breath, still struggling, she was sure, with the emotions Lydia's call caused to erupt. 'She happened to be the last in their suite of offices when some urgent information came through by fax,' he explained. 'It was important enough to necessitate someone informing me as soon as possible. And she was the only person there to do it!'

'Oh.' That was all Rachel could think of to say to that. 'Well, just make sure she never calls here again,' she added flatly, and in a tone which decidedly closed the subject.

But the uncomfortable silence that followed warned her there was more to come.

She was right. 'The thing is,' he began carefully, 'it means I have to go out again, almost immediately. A legal problem has developed with the Huddersfield take-over and I have to go back to the office to sort it out personally.'

The Harvey take-over, the Huddersfield take-over—what was the difference? 'Of course you do,' she agreed, with such acid understanding that it was like a slap in the face. 'And I have to put the children to bed.'

Pushing past him, she went to leave the room.

But Daniel stopped her. 'No.' Grabbing hold of her, he brought her to stand in front of him. 'I'm going to my own office, Rachel.' His eyes were a cool, steady, honest grey. 'Not Lydia's office. She has already faxed me the information I need—to my own office,' he emphasised clearly. 'I won't see her. I don't want to see her. We will have the full width of London between us—do you understand?'

Understand? Yes, she understood. He was demanding she trust his word. His steady gaze was insisting she trust his word.

A trust she did not feel she could give him.

Could maybe never give him again.

'Michael needs me,' she murmured, and pulled free to leave the room.

That had been Friday. On Monday he was going up to Huddersfield to tie up the loose ends of the deal before the Christmas break. And after an awful weekend, during which they paid a cool kind of courtesy to each other, Rachel could only feel relieved that he was going.

But he reached for her on Sunday night. And, in the middle of their desperate attempts to achieve some level of mutual satisfaction from their shared passion, he broke one of her strictest rules—he spoke to her. He asked her to forgive him. It made her cry out in pained protest at his spoiling what they were managing to share. Her wretchedness curbed his tongue, but when he came into her there was a new urgency about him that verged on the tormented, and afterwards she found herself desperately wanting to comfort him when he just turned and lay with his face pressed into the pillow, yet was unable to because it would feel so much that she was conceding something too important to him.

She only wished she knew what that important thing was! The trouble was, she was beginning to lose sight of what exactly was causing all the dissension between them.

Lydia, she reminded herself. Lydia.

Yet even that name was beginning to lose its ability to wound as deeply as it used to do.

Over the next few days she threw herself into a mad splurge of last-minute preparations for Christmas. She stubbornly ignored her continuing nervous stomach as she became engrossed in bedroom re-organisation until, by the evening Daniel was due home, she was beginning to feel so limp she wondered if giving in and taking to her bed might not be a bad idea.

They were all in the sitting-room, trying to erect the huge Christmas tree that had just been delivered, when the door opened and Daniel walked in. A rueful smile softened his harsh features as he took in the sight of all four of them struggling between the prickly branches of a disobliging tree.

'I see I'm still needed for a few small duties around here, then,' he mocked, bringing four heads whipping around in surprise.

The children deserted Rachel to fall on Daniel instead,

and he, with a cry of mock terror, fell down on the carpet as two wiry bodies landed on top of him laughing and whooping, while the third member of their little trio had to crawl his way over to his father as fast as his hands and knees could take him.

Rachel watched, her hands pricked full of pine needles but unaware of the stings, smiling stupidly at the mini-war taking place on her sitting-room floor.

And it was there, on a sudden surge of the sweetest insight she had ever experienced, that she saw the blistering truth as to why her life was so worth keeping as it was.

Family. Family love. A simple yet complicated interconnecting weave of love, from one to the other to the other, that bound them all together so tightly that even when one link broke and tried to tear them all apart it couldn't. Because the others held on so fast.

Made it worthwhile to hold on fast.

And Daniel like this was the old Daniel. Not the one so rushed off his feet that he was too tired to take time out to wrestle on the floor with his children: to enjoy them—simply enjoy as they tickled him and made him shriek for mercy.

Michael sat on his middle, patting hard on the steel wall of a chest with both hands. 'I give in—I give in!' Daniel cried as Sammy straddled his shoulders to hold him down so that Kate could tickle him ruthlessly, the sly pair knowing Daniel couldn't do a thing to save himself while Michael sat squarely on his middle. 'Help me, Rachel!' he pleaded. 'I need help!'

She let go of the tree, watching it warily for a moment to be sure it wouldn't fall down on top of them all before she went to pluck up Michael, tucking him under her arm so that she could tease Kate with a bit of her own medicine, leaving Daniel free to deal with Sam. In one swift economical movement he was on his feet with his eldest son wrapped in a bear-hug of a grip while he rained noisy wet kisses all over his disgusted face.

'Yuk!' Sammy protested, wriggling like an eel and loving every minute of it. There were not many ways to give six-year-old boys the kisses and cuddles they needed but were not allowed to admit to. But Daniel was using the best way right now, by making a game of it. And by the time he set Sam down on the floor the little boy was flushed with happiness and pretending utter disgust. Then he was laughing shrilly as Daniel went after a squealing Kate. She was easy to catch; it was very hard to feign reluctance when all you really wanted to do was to be wrapped in those big strong arms and hugged and kissed.

Michael watched, his little face alive with the fun of it all. And Rachel hugged him to her, gaining comfort from his warm little body, when really what she wanted to do was beg for her turn as, once upon a time, she would have done—quite brazenly.

That Daniel was thinking along similar lines was clear when he set Kate down on her feet, then fixed his uncertain gaze on Rachel. Feeling suddenly shy and self-conscious, she handed him Michael, lowering her fine-veined lids over her eyes as he took the hint and rolled back down on to the floor to tease his younger son into infectious baby giggles.

The Christmas tree chose that moment to begin creaking warningly. Rachel reached it in time, but not before she became lost in pine branches. Another hand, longer and stronger than hers, appeared just above her own, Daniel's lightning-quick reactions allowing him to leap off the floor and snake out a hand to take the weight of the tree from her, easily pushing it upright again. Rachel then found herself being disentangled by firm but gentle hands.

'You've scratched your cheek,' Daniel observed huskily, and lowered his mouth to place his lips on the tiny mark by the corner of her mouth. His tongue flicked out to soothe the tender spot, and she quivered.

'Hello,' he murmured softly, grey eyes gently noting the blushing shyness in her expression.

'Hello,' she answered huskily, having difficulty meeting his gaze. Then his mouth was lowering again, demanding a slower, deeper, much more intimate kiss. He felt warm and vital, the hard-packed leanness of his muscled body so achingly familiar to her own. And she closed her eyes, giving herself up to the sheer uncomplicated beauty of the embrace.

The doorbell chimed, breaking them reluctantly apart as the twins shot off with a yelp to let Daniel's mother in, since she was expected at that moment.

'Y-Your mother is taking them to the Christingle service,' Rachel breathlessly explained.

'She is?' he answered absently, his eyes smoky as they roamed her blushing face. 'Good,' he murmured, and kissed her again, softly, tenderly, lingeringly, his warm mouth clinging to hers even when his mother walked into the room and halted abruptly when she realised what she was walking in on.

Rachel didn't even hear her. A love she had thought she had lost for good was welling up inside her, fanning a beautiful sensual warmth into every part of her tingling frame, and with a sigh that was like the soft whisper of a breeze against his mouth she slid her hands up his arms and curled her fingers into the silken darkness of his hair.

They were both out of breath when they eventually broke apart. Daniel turned to smile at his mother, but his vision was not quite focused, and Jenny Masterson's smile was unsteady as she gazed at them both with undiluted hope written in her anxious eyes.

It was only after Rachel had helped bundle the children into their warm anoraks, while Daniel secured the tree, that she remembered the reorganisation that had gone on upstairs while he had been away, and she bit down on her bottom lip, wondering how she was going to tell him and weakly putting the moment off until she had no choice.

They waved the children and his mother off together, Daniel's arm a possessive clamp around Rachel's waist as Jenny trotted off with Michael wrapped up warm in his push-chair and the twins skipping along beside her, chatting away nineteen to the dozen.

Daniel closed the door. The silence inside the house seemed strange after the noise of a minute ago.

'Come with me while I change?' he invited, tentatively offering her his hand.

She took it meekly, letting him pull her up the stairs behind him to their bedroom where Daniel gave a contented sigh and moved away from her to begin tugging at his tie.

Rachel watched him from the door, her hands twisting together in front of her. 'Er...' she began.

He didn't seem to hear, his steps taking him right into the bathroom. Then...

'What the—?' He was out of the door like a bullet, staring at her incredulously, thinking, she knew, all kinds of things which had to hurt.

'I had to put my parents somewhere!' she burst out defensively. 'This was the only practical solution!' She waved an agitated hand at their room, where the bathroom already stood shiny clean and empty of all their personal toiletries. She had emptied one of her wardrobes into Daniel's. It had been a tight fit, and she was ruefully aware that their clothes were going to need a good pressing before they would be fit to wear again. But…

'And where,' he gritted, 'are you and I sleeping?'

Her hand fluttered in the vague direction of the other bedrooms. 'It worked out quite well in the end,' she told him nervously. 'I had two new beds delivered, one in Sam's room and one in Kate's. Y-Your mother can sleep in Kate's room with her.' His mother always slept over on Christmas Eve—she liked to be there to watch the children open their presents on Christmas morning. 'I'll sleep in Michael's room and y-you can sleep in Sam's. It's only for two nights, Daniel!' she appealed for his understanding when he looked ready to explode. 'You know we daren't put the twins together or they'll never sleep! And as it is the children are quite excited about it. They—'

'Hell and damnation!' he exploded anyway. 'What is it with you, Rachel?' he bit out furiously. 'Why the hell should I give up my bed for your parents? Why can't they sleep in the other beds? Or have you done this just to get another dig at me? Because if you have, I'm warning you, I've damned well had enough of it!'

Rachel bristled at the injustice. 'Since when have my parents been any trouble to you?' she retaliated. 'You only have to put up with them once a year! Show them some consideration, for goodness' sake! They'll be driving down here tomorrow directly from closing the shop, and they won't stop until they arrive. They're big-framed, Daniel! And getting on in years. They won't feel comfortable sharing with the twins!'

'I can't believe you've actually done this!' he rasped, too angry to listen to a thing she was saying. 'I come home after one hell of a week in Huddersfield—Huddersfield, for God's sake!' he derided, as though it were the end of the earth. 'Looking forward to a peaceful Christmas in my own home—*my own* home!—and find I've been chucked out of my bedroom by a vindictive wife who can't find enough ways to… It wouldn't be so bad.' He changed tack on a blankly staring Rachel, running his angry fingers through his hair. 'It wouldn't be so bad if the damned house was big enough for me to get lost in if I felt like it. But because *you* refuse to move to something better, *I* have to lose *my* home comforts, *Me*!' he choked. 'A damned cash million-aire—living in a poky little cardboard box with three noisy little brats and a wife who…'

His mouth snapped shut, his angry gaze at last focusing on Rachel's blanched face, 'Damn,' he sighed. 'Damn, damn—damn.'

'W-Why don't you go to Lydia, then?' she suggested shakily, her throat swelling on the thickness of unshed tears. 'Perhaps sh-she'll give you a better time all round!'

Spinning, she ran out of the room before he could say another thing! He thought her vindictive! He thought their home a poky little box! And his children! Those dear, sweet babies who loved him so utterly—he called them brats!

She banged the children's supper dishes with gusto, soapsuds flying everywhere. She could have put them all in the dishwasher, but this felt better, giving her something to vent her anger on!

Two hands appeared on either side of her, effectively trapping her against the kitchen sink. And a warm mouth came down to nuzzle her nape. 'Sorry,' Daniel murmured. 'I didn't mean a single word of it.'

She sniffed, scrubbing at a plate that was in danger of losing its pretty flower pattern. 'Why did you say it, then?'

'Because,' he confessed, then didn't bother finishing, preferring to taste her throat instead.

'Because?' she prompted, hunching her shoulder in an effort to stop him.

'Because I was disappointed,' he rumbled. 'Because I've thought of nothing else but that damned bed all week—with you in it. Because I'd forgotten all about the problem with your parents and I felt guilty for letting it slip my mind. Because,' he sighed out heavily, 'I don't want to sleep in Sam's room. I want to sleep with you. I want to wake up on Christmas morning with your face next to me on the pillow. Because—oh, there are a hundred damned becauses. But they all add up to one thing in the end. I blew my top because you were taking away from me the only place where I feel close to you any more. I need that bed, Rachel. I need it.'

On a sudden sob, she dropped the plate she had been wielding back into the water and spun around to bury her face in his chest. 'Oh, Daniel,' she whispered, 'I'm so *miserable*!'

'I know,' he sighed, holding her close, letting the tears flow, stroking her back, his dark head coming to rest comfortingly on the top of her own. And once again his big frame became her rock, the place to run for the comfort she had always found given so unstintingly.

Eventually she sniffed herself back to some kind of calm, and Daniel pushed up her chin so that he could inspect the damage. She let him, as mute and petulant as Kate.

'My mother will kill me if she sees you like this,' he grimaced. 'One look at you and she'll blame me without even a hearing!'

Rachel smiled despite herself. But Daniel was right. Jenny invariably came down on Rachel's side in a dispute, whether she was right or wrong.

'Forgive me?' he asked, gently pushing a wispy tendril of soft blonde hair away from her damp cheek. 'Call a truce, Rachel,' he urged. 'Let's make this a good

Christmas—hell,' he muttered, 'I'll even give up my damned bed if it makes you happy!'

'Who said it made me happy?' she objected, dipping her head so that she could rummage in his trouser pockets for his handkerchief, and having to suppress the urge to smile when her fingers brushed lightly down his groin so that he responded with a shuddering gasp.

'You provocative little witch!' he accused, knowing exactly why she had done it and ruefully amused by it. It revealed a glimpse of the old teasing Rachel—the one he'd thought lost to him forever. 'A truce, Rachel,' he pleaded huskily. 'Please.'

'You called the children brats!' she reminded him sternly.

'Did I say that?' He looked genuinely appalled.

'And more!' she complained.

'I wonder you didn't throw something at me,' he murmured contritely. 'Forgive me and call a truce?'

She pondered the suggestion, taking pleasure in the way his fingers were lightly caressing her face and throat. 'Are you really a cash millionaire?' she enquired curiously.

'Did I say that too?' His sleek brows arched. 'I must have been temporarily deranged.'

'Are you?' she insisted.

'If I say yes, will it gain me a bit of respect around here?' His smile was wry.

'It might do.'

'Then yes,' he nodded. 'You're looking at a cash millionaire—several times over, I might add, just to push up my rating, you understand.' It was said lightly, meant entirely as a tease, but it hurt something deep down inside her because she recognised that underlying the teasing was the real truth, that Daniel was indeed a very wealthy man and she hadn't even realised it. He was just Daniel to her. The man she had loved for what seemed all of her life.

'Truce?' he asked, lowering his mouth to nibble sensually at the corner of her mouth.

'Yes,' she mumbled, eyes closing in languid pleasure.

He lifted his head. 'Because of my millions?' he quizzed.

'Of course,' she smiled. 'Why else would I give in to you?'

He laughed, his manner at ease because, if he knew anything about Rachel, then he knew she was not mercenary. He dropped a kiss on the top of her head, then turned them both towards the kitchen door. 'Then come and talk to me while I change,' he invited, and led them both back up the stairs.

The bedroom was lit by its usual warm peachy glow. Daniel sent the bed a wistful glance as they passed by it.

'We can keep to our usual beds for tonight, of course,' Rachel remarked casually, and received a stinging slap to her behind for her tease, and they entered the bathroom laughing as light-heartedly as they used to do.

It was a nice Christmas, happy, relaxed, light-hearted—but soon over. And the time came for Rachel to decide if she was going to go back to Zac's class. Daniel made no comment, but his opinion was written all over his face whenever he caught her with her sketch-pad in her hands—which she in turn refused to comment on, simply because she wanted it to be her own decision with no manoeuvring from him.

So slowly, slowly, they slipped back to being guarded strangers in the same house. Rachel had to be aware that ninety nine per cent of the blame for this had to be because of their unsatisfactory achievements in bed. Daniel was a very sensual man, and her continued inability to give him all of herself challenged his virility. He hated the restrictions she placed on him: the darkness, the silence, the reluctance to go where their senses instinctively led them. And Rachel was afraid that if she didn't do something about it, then he might go in search of a fuller satisfaction elsewhere. Again.

Would that fear ever leave her now? she asked herself one morning, after a particularly disastrous loving the night before.

Daniel had been as wretched about his affair as she had been. But the knowledge that he could actually fall when the pressure became too great took away that necessary trust she needed to feel safe with him again.

Which left her with the most horrendous feelings of insecurity. An insecurity that played on her nerves to the extent that she was almost constantly plagued by an upset stomach that had never really improved in months.

The kind of months that started her thinking along lines that congealed the blood in her veins…

CHAPTER TEN

Two o'clock Wednesday afternoon, and Daniel was gathering together the stack of papers he had been working on for his next meeting when the telephone on his desk began to ring.

'A lady on the line for you, Mr Masterson. She says she's Mrs Masterson?'

An icy shiver shot down his spine. Rachel never called him here. An accident? he wondered with alarm. One of the children? 'Put her through,' he commanded tautly.

By the time his secretary connected him, his mind had conjured up so many lurid things that could have happened to one of his offspring that he was momentarily confused when it wasn't Rachel's voice he heard speaking, quick with urgency, but someone else entirely.

He shook his head to clear it. 'Will you begin again, Mother?' he requested of that other Mrs Masterson. 'I'm afraid I didn't take a single word of that in.'

Within minutes he was in his car and heading at speed for home. His mother had the door open for him even as he climbed out of the car, and he strode quickly inside.

'She's in there,' Jenny told her son, her lined face crinkling with concern. 'She's so upset, Daniel,' she whispered tearfully.

His face clenched as he turned to open the door, to find Rachel huddled into the corner of the sofa. Her face was buried in a cushion, deep broken sobs racking her slender frame. He approached her carefully, his hands trembling a little as he shrugged out of his jacket and loosened his tie before attempting to touch her.

'Rachel?' he prompted huskily, squatting down in front of her and reaching out to clasp one heaving shoulder gently.

'Go away,' she sobbed into the cushion.

He frowned, puzzled and just a little frightened. He had never seen her like this before—so broken up that she couldn't even tell him what was wrong. And he remained where he was, gently rubbing her shoulder while he tried to think what could have caused her to break down like this? The name Zac Callum hit his mind, and his chest tightened on a hot band of anger. If that bastard had done this to her! If the swine had dared to hurt her when she was only just recovering from the hurt he himself had inflicted on her...

'Rachel...' He moved closer, running shaky fingers through her hair—and was shocked by the clammy heat emanating from her. How long had she been like this? he wondered. 'For goodness' sake,' he pleaded, 'talk to me! Tell me what's wrong!'

The tousled head shook. He swallowed tensely, not knowing what to do. Then, with a grim resolve, he got up to collect her firmly in his arms, then sat down with her cradled on his lap, cushion and all.

At least she didn't fight him, he noted, but just curled up against him with the cushion pressed against her face and kept on crying. He listened, his tongue cleaving to the roof of his mouth at the sheer bloody wretchedness of the sound.

'It's all y-your fault,' she sobbed out suddenly.

His fault. He sighed, casting his mind back over the past few days, trying to discover what he had done this time to cause so much distress. He'd thought he'd been particularly diplomatic over the last week or so. He hadn't said one word about her damned art class! He had not forced his body on to her more than he could possibly help. In fact, he'd stayed out of her way as much as he could…

'Y-You were s-supposed to take c-care of it.' She damned him with that pathetically wretched voice which cut him to the quick.

He brushed his cheek over her hair. 'Take care of what?' he asked.

The sobs went deeper, threatening to choke her if she didn't calm down, and sighing, he took control of the situation, sitting her up and determinedly snatching the cushion away from her hot face. Her hands simply took its place.

'Calm down!' he commanded sternly, quietly appalled at the state she was in.

But, dutiful to that stern tone, Rachel tried to get hold of herself, dragging in some deep breaths that wavered heartrendingly. Daniel found his handkerchief, dragged down her hands, and gently wiped her tear-swollen face. She was so hot that he could actually feel the heat vibrating from her and, on another sigh, he stripped off the warm woollen jumper she was wearing, feeling her shiver as the cooler air hit her through her thin blouse.

'Now,' he said, 'let's hear what this is all about. You said it was something I've done, if I heard you correctly?'

She looked at him, her eyes swimming with hot watery tears. Her soft mouth wobbled, and Daniel almost smiled because she was staring at him through big wounded eyes much as his daughter would if she had not managed to get him to do what she wanted him to do. Only this wasn't Kate, he reminded himself grimly. This was Rachel. Rachel, who was no petulant child. She was brave and strong, despite that air of fragility she wore around her.

'Don't cry again,' he murmured roughly, when the tears began to run down her cheeks. 'Rachel, for goodness' sake—you have to tell me what's causing all this or how can I help?'

'You can't help! No one can help! I'm pregnant, Daniel! Pregnant!' she choked, then made a lurch for his throat where she began weeping all over again. She punched his chest with a clenched fist. 'It's all your fault! You said you would take care of it!'

He had been the one to 'take care of it' when she got pregnant with the twins! After that she had taken care of it—right up until she had developed a reaction to the Pill and had to stop taking it, so Daniel had taken charge again—and Michael came along!

'You're useless!' she spat at him, punching out at him again. 'You may be able to run a million damned companies!' she choked. 'But you're useless at everything else! I'm only twenty-five, for God's sake!' Her voice began to wobble again. 'At this r-rate you'll be nail-nailing down my coffin by the time I'm thirty!'

Now that deserved the smile it got from Daniel, but he pressed her face into his throat so that she wouldn't see it. 'Ssh,' he commanded. 'I'm still trying to take this in.'

But Rachel was angry now, and jerked into a sitting position on his lap to begin throwing at him all those self-pitying thoughts which had helped her to weep for such a long time. 'A proper little baby factory I've turned out to be!' she ground out scathingly. 'No wonder you keep me hidden away here under wraps, Daniel! Your big-time business colleagues would be shocked to discover what an efficient little production line you've set up in your own home! I bet—' she warmed to the idea '—if you put a team of your time and motions experts on me, they would have you up for contract abuse!'

'Shut up, Rachel!' This time he could not contain the need to laugh. 'I can't think while you're throwing all those crazy accusations at me!'

'Well, just think about this one!' she snapped, in a voice still thick with tears. 'I'm pregnant! And I don't want to be!'

Think on that as long as you want! she thought bitterly.

'How pregnant?' he asked after a long pause. He sounded tight-throated suddenly, as though the question had taken a lot of asking, and his face was suddenly white, that nerve in his clenched jaw jumping.

'Three months,' she told him, feeling a fool. Fancy not realising what was wrong with her—after all the practice she'd had, too!

'Three months,' he repeated, and the tension drained right out of him. 'Good God!' It hit him then, almost as hard as it had hit Rachel when the doctor had given her the news that morning. 'That means…'

'Yes.' She didn't need it spelled out for her; she could manage simple arithmetic. It must have happened the first time she had let him near her after she found out about Lydia, and everything went a little crazy.

'God.' He seemed stuck on blasphemies. 'I remember now, I never gave a thought to…'

Silence fell again, while they both pondered their own trains of thought. She still sat curled up against him, and Daniel was stroking absently at her hair. And suddenly it reminded her of another time when she'd sat with him like this, receiving those same soothing caresses while he came to terms with her news.

There had been no anger in him then. And there was none now.

'Well,' he said suddenly, 'that's it then.' He turned her face so that he could brush a kiss across her mouth. 'We'll *have* to buy a bigger house now. No bedrooms left in this one!'

With the twins—only they hadn't known then that she was having twins of course; that little shock had come much later, when she was more than five months pregnant—but with the twins, he had used a similar statement to announce his acceptance of his fate. 'We'll just have to get married,' he had said then. Same difference, Rachel thought with a mental shrug. Daniel had this capacity for accepting the inevitable.

She didn't go back to her art class. It was a decision reached entirely on her own. Drawing she had come to love again, but common sense told her that she would be doing herself no favours walking back into that class while Zac was still there. And although it was never mentioned by either of them, Daniel began taking her out on a Wednesday night—as if he wanted to compensate for what she had lost. But she did not stop drawing, and her sketch-pads could be found all over the house with their hurriedly drawn comical sketches scrawled in black on white paper.

They went house-hunting. And it took ages to find something which suited everyone. 'A case of too many cooks spoiling the broth!' she said drily to Daniel, after a weekend spent trailing around the local countryside viewing properties which did not suit one or the other's specific requirements.

'Why do you want something so big?' she complained once, when they'd arrived back home after viewing a huge mausoleum of a place that was just too grand for comfort. 'We may need something bigger, but not that big! It isn't as though we have to have all those extra rooms to entertain your business colleagues, is it?' He still kept a definite line between his home and his workplace and it still hurt her—hence the comment.

'We would have a damned hard job trying to entertain anyone here,' was his deriding reply. 'And I think, Rachel, that after all the hard work I've put in, making it possible for us to have virtually anything we want, you might allow me the pleasure of seeing something special for it!'

Then they found the ideal thing: an old manor-house built in warm red brick with long sash windows which let the natural light flood into the high-ceilinged rooms. It had its own acreage of land hemmed in by a six-foot-high brick wall lined with tall trees to keep the grounds very private. It suited Daniel's idea of prestige, and Rachel's idea of a home. The twins liked it because it had its own swimming-pool under glass at the rear, and stables. And, to clinch things, it had a small lodge-house by the electronically controlled gates which was ideal for Daniel's mother, who fell in love with the tiny cottage the moment she saw it.

It also had a ready-made live-in couple, who had been taking care of the house for over twenty years and were worried sick about what they were going to do once the manor-house was sold. Rachel's soft heart took them in and Daniel was happy to keep them because it meant fulfilling a couple more of his own requirements. They were getting a housekeeper to take some of the load off Rachel, and a gardener who was to double up as chauffeur and ferry the children to school and back every day instead of him and Rachel and the local taxi service doing it between them.

Rachel threw herself into the delights of completely re-decorating and refurbishing their new home, and found to her surprise that she possessed quite a flair for it. She was carrying this new baby better than she had Michael, and, as winter fell away to spring, the new house began to take shape enough for them to consider moving in.

Daniel was up to his neck in yet another take-over—a small Manchester-based engineering company he had once worked for himself but which was now in deep financial difficulties—so he was spending more time up north than he was at home, while Rachel busied herself trying to complete the house-move before her pregnancy became too advanced for her to do it comfortably.

Lydia had faded into the background over the past months. She no longer haunted their lovemaking, though Rachel still needed the darkness to hide in if she was to respond to Daniel at all. But at least she seemed to be coming to terms with a betrayal that had almost wrecked their marriage.

Daniel's seven-year itch, she cynically referred to it in the privacy of her own mind. If the same thing did not occur for another seven years, then maybe she could cope with that. For she knew for certain that she could never leave him now. Her life was too much bound to him by their mutual love of their children and this latest addition soon to come. But love for herself? She dismissed that ideal as a dream which belonged to Rachel the romantic child and not this older, far more awakened Rachel, who had learned to temper her emotions to suit their new relationship.

She was in their bedroom one afternoon when Daniel arrived home unexpectedly early from one of his quick trips to Manchester. He found her sitting on the floor surrounded by heaps of old clothes she was sorting out for jumble.

He looked tired out, and the way he glanced irritably at the mess told her that the never-ending sorting and packing was beginning to get him down. 'Why can't you employ someone to do all this for you?' he snapped out impatiently, shrugging out of his jacket and tie as he stepped carefully over the mess on his way to the bathroom.

'I'm not having strangers going through our personal belongings!' she protested. 'And how would they know what to throw out and what to keep?' she added sensibly. 'I have to do it myself!'

He didn't bother to reply, but the bathroom door shut with an expressive slam. A moment later and she was on her feet and rummaging for her sketch-pad. By the time Daniel returned to the bedroom, freshly showered and with just a towel slung around his hips, Rachel was sprawled across the bed with her pencil, busily drawing.

'What are you doing?' He came to lie beside her, receiving a scolding frown when he jolted her pencil.

'You cheeky witch!' he exclaimed when he saw what she'd drawn. Laughing, though, despite the fact that he could clearly recognise himself in the naked devil with horns and a forked tail taking a shower. But instead of water washing down over him, flames licked upwards while he stood there, wearing an expression of evil bliss. 'You cheeky witch,' he repeated ruefully—and filched the sketch-pad from her.

Rachel made a lurching dive to retrieve it, but he rolled on to his back, hooking his arm around her swollen waist to hold her still while he closed the pad, then began flicking slowly through the busy pages.

Rachel went very still, her heart thumping anxiously in her breast, watching his face intently as he studied each new sketch in turn. He wasn't laughing, but then he wasn't meant to. This was not one of Rachel's cartoon pads. And the only funny drawing in it was the one she had just done of him. No, this was her more serious work, until now kept right away from curious eyes.

The head and shoulders of Sam looked solemnly out on them from beneath faintly frowning brows, his hair ruthlessly flattened to his head as he insisted on its being. His chin was stubborn. He looked like Daniel—so much like Daniel that Rachel's heart contracted as she stared at him.

Kate looked pleased with herself, her golden hair a shimmering halo around her pretty face. She looked like the cat who had just stolen the cream—which she had, in a way, because that was how she had looked when she had just talked Daniel into letting her have a small pony when they moved into the new house. Kate had a mind of her own—stubborn, extrovert. She looked like Rachel, but she was not Rachel. She was too much her father's daughter for that.

Michael. There were more of him because he was the one Rachel spent more time with. There was one of him sleeping, with his padded bottom stuck up the air and poor old tattered teddy cushioned by his plump cheek. And one of him laughing, his small teeth standing out in his beaming round face. Then a serious one of him, face dark with concentration as he took that first wobbly step on his own.

'They're good,' Daniel said quietly.

Rachel took in a deep breath, her heart thudding now because she knew what was coming next. 'Thank you,' she said, and made a casual grab for the pad before he could turn to the next page. 'It gave me pleasure to do them.' She tugged, but Daniel was not letting go. Her nerve-ends began to tingle. He turned the next page—then went very still.

He had expected to see himself, she realised later. It seemed the logical conclusion to make when the pad was filled with drawings of the family. But it wasn't him.

It was her own face which gazed back at them. Rachel, with her hair a golden bob of fine-spun silk around a face that showed few lines of living. A young Rachel. A Rachel who had changed little over the years. Her mouth was small and soft, her nose delicately straight. But her eyes—those

wide-spaced expressive eyes—looked out on them with a
sadness in their gentle depths which tugged at the soul. To
her it was like looking at a stranger. She had hated it when
she'd finished it, could not see how accurately she had
caught the sad, wistful creature everyone else saw when
they looked at her these days. And she had shown her distaste of the drawing by scoring a cross through it from
corner to corner.

'Why did you do that?' Daniel asked sombrely, following one of the negative lines with a gentle finger which
paused at the corner of her mouth.

Rachel sat up and away from him. 'She isn't me,' she
said simply. 'I don't like her.'

He made no comment, but lay studying the drawing for
a long time, while Rachel felt a touch of her old restlessness
attack her and got up from the bed, pretending to return her
attention to the mounds of clothes scattering their bedroom
floor.

'None of me,' Daniel made wry note, when eventually
he turned to the next page only to find the devil leering
back at him.

Rachel's smile was forced. 'How can you say that,' she
mocked, 'when that is exactly how I see you?'

She couldn't explain why she had never attempted drawing him. She understood why herself, but those reasons did
not translate into words very well. Daniel was different. He
was one of the family—yet not. The other faces in the book
belonged—they were a part of her. Daniel used to be—the
most important part of her—but he wasn't any longer. He
had drifted away, become a blurred image in that place
inside her where those drawings came from.

He didn't love her as the others did.

Daniel was the broken link.

She reached out to take back the pad, and he let her this

time, watching her silently as she took it to store it away, in the bottom of her wardrobe, then closed the door on it before turning back to face him.

He was still lying on the bed, with only the towel covering the leashed power in his thighs.

'Where's Michael?' he asked softly.

Her insides curled. 'With your mother for the day.'

Their eyes held, and time stood breathlessly still in the quietness of the bedroom. He was asking something of her, his lazy eyes showing her the need beginning to burn inside him. She stood a mere arm's length away from him, nervous, unsure, blushing slightly, feeling the trailing beginnings of desire seep warmly into her blood, responding to the lean, muscular length of him stretched out on the bed.

Her gaze flicked down to the whorls of dark curling hair covering his wide chest, following restlessly the way they tapered like an arrow across the flat tautness of his stomach and disappeared beneath the covering towel. Daniel was tall, lean and essentially male, his legs two powerful limbs with long muscular thighs, and calves sprinkled liberally with crisp dark hair which she could actually feel rasp sensually against her own softer more delicate skin, even though she stood a good two feet away from him.

The sun was shining weakly through the window, and she realised with a small jolt that this was the first time in months that she'd openly gazed on his body like this. Her need for darkness had denied her this pleasure. Denied her the pleasure, too, of seeing the desire burn in his eyes.

His hand reached out, inviting her without words to come to him, and silently she placed her hand in his, drawn by a force too great to fight. His fingers closed around hers, being very careful not to break the hypnotising contact with her eyes as he slowly sat up and parted his thighs so that he could draw her between them. She was wearing very little, just a loose woollen dress and a pair of briefs. Daniel slid his hands around her thickened waist, then stroked them down her hips and thighs until he made contact with the hem of her dress.

She stopped breathing on an inward gasp. His caressing hands paused, his eyes dark and watchful, waiting to find out what that gasp meant. Then she was letting the air out of her lungs on a shaky sigh and her eyelids lowered, her soft lips parting as she bent to join her mouth with his.

He fell back and she went with him, her dress being stripped away from her body as they went. And, as quick as that, they were lost in each other, hungry, demanding, stroking and arousing in a sensual scramble of tangled limbs and intimate caresses and long, moist, drugging kisses.

She was ready for him—more than ready—as her senses began to draw together in that sweet, hot knot of need that made her pull him down on top of her, mouth urgent, hands clutching at the tautness of his hips in an effort to draw him deep inside her.

Then it happened. Loving him with every sense she had in her, Rachel allowed her eyes to open slowly, gaze into that stern, dark, beautiful face above her, see the sunlight play across his gleaming black hair, see the fierceness of his driving passion, his eyes glazed with the sheer intensity of it. Then the ghost of her hell came back to haunt her, and she snapped her eyes tight shut, whimpering in wretched frustration as her body began to tighten in rejection.

'No!' Daniel rasped, violence erupting inside him because he recognised what was happening to her. 'No, damn you, Rachel. No!'

She fought it, oh, she fought it with everything she could,

her fingers clinging to him, her breathing fast and labouring with the struggle.

'Look at me!' he demanded raspingly, struggling to hold back from making that ultimate union. 'For pity's sake, open your eyes and look at me!'

Her lids lifted slowly, eyes taking their time to focus on his dark face locked with tension. His eyes were shot through with a hot haunted need she could not deny. Daniel might not love her, but he desired her passionately—still, after almost eight years—still, when she was swollen with his child—still, with, during and through everything that had come between them over this last six months. Daniel still desired her with a need that made him tremble against her, and maybe that was enough...

'No!' he protested harshly as her lids began lowering back over her eyes. 'No—you won't shut me out this time, Rachel!'

His hands came up to take hold of her face, tightening until her eyes flickered open in frowning confusion.

'You want me,' he stated fiercely. 'But you won't have me unless you keep your eyes open and accept just who it is you want! Me!' he stated harshly. 'Me, Rachel. Faults and all. Me, the man I was before I let you down so badly and the man I am right now!'

'And if I can't do that?' she whispered wretchedly. 'What if I can never accept what you did to us?'

'Then you'll never have me again,' he answered grimly. 'Because I know I can't keep on making love to a woman who has to hide behind her closed eyes before she can accept me inside her.'

He pushed himself away from her then, while Rachel took in what he was actually saying. Daniel had just issued her with an ultimatum, she realised as she watched him stride back to the bathroom. He was telling her that he had done paying for his crime. He was, in short, telling her that she had to learn to trust him again or forget the physical side of their marriage.

She couldn't believe it—found it incredible the expert way he had just managed to turn the tables on her, making her the one who had to make the concessions from now on if there was to be a normal relationship between them in the future!

Resentment simmered, boiled, then died when it came to her that he could perhaps be right, and she did have to accept him, faults and all, if their marriage was going to survive—which only threw her into further confusion about what she was going to do.

She was still floundering on the question a week later when something happened which tossed all her other troubles into oblivion by comparison.

The twins disappeared.

CHAPTER ELEVEN

RACHEL blamed herself the moment she realised they had gone. It had been a week to top all weeks for tension in the home.

Daniel had gone into a cold withdrawal, making no effort to hide his anger with Rachel, so the whole household heaved a sigh of relief when he went off a couple of days later on a trip to Manchester.

But that wasn't all of it. It was the Easter break from school and the twins were at home all day. It didn't help Rachel's frayed nerves that they were excited about the coming move, that they seemed to be constantly under her feet, getting in the way so much that she caught herself snapping at them more often than was fair.

She was up to her neck in packing-cases when she heard the ring of the telephone and, on a muttered curse, she fought her way across the room on her way to answer it when it stopped.

That did her temper no good whatsoever, and her curses became richer as she fought her way back to where she had been working and got back to her packing again.

She was still grumbling to herself when Sammy and Kate sidled into the room. 'It was Daddy on the phone,' Sam informed her sullenly. He had not forgiven her yet for shouting at him for spilling orange juice all over the kitchen floor. He saw the scolding as an injustice because he had been getting the juice for Michael at the time, in his way saving Rachel the trouble, but Rachel had only seen the sticky orange mess she had to clean up and lost her temper.

'He said to tell you that he's on his way back from Man-chester.' The small boy relayed the message with the same haughty coolness his father would have used in the same mood. 'And that he has to go into the office first so he will be late home tonight.'

Well, bully for him! she thought grumpily. Let him hide in his office while she did all the hard graft! Playing the martyr, Rachel? She heard the acid echo of Daniel's voice sound so clearly in her head that she actually jumped and glanced round, half expecting to find him standing right behind her. He was not, of course, but the taunt went re-luctantly home.

'I asked him to come home and play with us instead,' put in a sulky Kate.

'And he, I suppose, put the phone down quick—in sheer fright!' She'd meant it as a sarcastic cut at Daniel, not at the twins, but they took it the wrong way, and Kate's face went red with anger.

'No, he didn't!' she cried. 'He said he wished he could play with us instead of doing stuffy work! And you're not a nice mummy!' she added heatedly.

Rachel caught a suspicion of tears in her daughter's eyes just before Kate disappeared, running back down the stairs with an equally disgruntled Sammy right behind her.

Sighing, she rested one weary hand on her swollen stom-ach and the other on her aching head, acknowledging that she'd probably deserved everything Kate had thrown at her, and fought her way back across the room to follow them down the stairs. The twins pointedly ignored her, pretend-ing to be engrossed in the television.

She picked Michael up from the floor, where he had been playing quite happily with his bricks, glanced at the other two in the hope they would look at her so that she could say she was sorry, when they didn't felt irritation swell within her yet again, and flounced out of the room with her youngest, leaving them to watch their TV programme in peace.

An hour later and she was going demented. She had looked everywhere she could think of. But the twins seemed to have disappeared off the face of the earth! She had driven over to the park, hoping to find them playing on the swings. To Daniel's mother's house—knowing that Jenny was out for the whole day visiting friends, and equally sure that the twins did not know that and could well have walked around to her house in search of some sympathy and comfort. She had checked and double-checked the house, the garden and even rung the new house in the vague hope that they had somehow found their way there. But they hadn't, and she was just reaching the stage when she knew she was going to have to call in the police when the telephone began to ring.

She snatched it up, white with strain and trembling so badly that she could barely hold the receiver to her ear.

'Mrs Masterson?' an uncertain voice enquired.

'Yes,' she whispered through chattering teeth.

'Mrs Masterson, this is your husband's secretary…'

Her heart leaped to her throat. 'I-Is Daniel there?' she asked.

'No, he hasn't arrived yet,' the voice said. 'But your children have turned up here just now asking for him and I—'

'They're there?' Rachel cut in shrilly.

'Yes,' the voice assured gently, hearing her distress. 'Yes, they're here.'

'Oh, God.' An ice-cold fist went up to her mouth, stopping the well of tears. 'Are they all right?'

'Yes,' she was assured once again. 'They're fine—really.'

Rachel dropped down on the bottom stair as relief—blessed, blessed relief—took the strength right out of her. Then she was almost instantly up on her feet again. 'W-Will you hang on to them for me, please?' she whispered. 'I'm on my way. I'm—on my way...'

She dropped the phone, gave an odd, choked little laugh, then a single wretched sob, and then was rushing to go and get Michael.

Rachel arrived at Masterson Holdings just as the lunch-break was coming to an end, and the ultra-modern reception area was teeming with people on their way back to their respective offices.

Her cheeks flushed with rushing, eyes slightly dazed by shock, and still dressed in the same white stretchy leggings and one of Daniel's old pale blue work-shirts that she had been wearing all day, she came to a halt just inside the plate-glass entrance and stared bewilderedly around her while Michael did the same from his comfortable position on her rounded hip.

The children were nowhere to be seen. Her heart gave a sickening lurch and she started forwards, making for the reception desk she could see across the spacious foyer, where a pretty young girl sat flirting with a young man who was half sitting on the corner of her desk.

'Excuse me,' she interrupted a little breathlessly. 'I'm Rachel Masterson. My children. They—'

'Mrs Masterson!' The young girl came to her feet, her brown eyes widening as they took in every detail of Rachel as if she couldn't quite believe what she was seeing. Rachel didn't blame her—she knew she must look a sight—but neither did she care. She just wanted to see Sam and Kate—needed to see them.

'My children,' she repeated as the young man shot off the desk and almost to attention. 'Where are they?' she demanded, unaware that the receptionist's voice had carried right across the foyer and now everyone in it was staring curiously at her.

'Oh, Mr Masterson arrived not ten minutes ago,' the young girl informed her. 'He has them in his office and said for you to—'

'I'll take you up to him if you like,' the young man offered.

Rachel turned a distracted expression on him and nodded in agreement. 'Thank you,' she whispered, and followed him over to the bank of lifts, too distraught to notice the sea of curious faces turned her way.

The lift took them upwards, and ejected them on to a thick grey carpet that muffled their steps as they walked towards a pair of matt grey-painted doors. Rachel followed her guide more slowly, feeling odd inside, trembly and weak-limbed. The young man knocked, waited a moment, then opened the doors before standing back so Rachel could go by him.

She paused on the threshold, glanced warily at Daniel who was leaning against a large grey grained desk, his arms folded across his chest, flicked her gaze to the two woe-begone figures who were sitting very close together on a long leather settee, felt the tears flood into her eyes, put Michael to the floor, choked out thickly, 'Oh, Sammy—Kate!' then fainted clean away.

She came round to find herself lying on the settee with something cool and damp across her forehead—and four faces with varying similarities about them watching her anxiously. She smiled weakly, and received four varying but similar smiles by return.

Daniel was squatting down beside her with Michael balanced on his lap and one of his hands warmly clasping one of hers. Sammy and Kate flanked him, leaning sombrely against a broad shoulder each. They all looked rather sweet like that, and she wished she had some paper and a pencil close by so that she could catch the scene forever.

'How do you feel?' Daniel asked in a gritty voice.

'Woozy,' she smiled ruefully, then turned her attention to the two runaways. 'I'm sorry,' she whispered painfully, and received two sobbing bundles into her arms.

They sobbed out their regrets, their apologies, their love, and their fear when they saw her faint. Then they were snuffling out the excitement of their adventure: ringing for a taxi, pooling their saved pocket money, arriving here to find Daddy not here and putting everyone into a panic.

'And frightening your mother half out of her wits,' Daniel silenced them dampeningly.

He looked hard at Kate, who lowered her head in mute contrition. 'It was all very neatly worked out.' Daniel took up the story. 'They rang the taxi firm you use to ferry them to school when I'm away,' he explained. 'Said you were sick in bed and wanted them bringing to me. They even produced one of my business cards with this address on to make it all look official.' He glared at Kate. 'All very slick,' he clipped. 'Very believable.'

'Oh, Kate,' Rachel said gravely, remembering how important Kate had felt when Rachel gave her the task of ringing the taxi firm to order a car to take the twins to school on those mornings Daniel wasn't around to take them.

But to abuse that bit of responsibility in such a way...!

The poor child's head sank lower.

'I thought of using Daddy's business card,' Sammy put in, gallantly prepared to share the blame.

But they all knew it was the more precocious Kate who would have thought up the whole thing. 'I'm sorry,' the little girl whispered, and Rachel saw with an ache her small hand lift to wipe the tears from her lowered cheeks.

The tension was rife, the fact that Kate wasn't going to her Daddy for a comforting hug telling Rachel that there had been some tough reprimands before she'd arrived.

Her gaze drifted to Daniel. He looked drawn and pale, his mouth a grim tight line that warned of a simmering anger. He held Michael against him, big hands spanning the little body as though he needed to feel the living comfort of this youngest child of theirs because he was too angry to give in to what was really troubling him—the need to hold the twins close too.

He caught her looking at him, and grimaced. 'My secretary is preparing some coffee,' he said. 'As soon as it comes I'll have her take the children down to the cafeteria for some lunch. Then we talk.'

That sounded ominous. Rachel dropped her gaze and eased herself into a sitting position, just as a young woman with a pleasant face walked in with a loaded tray.

Still holding Michael, Daniel got up and walked over to her as she placed the tray on his desk. He spoke quietly for a moment, then called the twins over. They snapped into action with an obedience that confirmed Rachel's suspicions that Daniel had issued a severe scold to both of them.

A moment later Michael was going trustingly into the other woman's arms, and she took the children out while Daniel turned his attention to the coffee.

He didn't speak, not until he had offered her the strong drink and sat himself down beside her to watch her drink the whole cupful.

'Right. What happened?' he said quietly then.

She shrugged guiltily. 'I've been impatient with them,' she admitted. 'Today perhaps more than usual. They were feeling neglected, I think—pushed away. So they went in

search of comfort elsewhere.' She put down her cup when
the tears threatened to come again. 'I thought they'd gone
to your mother's... I searched everywhere for them...
B-But it never entered my h-head that they m-might try to
come h-here!'

'It's OK.' He covered her twisting hands. 'Don't upset
yourself any more. They're fine. You've seen that they're
fine.'

She nodded, fighting to get hold of herself.

'I'm sorry,' she whispered after a while.

'What for?' His head shot round to stare at her.

'For being a poor mother to your children,' she said. 'For
intruding,' she added, 'here.'

'Sometimes, Rachel,' Daniel sighed impatiently, 'I wonder what actually goes on in that head of yours!'

'Did you smack them?'

He frowned at the abrupt change of subject. Then, 'No,
I managed to control that particular urge,' he said drily.
'But that didn't stop my tongue! What they did was stupid,
dangerous and downright wilful!' Angrily he shook his
dark head. 'Sammy took his medicine on the chin, but Kate
was appalled.' He grimaced. 'I don't think I've ever
shouted at her like that before.'

'She'll forgive you,' Rachel assured him. Kate adored
her darling daddy.

'Not if she's like her mother she won't,' he grunted, and
Rachel lowered her eyes.

'It—it isn't a case of forgiveness,' she murmured. 'It's
trying to forget it I find I can't do. You shattered my whole
world, Daniel!'

'I know.' Grimly he looked down at their clasped hands.
'Shattered my own at the same time, if you must know.
Not that that means anything.' He shrugged. 'I deserved it.
You didn't.'

'Then why did you do it?' she asked in wretched bewilderment.

Daniel sighed, the sound seeming to come from deep inside his rigid chest, and he let go of her hand so that he could rake his fingers through his hair.

'Because she was there,' he answered brutally, and winced at Rachel's dismayed gasp.

'Y-You must have hurt her very badly.'

'Did I?' His mouth twisted cynically. 'She isn't of your ilk, Rachel. Women like Lydia have thicker skins. They don't hurt that easily.'

'And that makes it all right, does it?'

'No.' Hunching forward, he rested his elbows on his spread knees and stared grimly at the carpet. 'But I can't feel guilt for her hurt feelings when she gave no thought to mine.'

Rachel frowned at that, not understanding what he was getting at.

Daniel saw the frown and sighed again. 'If I try to explain it all to you, Rachel,' he offered, 'will you listen?'

Would she? Did she want to know? Could she take the full sordid truth of it? Her eyes drifted away from him, pained and bleak, soft mouth quivering with a vulnerable uncertainty.

His hand came out to cover hers, warm and strengthening. 'Please,' he asked again. 'You were and still are the only woman I have ever loved, Rachel. If you can't let yourself hear anything else, then, please—hear that, because it's the truth.'

'Then why Lydia?' she flashed, spinning her head back to lash him with her eyes.

His mouth straightened, the attractive curve of his lips becoming lost in the grim tight line. He took his hand away, letting it drop loosely between his spread knees. 'Because,' he said, 'for a short while last year, I lost control—not just with what was happening to you and me,' he enlarged, 'but here too.' His grey eyes skimmed the length of his plush office. 'Lydia was a safety-valve. Pure and simple, very basic.' He fixed her with a grim look. 'I was under terrible pressure, and I used her, quite frankly, to relieve some of it.'

Was that supposed to reassure her? Rachel stared at him, the rumblings of anger beginning to bubble up inside her. 'So now I'm supposed to forgive—forget,' she said. 'And sit back and wait for the next time you're under pressure like that and feel the need to *relieve* it with some other accommodating fool who happens to be available?'

'No.' Unlike her, Daniel did not harden his tone. 'Because it won't happen again.'

The sceptical look she sent him was her opinion of that.

'It won't happen again,' he repeated patiently, 'because it didn't work the first time.' He studied her hurt and angry face to see if she understood what he was getting at, then allowed himself a small wry smile when he realised she certainly did not. 'You and your undying innocence,' he murmured drily.

'I stopped being an innocent, Daniel,' she derided, 'at the age of seventeen, when you took innocence from me!'

'You gave it, Rachel,' he corrected. 'You gave it freely.'

She flushed—couldn't help it because he was so damned right! And she hadn't just given, she'd virtually thrown herself at him.

'And, believe it or not,' he went on, 'I took when I'd had no intention of taking. No—' he reached out to grip her hands again '—don't take that the way I made it sound,' he begged. 'I wanted you, Rachel. My God,' he sighed, 'I *always* want you! But you were seventeen years old, for God's sake! And I was a reasonably experienced man of twenty-four! I knew that, in all decency, I should turn and walk away from you before things became too serious! But I couldn't,' he admitted. 'So I was determined to keep the relationship light—but I couldn't even manage that.' His jaw clenched momentarily. 'In the end, I found myself so obsessed by you that my work began to suffer. And yours did too,' he reminded her. 'You were heading for straight As in your exams before I came along. But instead of submerging yourself in study, as you should have been doing, you were out with me. And your parents began to get at me…'

Her eyes widened in surprise at that piece of news. She hadn't been aware that her parents had done anything but smile warily at him when Daniel used to collect her from home.

'They disapproved,' he continued. 'And rightly so. I was putting at risk all those years of schooling you'd already put in. And, because of you, I had put in abeyance all the big plans I had mapped out for my own career.'

'This?' she asked, meaning the office they were sitting in which made its own statement of his successful achievements.

He nodded. 'Or something like this.'

'So you fulfilled your dreams in the end, despite me,' she remarked a trifle bitterly.

'But at the expense of yours,' he added.

'Mine? How do you know what my dreams were if you never bothered to ask?' she queried.

'Art,' he stated. 'University first, then a career in art. Advertising, maybe, or design. It was all you thought about then.'

'Was it?' Her tone mocked his confidence. 'Which just goes to show how little you really know about me.'

His eyes flashed up to hers, dark and intense. 'Then what

did you want?' he asked, and he swallowed tensely, as if he didn't really want to hear the answer.

Rachel derided him with a look. You, she wanted to say. All I ever wanted from life was you. 'Let's just say I probably got what I deserved,' she mocked instead, and knew the words hurt him.

'I was about to get out of your life eight years ago when you told me you were pregnant,' he went on grimly, and Rachel closed her eyes, accepting that it was his turn to hurt her. 'I'd spent that fortnight down here in London, if you remember,' he said. 'But what you didn't know was that I'd been attending a series of interviews for a job which would have taken me out of the country and as far away from you as I could get.'

She'd suspected it, Rachel thought wretchedly. Ever since Lydia had opened her eyes to what she and Daniel really were to each other, she had suspected her pregnancy had trapped him. Daniel had not wanted to marry her; he simply hadn't been given the choice.

'No—' again he grabbed her hands and squeezed them tightly '—you're mistaking my reasons. I didn't want to leave you!' he stated fiercely. 'But I was prepared to get out of your life for your sake! You were too young and had too much going for you for me to tie you down! The job offer was like a crossroads I had reached, and I accepted it because I believed it was the best thing to do for both of us! But it wasn't an easy decision and I was feeling bloody wretched by the time I got back from London with my cool goodbyes all rehearsed in my mind.'

He stopped, his eyes darkening on a remembered pain. 'Then there you were,' he murmured thickly, 'standing right in front of me, looking up at me with all that—all that...' He pushed a hand to his eyes, covering them for a moment with fingers which shook. 'And I stood there, dy-

ing inside because I was going to have to let it all go. The
next thing I knew—' he swallowed '—we were making
love when we should not have been, making things worse,
because how the hell do you tell the woman you've just
drowned yourself in that you're going to leave her?' he
choked, too lost in his own pained memories to notice how
still and pale Rachel had become. 'Then, while I was struggling to say the damned words, you laid your head on my
knee and said calmly, "I'm pregnant, Daniel. What shall
we do?"' He laughed softly, shaking his dark head. 'It was
like being handed a reprieve with the hangman's noose already tied around my neck! I felt freed—alive—so alive
that all I could do was sit there—' he spread his trembling
hand out expressively '—and let the sheer bloody joy of it
wash over me! I didn't have to let you go, because you
needed me. You—needed—me!' he repeated hoarsely. 'I
could dismiss your dreams of a career. I could dismiss your
youth. And I could do what I'd really wanted to do and
gather you in, keep you close so no one else would know
what a wonderful, beautiful treasure I'd got!'

He sucked in a deep breath of air, then let it out again
slowly. 'So, we got married,' he went on less emotionally.
'And came down here to live in that poky little flat in
Camden Town. We had hardly any money, barely a possession we could call our own, but I don't think I've ever
felt so happy in my entire life! Then the twins arrived, and
I had a stroke of luck which gave me the chance to try
something I'd always wanted to do. You know how I used
to dabble in stocks and shares then?' She nodded. 'Well,
after we married, I hung on to those I thought might bring
in a good return one day, and one particular block did,' he
said. 'It was my first real killing on the market, and I had
a choice; buy you a nice little house with the money, or

feed it straight back into the market. I fed it,' he confessed, as if it were a mortal sin.

Which perhaps it had been at the time, Rachel allowed, if only because he hadn't bothered to discuss what he wanted to do with her first. But then—she gave a mental shrug—perhaps Daniel would not be the man he was today if he had needed constantly to refer to others before he made a decision to take a risk.

'Then I spent the next few months feeling as guilty as hell when the flat became impossible to live in with two small babies and all the paraphernalia that comes with them. Then the stock began to pay big dividends, shifting up the market ladder at such a rate that I made my second killing in as many months! And after that—' he shrugged '—I never had to look back. We bought the house. I set up my own company, diversifying into helping out small ailing companies by gaining majority stock, then feeding more money into them to make them more efficient. And Masterson Holdings grew steadily, until it became what you see today. But not without its sacrifices,' he added grimly. 'The bigger the company got, the more time I had to spend working in it. And the sheer nature of my business meant I had to move in certain social circles if I was to keep an ear to what was going on in the business world. But the more I saw of that world, the more determined I became that none of its ugly taint was going to rub off on you! You were the rose-garden in the middle of the vile jungle I fought in,' he likened huskily. 'You were the only constant thing in my life. I would come home to you and see the sweet seventeen-year-old I first fell in love with, and I knew I would fight the very devil himself to keep you that way!'

He took another deep breath, his eyes hooded a little because he was revealing to her so much of the inner man he usually kept hidden away—the one she had been curious to know but had never looked closely enough to find for herself.

'I think someone up there must have known it,' he said ruefully then. 'Because the next thing I know you're pregnant with Michael, and not having an easy time of it. And one of my newest acquisitions becomes involved in a nasty little fraud scandal which takes months of legal battling to sort out. I'm away more than I'm at home where I should be, making things easier for you. You can be bloody stubborn sometimes, Rachel,' he inserted gruffly. 'We had more money than we could ever spend even if we tried, and you wouldn't let me hire anyone to help you.'

Her chin came up. 'If you can run this place singlehanded, Daniel, then surely I can take care of one small house and three even smaller children!'

He sighed, hearing the self-defence behind the attack. 'And we all have our limits of endurance,' he pointed out. 'You almost reached yours after Michael was born and he gave you hell for four months solid. And the twins developed a severe strain of measles.'

'And I found out about your affair with Lydia,' she added coolly.

But Daniel shook his head. 'No,' he said. 'That was the result of my reaching my limits of endurance, Rachel. I almost lost everything in the ugliest hostile take-over attempt I've ever heard of. Harveys—a bigger holding company than mine—decided it wanted me out of the running, and it went for me with every weapon it had. Including trying to slap a fraud charge on me.'

CHAPTER TWELVE

'THE Harvey take-over?'

But she'd always assumed that it had been Daniel taking them over—not the other way round!

He nodded, unaware how new comprehension was holding her still with shock.

'It was bitter and it was bloody,' he said. 'And I had to take risks that made my mind boggle when I thought about them after it was all over. And where, at any other difficult period, I'd always had you to turn to for some blessed relief from it all, you were out of reach—tired and weak, and run off your feet trying to share yourself between two sick children and a very demanding baby and, selfish as I know it sounds,' he sighed out heavily, 'I resented the whole bloody lot of them! I needed you, Rachel! But you couldn't be reached! And—God forgive me—Lydia could.' He sucked in an anguished breath and let it out again. 'With Lydia's frankly brilliant help,' he conceded, 'I won the battle with Harveys. But for some reason that same God only knows, because I know I can't work it out, the relief of it sent me staggering over those limits of endurance I mentioned, and right into her arms.'

'How long?'

He glanced at her, his brows pulled into a puzzled frown. 'How long, what?'

'Did you have her as your mistress—how long?' she repeated rawly.

He shook his head, an odd expression twisting at the corners of his mouth. 'She never was,' he admitted. 'Not in the sense you're implying anyway. I have tried to tell

178

you that once or twice,' he added wryly, 'but you refused so much as to listen, never mind believe, and—God knows,' he sighed, scraping his fingers through his dark hair, 'I didn't blame you. After all, I'd been unfaithful to you in every way but the ultimate act, indulging in my own light relief from all the pressures by taking Lydia out instead of coming home to you. Wining her, dining her...' His shoulders hunched as if the memory clenched at something vicious inside him.

'Mandy told me you were seen coming out of Lydia's flat,' Rachel put in huskily.

He nodded. 'After my battle with Harveys, I went a little crazy,' he confessed. She could see he didn't like admitting that; the self-contempt was etched into his rigid jaw. 'I just sat here and drank myself stupid until I wasn't fit to drive myself home. Lydia coaxed me into her car and drove me to her flat to sober up. Oh,' he added with a cynical twist to his mouth, 'don't get me wrong. She knew what she was doing and I knew what she was expecting of me when I let her take me there but—' he stopped to smile bleakly. 'In the end, I couldn't. She wasn't you and, drunk or not, the very thought of laying a hand on her made my skin crawl. She must have seen it,' he grimaced, 'because she just walked out of the room. I fell into a drunken stupor and awoke in a strange bed the next morning. Where she slept that night I have no idea, but she came back into the room just as I was struggling to pull myself together and trying to remember just what the hell I had done, already horrified and disgusted with my own behaviour even before she smiled and told me that I wasn't bad for a man with as much alcohol inside me as I'd had.'

He stopped to swallow and Rachel went pale, her heart dropping with a sickening thump to her stomach. 'She kept me wallowing in my own self-disgust for months before she told me the truth. It was her way of getting revenge on me, I think,' he said, 'because I took my business away from her and gave it to one of her partners. The night she spoke to you on the telephone was a vindictive attempt to hurt me through you. And the last straw as far as I was concerned. When I called her back I informed her that I was going to remove my business right out of her sphere. Now I'm talking real money here, Rachel,' he inserted grimly, 'a very lucrative account. And the fact that she had now managed to lose it completely was not going to sit well with her co-partners, which frightened her—so much so that she lost control of her tongue. The insults which flew between the two of us then were so vile they were unrepeatable, but one thing she did let slip, which went at least some way to making me feel better about myself— she told me I never touched her. Oh,' he added deridingly, 'not in those words exactly. She was out to slay and used the kind of insults gauged to cut a man's ego in half. But to me they were like music to my ears! I never touched her and, oddly, I knew suddenly that she was telling the truth at last. Knew because my own instincts had been telling me the self-same thing through all the weeks she kept me dangling on that tormenting string.

'And that—' he turned to look her directly in the eye for the first time '—is the full unvarnished truth of it—if you can bring yourself to believe it, of course, and I wouldn't blame you in the least if you couldn't.'

Rachel lowered her eyes, staring at her hands where they twisted tensely together on her lap. She wanted to believe him, needed to believe him, but...

'Money, power—you can keep them,' he ordained huskily. 'If I can have your forgiveness in return.'

'You already have that,' she told him irritably. But the doubts still clouded her eyes.

'Then what else do you want me to say?' he sighed in

frustration. 'I cannot make your mind forget! Only you can do that.'

Impatiently she got up, angry suddenly that he was laying the problem their marriage had become on her. He had said a lot—revealed a lot—about himself, how he thought and felt. But none of it helped how she thought and felt; none of it revealed anything about the inner Rachel.

And maybe that was her problem, she conceded, feeling his eyes following her as she moved restlessly about the office. She, like Daniel, had always kept a part of herself hidden away. Dreams, he'd called them. But how was he supposed to know her dreams were fulfilled in him, in being his wife, the mother of his children, when she'd never actually said it?

Could she say it now? With all the hurt and misery she had carried around with her over the last months, could she afford to be as open and as honest with him as he had just been with her? To save what was left of their marriage, could she do it? Could—dared—she put her love on the line for him again?

Sighing into the heavy silence, she turned back to face him. Then she saw them, hanging in a neat row on the wall above Daniel's head. And her heart stopped beating.

Sam, Kate, Michael and herself. All professionally mounted and framed. Her very own sketches looking down at her from the wall of Daniel's office.

'I stole them,' he confessed, coming to his feet as she walked slowly towards them. 'I wanted them to look at whenever I needed— Do you mind?' he asked anxiously.

Rachel was amazed she hadn't missed them! Then she remembered the turmoil still waiting for her at home and smiled to herself. She wouldn't miss a three-piece suite in that chaos! 'You've managed to get the cross removed,' she noted, staring at her own face and feeling oddly exposed by what it revealed. 'It isn't a good likeness of me.' She dismissed what her own eyes were telling her.

'It *is* you,' Daniel insisted. 'The real you. They all are to me,' he added, with a quiet pride which warmed her right through. 'Quite a family gallery, when you think about it.' He smiled wryly.

'Except you're not there.'

'No.' His smile died. 'Why is that, Rachel?' he enquired. 'Why was there no portrait of me in any of your books?'

He'd searched through them all? She hesitated over her reply, then told the truth. It was time for the truth, she accepted suddenly. The full truth. 'They all love me,' she explained, nodding towards the three faces of their children. 'I didn't think you did any more. I tried to draw you,' she added quickly, before he could say anything to that, 'but the features kept distorting so I gave up in the end…'

'Did Callum see these?'

'What?' The harshness of his tone threw her for a moment, and she had to think who Callum was. Then, 'Oh, no,' she replied. 'Nobody saw these other than you.'

'How serious did things get between you two?'

'It didn't get serious at all.' She shrugged Zac Callum off as though he were unimportant.

But Daniel wasn't ready to dismiss the other man. 'You kissed him!' he muttered. 'I saw you!'

'One hasty kiss in the front seat of a car?' she mocked his jealousy, then added softly, 'That's all it was—that's all!'

But he wasn't convinced. His fingers came to clench on her shoulders as he frowned darkly down on her. Rachel sighed, noting that he had managed to do it again and turn the tables on her so that she was having to defend herself against something that she had not even done! Then she smiled at the absolute ridiculousness of it all.

'You look like that devil again.' Her eyes twinkled at him. 'You know, the one who takes showers in vats of fire!'

'I'm going to kiss you,' he growled.

'What—here in your very office?' she mocked. 'Wrong setting, darling. I belong in your other world, remember?'

He kissed her, angrily and passionately. He kissed her until she swayed in his arms. He kissed her until her hands crept round his neck and hung on, fingers curling into the silken dark hair at his nape. He kissed her until her tongue linked sensually with his, and her breasts began to respond, and his own body pulsed urgently against the firm swelling wall of her stomach. He kissed her until she was breathless, gasping, eager, hungry and totally, utterly lost in him.

Then, 'I love you, Rachel,' he whispered urgently.

'I know.' Softly, she pressed her lips to his taut throat. 'I think I can let myself believe you again.'

He sighed then in gruff relief, and took her mouth again, kissing her long and slow and deeply.

One of his telephones took that moment to start ringing. Daniel turned to glare at it, then took hold of her hand and drew her with him over to his desk. 'Don't move,' he said as he let go of her so that he could reach out for the phone, then hitched one lean hip on the edge of the desk and barked out his name.

It was amazing how smoothly he switched from passionate lover to cool, collected businessman, she noted, hearing nothing of what he was saying as she curiously studied his face. He looked leaner somehow, more finely honed, as if his features had actually taken on a physical alteration to suit the man he was being now: sharp, shrewd, assertive. His eyes were cool—even though they never lost contact with her own. And his mouth was thinner, losing all that beautiful sensuality her kisses had given it.

She smiled ruefully, and he frowned an enquiry at her without faltering in the discussion he was having with his caller. And some little devil in her made her want to crack the tycoon armour, making her reach out to stroke a caressing hand along his thigh.

He almost choked on an inward gasp, his own hand coming to clamp fiercely on top of hers. The eyes flashed, the voice faltered, and Rachel laughed.

'I'll call you back,' he ground out, and slammed down the phone. 'That was an important client!' he accused, pulling her towards him. 'You did that on purpose!'

'I love you, Daniel,' she told him softly.

He went pale, swallowing. 'Say that again,' he ordered thickly.

Rachel reached up and pressed a kiss to his mouth. 'I love you,' she repeated, finding it easier now that she'd let herself say it.

Daniel inhaled deeply, his nostrils flaring as though he was savouring the very scent of the words. 'I've missed you telling me that,' he said as he exhaled again. 'I've missed having the light on your face when you say it.' He lifted a hand to her cheek, cupping it gently where the afternoon sunlight caressed her skin.

'I loved you when I was a child of seventeen,' she told him softly. 'And I've never actually stopped loving you since. It just got—bruised badly, that's all.'

'So you hid it all away and made our nights into torments of pure hell.' His chest lifted and fell on a heavy sigh. 'All those terrible silent lovings, Rachel. And the darkness.' He sighed at the pain of it all. 'Now there was a punishment. Those dark silent lovings.'

'Let's go home,' she murmured, wanting to hold him close, hold him against her, naked and gleaming in the light. 'Can you leave here just like that?' she then asked anxiously, remembering that all of this was, after all, his responsibility.

'I can do anything I like!' he claimed haughtily, straightening from the desk. 'I'm the boss. I own this lot!'

'Mmm,' she murmured. 'I'd forgotten that—cash millionaire, I think I recall you saying once.' Her blue eyes looked up at him speculatively. 'That means half your assets are mine if we get divorced. I wonder if it would be worth the—'

Taking her firmly by the shoulders he turned her towards the door. 'We're going home—to the new house, not the old one,' he said threateningly. 'Then we're going to dump the kids on our new housekeeper while we use one of the finished bedrooms so I can show you which *asset* of mine is more important to you!'

'Sounds interesting,' she mused.

'It will be more than interesting,' he promised threateningly.

'I am in a rather delicate condition, you know,' she reminded him.

'That never caused problems before.' He dismissed that argument. 'In fact,' he added silkily, 'I recall from past experience that you're rather more—sensitive at times like this.'

Just then the door to his office opened, and three children scrambled in, saving Rachel from having to refute that last provoking remark.

Daniel stooped to pick up Michael, who was falling asleep on his feet. The baby's head flopped on to his shoulder and Rachel smiled lovingly at them both.

They rode down in the lift and walked off towards the car park, Daniel carrying the sleeping baby, his free arm still resting possessively across Rachel's shoulders. Sam was a tornado fighter plane, bent on circling them all as they walked. Kate held tightly to her mother's hand. She had pulled Rachel's face down and kissed her a few moments ago, her blue eyes full of silent remorse. 'I'll never do it again, Mummy,' she promised solemnly. And Rachel knew she wouldn't. Kate had learned her lesson the hard way.

It was a sunny day, and half of Masterson Holdings seemingly happened to be gazing out of the office windows as their employer and his family made their way across the car park.

'I just can't believe it of him,' one man said. 'I knew he was married, but three—nearly four kids!'

'I've been working for him for years,' someone else put in. 'And I never knew he was married. He's always been such a ruthless swine, so sharp you could cut yourself on him. What the hell made a sweet creature like her marry a man like that?'

'He doesn't look so sharp and ruthless now,' the first remarked ruefully. 'In fact he looks kind of cute. Perhaps he's different at home.'

'Or maybe she's not so sweet and innocent as she looks,' the second leered. 'After all—four kids? That takes a lot of loving…'

'What about my car?' Rachel protested as Daniel herded them towards his.

'I'll get it delivered this afternoon.'

'Not while I have the keys right here, you won't,' she pointed out with perfect feminine calm.

Daniel muttered something beneath his breath, swapped the sleeping Michael for the car keys and commanded the twins to get in the back of the car. They scrambled in, he closed the door, then opened the front passenger door and carefully helped Rachel inside.

The faces pressed to the office windows watched him stalk back into the building only to reappear again a few minutes later with young Archer from Sales—the same young man who had escorted Rachel to Daniel's office earlier.

Daniel handed him the keys and pointed to the white Escort. The two men parted and Daniel climbed into the BMW. A moment later he was climbing out again and opening the rear door. The twins scrambled out. He came around to open the front passenger door and took the sleeping child from Rachel, then helped her climb out. Then they were all trooping across the car park towards the Escort, where words were exchanged with Archer, plus sets of keys, then the family were opening doors to the Escort and the reason for this swap became clear when the baby was strapped into a child safety seat. Archer was about to make for the BMW when he was stopped by Kate. She gazed pleadingly at her father, who glanced enquiringly at Archer, who shrugged and grinned and held out his hand. The daughter demanded her father's cheek for a thank you kiss, gave it, then was skipping off beside Archer and the rest were scrambling into the Escort.

'Good God,' someone gasped. 'They've got him wrapped around their little finger! I wonder what the formula for that is? It could be worth a fortune bottled!'

'Blue eyes, blonde hair and the most delicious body even while pregnant,' someone listed.

'I thought he had something going with Lydia Marsden not so long ago,' someone else murmured thoughtfully.

'Lydia Marsden!' the scathing cry went up.

'Sorry,' the other man shrugged. 'Stupid idea.'

'Nice kids,' someone said.

'Nice wife,' said another.

'Nice car,' laughed the next.

'Nice home?' The joke continued down the line.

'Nice business,' sighed someone wistfully.

'Nice dole queue if you don't get back to work!' shouted out a voice which drowned out all the rest.

'Remind me to have a safety seat fitted into my car, will

you?' Daniel muttered as he climbed behind the wheel of the Escort and readjusted the seat to fit his longer frame.

'What—and ruin your macho ruthless tycoon image?' Rachel mocked.

'What macho ruthless tycoon image?' he derided. 'Did you bother to look up at the windows in my building?'

'No—why?' She turned to look now, though, saw the long row of curious faces and blushed hotly. 'Will they tease you about us?' she whispered anxiously.

'Not to my face, if they have a healthy sense of self-preservation,' he grunted, then sighed. 'Though God knows what they'll say behind my back.'

'Never mind.' Rachel put a comforting hand on his thigh. 'We all love you. Macho ruthless tycoon or not.'

'Keep your hand where it is,' he muttered tensely, 'and I'll be labelled a damned sex maniac!'

'What's a sex maniac?' a young voice enquired from the back.

Rachel choked back a giggle and snatched her hand away. Daniel looked heavenwards and sighed. 'When you're older, son,' he answered drily. 'I'll explain when you're older.'

'Will you explain it to me when I'm older too?' Rachel asked guilelessly.

His eyes flashed her a burning look. 'I'll do better than that. I'll show you just as soon as I can get you alone!' he promised.

'With the light on, so I can—'

'Don't, Rachel!' he groaned, closing his eyes on a spasm of pain. 'You don't know how much I want to do that.'

'Yes, I do,' she said, and her eyes told him why.

Daniel's darkened. 'Just hold that thought,' he commanded, and put the car into gear.

Miranda Lee is Australian, living near Sydney. Born and raised in the bush, she was boarding-school educated and briefly pursued a classical music career before moving to Sydney and embracing the world of computers. Happily married, with three daughters, she began writing when family commitments kept her at home. She likes to create stories that are believable, modern, fast-paced and sexy. Her interests include reading meaty sagas, doing word puzzles, gambling and going to the movies.

Look out for THE PLAYBOY IN PURSUIT
by Miranda Lee
in Modern Romance™, January 2001

MARRIAGE IN JEOPARDY

by

MIRANDA LEE

CHAPTER ONE

THE first inkling Juliana had that something was wrong came with Stewart's telephone call to her office. Not that this was unusual. Blake's secretary often called her to relay messages from her husband. It was Stewart's tone of voice that disturbed her. He sounded almost…rattled.

'Mrs Preston, have you by any chance heard from Mr Preston today?' he asked after announcing himself.

'No, Stewart, I haven't. Why? Is there some problem?'

His hesitation to answer sent Juliana snapping forward on her chair. 'What is it?' she said sharply. 'What's happened?'

Her anxious quizzing seemed to shock Stewart back into his more characteristic role as Blake's unflappable right-hand man. 'No need to be alarmed, Mrs Preston,' he replied in that maddeningly phlegmatic voice he usually used. It's just that when I rang the Sydney office a minute ago they hadn't seen hide nor hair of Mr Preston all day. The manager sounded most relieved, I might add.'

'The *Sydney* office? Why would Blake be in the Sydney office? Wasn't he flying straight home from Manila today?'

5

'You mean Mr Preston didn't tell you of his change of plan?'

Juliana bit her bottom lip in a vain attempt to stop dismay from swamping her. This was one aspect of her marriage that had been bothering her more and more of late. Blake's obsession with personal space. He hated answering to anyone, especially his wife. Juliana knew *why* this was so, but knowing why did not make it any easier to bear.

'No, Stewart,' she admitted. 'He didn't.'

'I see.' The secretary was unable to hide the sardonic edge in his voice.

What do you see? Juliana agonised with a rush of fierce emotion. A marriage without love? A woman prepared to accept any kind of treatment in exchange for money and position?

Her heart ached with the desire to explain that her relationship with Blake was not really like that. OK, so maybe their marriage *had* been entered into with their heads, rather than their hearts. But that didn't mean they didn't care for each other, that they hadn't become the most important people in each other's lives.

If she came across as a cool, reserved spouse then that was because Blake liked her that way. Surely Stewart could appreciate that. He himself had been hired as Blake's secretary and assistant because he possessed the very qualities Blake demanded in all those close to him. He was self-sufficient, self-reliant, self-contained. Like herself.

Only she didn't feel self-contained at that moment. She felt extremely vulnerable. And worried.

'Please, Stewart,' she went on, her voice unsteady. 'Don't leave me in the dark. Tell me what's going on.'

Once again, the man hesitated. Clearly, he'd been well trained by Blake over what the boss's wife should and shouldn't know.

Juliana felt the beginnings of panic. '*Please*,' she pleaded. Oh, God, if something had happened to Blake she didn't know what she would do.

'Mr Preston will be very cross with me,' the man muttered, 'but I suppose you have a right to know since my call has obviously upset you. Your husband sent me a fax yesterday to say he'd finished in Manila a day early and had decided to drop off at our Sydney branch for a totally unannounced visit on the way home, but that he would still be arriving in Melbourne by five-thirty.'

'But you said he *hasn't* dropped in at the Sydney office!'

'Which is no reason to panic, Mrs Preston. As you well know, it's not unlike your husband not to let even me know of last-minute changes of plans. Maybe he's stayed on in Manila. Or maybe he's gone to the Brisbane office instead. He's sure to turn up at Tullamarine airport as per schedule. The boss is very reliable like that. I'll just mosey on out to the airport to meet him and you pop on home and dress for dinner. I've booked a table for you and Mr Preston at Don Giovanni's for eight-thirty.'

'But what if his plane doesn't arrive?' Juliana cried,

unable to think of something as ridiculous as dressing for dinner when for all she knew her Blake might be in mortal danger.

'It will, Mrs Preston. Be assured of that. Now do stop worrying, and please…let this incident be our little secret. Your husband would be far from pleased if he knew I'd bothered you with this minor misunderstanding. Do I have your reassurance that you won't mention it to him?'

Juliana sighed. 'I suppose so, but please call me at home as soon as Blake's plane touches down, otherwise I'll worry myself to death.'

'I'll certainly do that, Mrs Preston,' he finished with far more warmth than usual.

Juliana hung up, aware that nothing would make her feel better till Blake was home again, safe and sound. Three weeks he'd been away. Three long, lonely weeks. She'd been so looking forward to tonight, to dinner, then afterwards. Now…

Her heart squeezed tight. What if something awful had happened? What if she never saw Blake again?

I'm being maudlin, she told herself abruptly. Maudlin and melodramatic and ridiculous. Just because I've been having some small doubts about my marriage lately. Stewart's right, Blake does this sort of thing all the time. He'll show up as he always does, smoothly elegant and totally unruffled. There's absolutely no reason to worry, let alone panic.

Still, Juliana could not settle to any more work that afternoon and was glad to leave the office at four-thirty, anxious to be home for Stewart's call. The

Preston mansion was only a few miles from the city, overlooking the Eastern side of Port Phillip Bay, but Juliana caught the Friday afternoon rush, and the drive home took over an hour.

The telephone was ringing as she let herself into the house via the garages shortly after five-thirty. Since it was Mrs Dawson's night off, there was no one to answer it, and Juliana hoped it would keep ringing till she could reach the closest extension. Hurrying through the laundry and into the kitchen, she dropped her coat and handbag on the breakfast counter and snatched the receiver down from the wall. 'Yes?'

'Mrs Preston?'

'Stewart! Oh, thank God you didn't hang up. I was just letting myself in and I ran. But everything's all right now,' she sighed happily. 'Blake's jet landed on time, I gather?'

'Well—er—'

Juliana froze.

'Mr Preston's plane *hasn't* arrived as yet, I'm sorry to say, and I've been having some trouble locating him. I've been in contact with Manila, and it seems Mr Preston left on time yesterday, with Sydney as his intended destination, but the airports there are insistent he did not land anywhere in Sydney at all either yesterday or today.'

All the blood began draining from Juliana's face. 'Dear heaven…' She dragged over a kitchen stool and slumped down on it before she fell down. 'Have… have you contacted the various authorities?'

'I certainly have. They're making enquiries.'

'Making enquiries,' she repeated limply.

'Please try not to worry, Mrs Preston. I'm sure everything will be all right.'

'Do…do you think I should come out to the airport myself?'

'I don't think that would be wise,' came the firm advice. 'Especially if Mr Preston arrives shortly, as I'm sure he will. You know how he hates being fussed over. He'd much prefer you to wait for him at home, as you always do.'

Juliana flinched at what sounded like a reproof. The only reason she didn't meet or see her husband off at airports was because he always insisted she didn't, not because she didn't want to. This was another aspect of her marriage that was beginning to trouble her: other people's perceptions of it. Still, this was hardly the time to be worrying about appearances.

'You promise to ring me,' she said shakily, 'as soon as you know anything? Anything at all.'

'I promise, Mrs Preston. Must go. Bye.'

Juliana finally hung up the receiver. Oh, God… Blake…

For a moment she buried her face in her hands, terrified by the images that kept bombarding her mind. Blake…lying dead in a twisted mangle of metal on some mountainside. Blake…sinking to the bottom of the ocean in a cold coffin of steel. Or worst of all…his beautiful body charred beyond all recognition. Planes often burst into flames when they crashed.

Her loud cry of utter desolation shocked even herself.

Juliana's lovely hazel eyes opened wide. She sat up straight in the stool. Dear heaven, she thought with a wild churning of her stomach. Dear heaven…

Juliana sat in the dark in her living-room, all alone. She was grateful that it was Mrs Dawson's night off, grateful that she didn't have to put up with the woman's scepticism over her distress. Blake's housekeeper had made it perfectly plain without being overtly rude that she didn't approve of her employer's wife, always calling Juliana 'Mrs Preston' in a stiffly formal manner.

Two hours had passed since Stewart's call. It felt like two years.

The sudden sound of the phone ringing sent Juliana leaping to her feet. Heart pounding madly, she raced across the room, hesitating fearfully before snatching the dreaded instrument up to her ear. 'Yes?'

'Stewart Margin here again, Mrs Preston. No need to worry any longer. Mr Preston is perfectly all right.'

Juliana swayed, gripping the edge of the telephone table as a steadier. 'Oh, thank the lord,' she whispered huskily. 'Thank the lord…'

She closed her eyes for a second to say another private prayer of thanks. Blake hadn't been killed in a plane crash after all! Soon he would breeze in through their front door, splendid as always in one of his immaculate business suits. He would toss aside his crocodile-skin briefcase before reefing his tie off then heading straight for the drinks cabinet where he would pour himself a hefty Scotch and call out to her. 'Come and join me, Juliana, and tell me about your day. Mine's been hell!'

Oh, Blake... What would I have done if something had happened to you? How would I have survived?

She paled as the realisation that had come to her earlier on struck again with sickening force, a realisation which could threaten her future happiness almost as much as Blake's dying. A small sob escaped her throat, her knuckles whitening as her nails dug into the wood.

'Mrs Preston? Are you all right?'

No, she cried in silent anguish. I'm not all right. I'm never going to be all right again. Don't you see? Somewhere along the line I've fallen in love with my husband! Why, if he walked in right now I would throw myself into his arms, weeping and making a complete fool of myself.

And what would Blake do? He would stare down at me in appalled horror, coldly withdrawing from such a display of emotional possessiveness. Oh, how he hated women who clung, who needed, who *loved* like that.

God! Whatever am I going to do?

Ask about your husband, you little idiot, the voice of common sense suggested. But ask *calmly*.

She gulped and set about gathering her wits. For if she didn't she might as well ask Blake for a divorce this very night.

'I am now,' she assured Blake's secretary. 'Has my husband's plane actually arrived?'

'No. He's coming in on a commercial flight that lands in…let's see now…in about ten minutes' time.'

'A *commercial* flight? What happened to his Lear-jet? Did it break down somewhere?'

'In a way. It appears that some time after take-off from Manila yesterday Mr Preston's plane went through a cloud of volcanic dust that clogged up the engines—and the on-board electronics—so badly that the pilot had to make an emergency landing.'

'An emergency landing? But *where*? Why weren't we *told*?'

'Fortunately the pilot knew of an American airforce strip on a nearby island, but unfortunately it was abandoned. It took some time for them to be able to contact authorities and get a helicopter to take them back to Manila. Blake had a message sent through to Tullamarine airport but it was misplaced temporarily during a change-over of staff. It's always rather hectic here during Friday evening peak hour. Not that that's any excuse really. Still, all's well that ends well, Mrs Preston. The boss is safe and sound.'

For the second time that day Juliana heard traces of emotion in Stewart Margin's voice. So he too had been worried. And he too was relieved.

A softly ironic smile passed over her lips. And why wouldn't he be? Without Blake as company director, Preston's Toys and Games would probably quickly revert to the almost bankrupt business it had been when he'd taken over a few years before. Without Blake, Stewart Margin might be swiftly without a job.

Without Blake…

Juliana shivered. If only her own relief weren't tinged with this awful apprehension.

If only this incident hadn't happened at all! she agonised. Then she might never have realised the depth of her feelings. She would have been able to go on in blissful ignorance, happily being the sort of wife Blake wanted without worrying that any moment she might betray herself and, in doing so, lose him.

But have you been happy being that sort of wife? came a dark voice from deep inside. *Really* happy? What about all those niggling little doubts of late?

'Mrs Preston? Are you sure you're all right?'

Juliana scooped in a steadying breath. 'I *am* still a little shaken,' she admitted. 'I'll be fine by the time Blake arrives home. But, as you mentioned earlier, my husband does hate any fuss, so best he doesn't know the extent of my concern over this matter.'

'Of course, Mrs Preston. I wouldn't *dream* of telling him.'

'Good. Let me know if there are any more delays, will you?'

'Certainly.'

When Juliana hung up the phone she didn't know whether to laugh or cry. She felt both elated and devastated. In the space of a couple of hours she had been through an emotional mill. She was *still* going through it.

She turned to walk somewhat dazedly out into the deserted kitchen, switching on the electric kettle for a cup of coffee. Would Blake still want to go out for dinner when he got home? she wondered distractedly.

She doubted it. He was sure to have been fed on the plane.

There was one thing, however, that he might want tonight after being away for so long.

Juliana shuddered. An odd reaction, she realised, for a woman who had found nothing but pleasure in her husband's arms.

But with her newly discovered love burning in her heart Juliana could see that the intimate side of their marriage left a lot to be desired. Blake conducted their sex-life in a coolly clinical fashion, without any spontaneity or real passion. They had separate bedrooms, their sexual encounters always pre-arranged. He even marked the calendar in his study with the dates on which she would be...indisposed. Being on the Pill, Juliana could provide this information in advance.

She wished now that this were one of those days. But it wasn't.

Of course she could *understand* Blake's aversion to sharing a room with her. It was his way of keeping her at a safe distance, making sure she didn't start demanding any more than he was prepared to give.

But *understanding* did not make the situation sit better around her heart.

She cringed now to think of the way Blake would give her the nod before retiring whenever he wished to sleep with her; the way he didn't come into her room till she was showered and already in bed; the way he never stayed the whole night with her, going back to his own room once he was finished.

Juliana shook her head in distress. God, it was little better than legal prostitution.

No, no, she denied quickly. That was being unfair to Blake and their marriage. Their sex-life was only one aspect of their relationship. They were partners in more ways than just in bed. They went everywhere together. They were good friends. They always had been.

Was she going to ruin what they had simply because she'd been silly enough to fall in love? She would be crazy to. Her marriage was stronger than most. They were going to try for a baby next year. Madness to throw that all away by wanting the one thing she couldn't have.

So Blake didn't love her. He *did* care for her in his own peculiar way. So he wasn't swept away by passion for her at odd times during the day. He *did* make love to her quite beautifully when he came to her bed. And that was often enough.

For pity's sake, what did she want out of life? She had it good, had what she'd always wanted. Financial security; a solid marriage; a good job. All she had to do was keep her love under control and simply go on as before.

Which included not making any objections to the way Blake conducted their sex-life.

But, dear heaven, she hoped he would be too tired to come to her bed tonight. She didn't think she could bear to have him touch her just now. She was sure to do something silly, sure to give herself away.

There again, she did so long to hold him. Just hold him.

But Blake didn't know how to just be held. He never, ever touched Juliana at all except when he climbed into her bed. Not for him the simple holding of hands or the putting of an affectionate arm around her shoulder or waist. He was not, and never would be, a toucher.

And Juliana knew why.

Bitterness rose in her chest. His mother had a lot to answer for.

The telephone ringing again cut through the silence of the house.

Juliana stiffened.

It was Blake. She just *knew* it was Blake, ringing before he left the airport.

Though never liking her to call him at all, he often phoned her. It was another of his quirks about wives which Juliana fully understood. His mother had driven his father crazy with constant telephone calls, especially when he was away on business. They had not been chatty, affectionate calls, but jealously possessive calls, always wanting to know where he was, what he was doing, where he was going, when he would be home.

Then, once he *was* home, she never let him out of her sight, always touching him, kissing him, pawing at him. Noreen Preston had been a neurotically insecure women who'd loved her handsome husband to her—and everyone else's—distraction.

Juliana knew all this, not because Blake had told

her. Her mother had told her. Her mother, who had been the live-in cook here in the Preston household for almost twenty years, her long employ coming to an abrupt halt a year ago when she was accidentally killed by a hit-and-run driver.

Juliana closed her eyes against the rush of tears.

Poor Mum…

Yet she knew her mother would not have wanted her pity. Or her grief. Lily Mason had been an open-hearted, kind-natured woman who'd embraced life with a naïve optimism that left little room for regrets and remorse. Unfortunately, however, this same naïve optimism made her vulnerable to certain types of men, ones whom Lily always thought loved and needed her.

All they had loved and needed, Juliana thought bitterly, was her mother's quite beautiful body in bed. Not one of them had ever offered to support her, or marry her, not even Juliana's father, who had apparently disappeared into the wide blue yonder as soon as he'd found out his teenage girlfriend was pregnant.

At least Lily hadn't made the mistake of letting any of these men live with herself and her daughter. Juliana was spared that. But even as a young child tucked up in bed she'd heard her mother sneaking men into her room late at night.

This had stopped for a while when Lily and her daughter had moved into the flat above the Prestons' garage. But not for long. Lily merely moved her assignation time to during the day, Juliana often smelling male aftershave and cigar smoke when she came home from school.

The insistent ring of the telephone brought Juliana back to reality. What on earth was she doing, mentally rumaging over all this dirty linen? The past might hold explanations for why people did what they did—herself and Blake included—but it didn't give her any weapons with which to handle the present and the future.

All she could do was gather herself and answer the telephone, and, if it was Blake, show him that nothing had changed between them. Nothing at all.

She reached up and lifted the receiver down to her ear, telling herself to act as if she were taking a business call at work. As public relations officer for a large international cosmetic company Juliana had had plenty of practice at appearing cool under stress.

'Juliana Preston,' she said with superb calm.

'Blake here, Juliana.'

'Blake!' she exclaimed with a forced lilt in her voice. 'You bad man, you had me so worried.' Her tone betrayed not the slightest hint of any real worry.

He laughed his attractively lazy laugh, reinforcing her belief that this was the way to play the situation.

'And there I'd been,' she went on lightly, 'thinking you'd made me into a premature widow.'

'Thinking, or hoping?' he drawled. 'And don't you mean a *merry* widow? I'm worth a bundle. Even more after the deals I've just made.'

Juliana's skin crawled at the mention of money. It was bad enough having people like Stewart and Mrs Dawson believing she'd married Blake for his money, worse to have her husband voicing the same opinion.

Maybe it had been partly true. Once. But not now. Not any more…

How ironic that Blake would hate to think that was so. He *liked* the arrangement they had come to, the sort of marriage he'd insisted upon and which Juliana had thought she'd wanted too, at the time. God! If only she were able to take him into her confidence, to tell him of her newly discovered love.

But that was impossible. He didn't want her to love him. In fact, he would hate the idea. The truth was, if she wished to continue being Mrs Blake Preston she would have to hide her love behind the sort of wife she'd successfully been up till now, but which she suspected would prove hard to be in the future.

'Everything went well, then?' she asked, keeping her voice amazingly cool.

'Fantastic!' he returned. 'I love doing business with the Asians—they're a real challenge.'

She forced a laugh. 'And how you do like a challenge!'

'Do I?'

'You know you do. That's the only reason you came back into the fold of the family business. Because it was on the skids. You liked to think you could resurrect it from the ashes like the phoenix.'

He chuckled. 'You could be right. But aren't you going to ask me what happened to my plane?'

'Stewart gave me the general idea. You can tell me more later.'

'Such restraint. Sometimes, Juliana,' he said with a dry laugh, 'I almost think you don't love me.'

Her heart squeezed tight. 'Whatever would give you that idea?' she tossed off.

He laughed again. 'Can I hope you'll be a bit more enthusiastic about my return later tonight?'

All her insides tightened. 'I would have thought you'd be too tired for that after your little adventure.'

'I slept on the plane.'

The implication behind his words was clear. He wasn't too tired. He would definitely be coming to her bed tonight.

Oddly enough, this thought didn't produce the re-action in Juliana that she might have expected, given her earlier apprehension. It actually sent a hot wave of desire racing through her body, bringing a flushed heat to her face.

She was shocked. She wasn't the easiest woman to arouse, Blake always having to take his time before she was ready for him. She suspected that her mother's promiscuous behaviour had instilled in her an instinc-tive fear of appearing sexually easy—hence the diffi-culty she had always found in surrendering her body to a man. Even with Blake, who seemed to know ex-actly what to do to relax, then excite her, she was still somewhat inhibited. There were several sexual activ-ities and positions she not only would not permit, but which had previously repelled her.

Now, Juliana could hardly believe the images that kept flashing into her mind, or the way her heart was racing.

Had falling in love within the security of marriage finally released in her the sort of sensuality Lily's daughter should always have possessed? Had she sub-consciously locked a highly sexed nature away within a tightly controlled shell, for fear of turning out like her mother?

Perhaps. Only time would tell, she realised shakily. Time. And tonight…

'Maybe I'll have a headache,' she said, seeking to defuse her tension with humour.

'I'll bring some aspirin home with me,' Blake countered drily.

'What if I just said no?'

'You never have before.'

'Maybe I've found somebody else to keep me happy while you're away.'

Blake laughed. 'Is that so? Well, you'll just have to tell him your hubby's home and he isn't needed any more. Now I suggest you have a nice relaxing bath and I'll be with you as soon as I can.'

After his abrupt hanging-up, Juliana stared down into the dead receiver, not sure how to take Blake's amused indifference to her taunt about another man. It crossed her mind that he might react the same way even if she hadn't been joking.

Wouldn't he *care* if she had an affair? she worried with a sudden and quite dampening dismay. Was he himself doing the same with other women during his business trips away?

She had never thought to question his faithfulness before, had never been ripped to pieces inside by the shards of jealousy that were even now slicing deeply into her heart. The thought of him touching another woman as he touched her…

A violent shudder ran through her before she was able to pull herself together with some solid reasonings.

Blake had *never* given her a reason to be jealous on his business trips. It wasn't as though he ever took a female secretary or assistant with him. He didn't have one. His faithful Girl Friday was a man—Stewart.

OK, so he didn't ring her every single day as some husbands would. And he never brought her a gift home, to show that he had been thinking of her while he was away.

But she fully understood why he didn't do either of those things.

Once he arrived home he always showed her in bed how much he had missed her, never missing a night for at least a week. Would he be like that if he was having other women on the side? No, of course not, Juliana reasoned. His offhand response was just his being as flippant with her as she had been with him. She was imagining things.

But her imaginings demonstrated perhaps what was to be feared in falling in love. She could almost understand Blake's deep aversion to it. Love made you irrational, panicky, insecure. Especially when that love was not returned.

The automatic kettle made a click as it switched itself off. Juliana stared at it. She didn't feel like coffee any more. A swift glance at the wall-clock showed it was ten to nine. Blake could be here in a little over an hour.

She shivered again. What to do?

Perhaps she should have that bath he'd told her to have. It might relax her, calm her nerves.

Juliana moved slowly from the living-room out into the large foyer from which the semi-circular staircase rose in all its magnificent glory. Hesitating for a moment on the first step, her hand curled over the knob at the end of the elegantly carved balustrade, Juliana's mind slipped back nineteen years to the first time she actually saw this house, and this imposing staircase.

Who would have dreamt that the little girl who had stared with open-mouthed awe at the riches contained within the hallowed walls of the Preston mansion would one day be mistress of that same house? And who would have believed that she would ever find herself in the same situation as the tragic Noreen Preston, in love with a husband who didn't love her back?

For a moment, Juliana's stomach churned. But then she straightened her spine and continued up the stairs.

There was one major difference between herself and Noreen Preston. *She* was from tougher stock. Far tougher. No way would she ever commit suicide because she found out her husband was having an affair with another woman. She would fight for what she wanted, fight to the death.

And, as of now, she wanted Blake. More than she could ever have envisaged.

CHAPTER TWO

HALF an hour later, Juliana was lying in her bath, remembering that there had once been a time when she and Blake had been so close, she could have told him anything. But of course that had been years ago, and so much had changed since then...

The first time Juliana saw Blake he'd frightened the life out of her. She'd only been nine at the time. It was on her mother's second day as cook in the Preston household. Mr and Mrs Preston had kindly given Juliana permission to use their swimming-pool and, since it was an awfully hot day, smack-dab in the middle of the summer holidays, she had been only too happy to accept their generous offer.

So, garbed in her cheap multi-coloured costume, Juliana made her way out on to the vast back patio and pool complex. And it was while she was gaping at the Olympic-size pool, complete with extravagant surroundings, that the accident happened.

Blake, then fifteen, was making his first attempt at a backward somersault from the diving-board. Apparently, he didn't jump far enough away from the end of the board, for he banged the back of his head during the turn, splashing into the water then sinking like a stone to the bottom.

'Blake!' screamed a girl who was lying sunbathing

on a deckchair. Juliana was to find out later that she was Blake's eleven-year-old sister, Barbara. But for now Juliana's attention was all on the unconscious shape at the bottom of the pool.

She didn't stop to think. She simply dived in, dog-paddled down to him and dragged him up to the surface. 'H…help me!' she spluttered out to Barbara, who was standing open-mouthed by the side of the pool.

Somehow, with her inept help, Juliana managed to pull Blake out.

'He's dead!' his sister cried. 'Oh, my God, he's dead.'

'No, he's not,' Juliana refuted, though frightened that he might be. 'Go and tell my mum to ring an ambulance!' she ordered. 'The *cook*!' she screamed when Barbara looked blankly at her. 'My mum's the new cook!'

Barbara ran while Juliana set about doing what she'd seen on television a few times but which she had no real experience with: mouth-to-mouth resuscitation. But she must have done something right, for by the time her mother ran out to tell her the ambulance was on its way Blake started coughing back to consciousness. By the time the paramedics arrived he only needed a little oxygen to be on the way to full recovery.

'I reckon you saved his life, little lady,' one of the paramedics praised.

'Really?' she grinned, widely pleased with herself.

'Yes, really,' the man said. 'Your mum should be very proud of you.'

Behind the ambulance officer's back Barbara pulled a face at Juliana, which set the tone of their relationship from that day forward. Barbara never let an opportunity go by to express her disgust and disapproval that the cook's child was allowed the run of the house, let alone *her* pool. Blake, however, immediately became Juliana's firm ally, defending her against Barbara's bitchy snobbery and generally being very nice to her.

Oddly enough, despite the six-year age-difference, he really seemed to find Juliana's company enjoyable. Maybe because she was a bit of a tomboy, and would join in with his leisure activities. They swam together, dived together, played board games together. Juliana also believed he found her a pleasant change from all Barbara's girlfriends who went ga-ga over him all the time. He clearly found their drippy drooling both embarrassing and repugnant.

Still, Juliana wasn't blind. She could see that at fifteen Blake was a well-grown and very handsome young man. His blue-eyed blond looks and well-shaped bronzed body drew the girls in droves. Barbara's classmates found any excuse to visit the Preston household. Not that he ever took any notice of them. They were too young for him, for a start. Generally speaking, he didn't seem to like girls at all. If he *did* have any girlfriends during his high-school years, he kept them a secret.

Juliana was the only female given the privilege of

Blake's company and conversation, much to Barbara's friends' pique. They repaid her in a myriad spiteful little ways, from openly insulting her background to pretending to be friendly before cutting her dead. Once they even gave her an invitation to a non-existent birthday party.

Juliana could still remember her humiliation when she turned up at the address, only to be bluntly told there was no party there that day. Not wanting to upset her mother—who'd been so pleased by the invitation—she spent all afternoon in the park before returning home and pretending the party had been fantastic.

It was only when she told Blake later about the incident and he gave her a look of such pained apology that she finally burst into tears. He hugged her, something he *never* did, and told her not to worry, that people like that would eventually get their come-uppance.

But Juliana privately believed the privileged rich rarely got their come-uppance. It was the working-class poor who always suffered, who were put upon and discriminated against. The rich never lived in back rooms or wore hand-me-down clothes. They certainly didn't know what it was like not to be able to go on school excursions because they didn't have the money.

By the time Juliana turned twelve she'd decided that one day she was going to be rich too.

'When I grow up,' she told Blake shortly after her twelfth birthday, 'I'm going to marry a millionaire.'

Blake glanced up from his desk with a surprised

look on his face. 'I don't believe you said that. I thought you despised the wealthy.'

Juliana was lying face-down on his bed, her face propped up in her hands. 'I'm going to start a different brand of wealthy. I'll give a lot of my money to charity and be kind to my servants.'

'What do you mean, be kind to your servants?' he said sharply. 'Mum and Dad are kind to your mother. Besides, you always said people shouldn't *have* servants at all.'

'Employees, then,' she argued stubbornly. 'I'll have to employ someone to clean and cook for me. I'm going to have a career.'

'Why have a career,' he scoffed, 'if you're going to marry for money? Rich men's wives don't work. They have lunches and their hair done.'

'I'm going to be different.'

'Are you, by gum?' He laughed at last.

'Yes, I am!'

'And what if you can't find a rich man to marry you?' he mocked. 'The rich marry the rich, or didn't you know that?'

Juliana frowned. She hadn't thought of that. But she wasn't about to have her dream shattered by cold, hard reality. Sitting up abruptly, she tossed her long straight brown hair back over her skinny shoulders, her pointy chin lifting defiantly. 'I'm going to be so beautiful when I grow up that millionaires will be hammering at my door!'

'*You*! *Beautiful*?'

His laughter cut to the quick. For Juliana knew she

was a bit of a scarecrow, with her long, bony body and equally long, bony face. Only her eyes carried any promise of future beauty, being slanty and exotic-looking, their colour a chameleon hazel which changed colour with whatever she was wearing.

'You wait and see,' she pouted. 'My mother says I'm going to grow up quite lovely. She says I could be a model with my height and bone-structure.'

'Your mother has rose-coloured glasses,' Blake muttered. 'About everyone and everything.'

'You leave my mother alone. She's a fantastic person. You're just jealous because your mother hasn't time for anyone except your father!'

'I don't give a damn about my mother,' he scowled. 'Now get lost, rake-bones. I've got to get on with this study.'

'You're always studying these days,' she complained.

'Yeah, well, I want to grow up smart, not beautiful. My HSC is in a couple of months and I have to get well over four hundred to get into my course at uni next year. So for pity's sake get out of here, Juliana, and let me get some work done.'

She flounced out, thinking grouchily to herself that he didn't have to grow up beautiful because he already was, the lucky devil!

Juliana's dream of even becoming passably attractive came to an abrupt halt the following year. Puberty came in a rush and, horror of horrors, she broke out in a bad case of acne. All of a sudden she felt so ugly and awful that during her spare time she remained hidden in her bedroom. To make matters worse, that same year her mother sent her to the same toffee-nosed private school Barbara went to, the result of having saved like a lunatic during her four years' employ at the Prestons'.

Little did Lily know that the sacrifices she had made for her much loved child's future were not bringing Juliana much present happiness. She was going through hell during her first year of high school among the daughters of millionaires. Never before had the difference between her world and the world of wealth and privilege been so painful. The children of the rich did not tolerate outsiders kindly.

The acne was the last straw for Juliana. Oh, how she would cry when she looked at herself in the mirror every morning. She was absolutely hideous!

Her only reprieve was that Blake was away on campus at university, doing his first year of an economics and law degree. She was afraid he might tease her about her skin. It was bad enough having Barbara calling her names like 'pizza-face' on the way to and from school every day.

But Blake was to be home soon on his mid-term break, and Juliana was simply dreading the day he would come over and call up to her to come swimming with him.

The day dawned, however, and when she refused to come down from the flat above the garages Blake thumped up the stairs, banged on the door and demanded to know what was the damn matter with her.

'I'm not leaving, Juliana,' he pronounced forcefully.

'So you might as well come out here and tell me what's what. And don't give me any garbage about your not liking the water any more because I won't believe you.'

Wretched with embarrassment and misery, she finally opened the door.

'Well?' he said, looking her in the face with only puzzlement on his.

'Can't you *see*?' she wailed.

'See what?'

'My skin,' she groaned.

The light dawned in his eyes. 'Oh, you mean the acne.'

She looked down at the floor in an agony of wretchedness and frustration. 'Of course I mean the acne,' she grumbled.

He put out a hand and tipped up her chin, scanning her face. 'They're not that bad, sweetie,' he said so tenderly that she promptly burst into tears.

'They are too!' she sobbed, and struck away his hand. 'What would you know? You've never had a pimple in your life! They're ugly. I'm ugly.'

Blake sighed. 'You're not ugly, Juliana. Fact is, I suspect you're going to become the beauty you always wanted to be. Why, you've grown so tall and graceful this past year. And you're not nearly as skinny as you used to be,' he added, flicking a rueful glance at her sprouting breasts. 'But if you're so unhappy with your skin, why don't you do something about it?'

'Like what? Mum says there's not much I can do

except keep it clean. She said I'll grow out of it in God's own good time.'

'God helps those who help themselves,' he said sharply. 'Come on. I'm taking you to the doctor. I know there are things they can do for acne these days.'

'Do you really think so?' Juliana said hopefully.

'I know so!'

An hour later she came home armed with an antibiotic lotion for her skin which the doctor said had proved very successful with other patients, particularly girls. Juliana set about using it morning and night, and it wasn't long before she saw a quite dramatic improvement.

'It's a miracle!' she exclaimed to Blake in the pool a week later.

'I don't believe in miracles,' he returned with such a dark scowl that Juliana was taken aback. She frowned at him. He'd changed since going to university, she realised with a pang of true regret. Why did people have to change? First herself, and now Blake.

Her eyes followed him as he swam over to the edge of the pool and levered himself out of the water, the action showing a muscle structure in his back and arms she'd never noticed before.

'Have you been doing weights?' she asked.

He shrugged. 'A little. They have a good gym at the uni. It keeps me out of trouble.'

'What kind of trouble?'

His blue eyes flashed with exasperation, but he said nothing.

Juliana swam over and scrambled out to sit next to Blake, blushing when she noticed that one of her nipples had popped out of the tiny bra-top. She stuffed it back in, relieved that Blake wasn't looking at her.

There was no doubt about it, though. She would have to ask her mother for a new costume before the swimming carnival at school next week. This one was getting too small for her rapidly growing body.

'Can I feel your muscles?' she asked Blake, dripping water all over his thighs as she bent over to curve her hands around his biceps. 'Gosh, they're really something. Your back looks fantastic too.'

When she ran a quite innocent hand across his shoulder-blades, Blake stiffened. 'Cut it out,' he snapped, then abruptly dived into the pool.

Juliana stared after him, hurt and confused. What had she done?

But then she sighed her understanding. She'd touched him. Blake hated girls touching him.

Still, she would have thought he didn't think of her as a girl, just as she never thought of him as a boy. They were simply good friends.

It wasn't long, however, before Blake put aside his aversion to girls touching him. A never-ending stream of nubile young women began accompanying him whenever he came home from university.

Blondes, brunettes, redheads—Blake didn't seem to have any preference. The only thing the girls had in common was that none of them lasted very long. A few weeks at most.

At first Juliana had felt a sharp jealousy, for Blake

never seemed to have time for her any more. But gradually her feelings changed to bitter resignation. Her close relationship with the son and heir to the Preston fortune had drawn to a close. She was once again nothing more than the cook's daughter, whose presence was tolerated though no longer sought out.

Only once during her school years did she cross Blake's path in anything other than a 'hi, there, how's things, see you later' fashion. It was to prove a very memorable experience.

She was sixteen at the time. It was the night of her graduation ball to which she had worn Barbara's gown of two years before, given to her mother by an uncharacteristically sweet-tongued Barbara.

'Mummy paid a fortune for this, Lily,' she said as she handed over the exquisite ivory satin gown. 'It seems a shame that it's only been worn once. I'm sure Juliana would look divine in it. Much better than I did. She's so tall and slender.'

Naturally, her kind-hearted and still amazingly naïve mother had not seen the malice behind the offer. All she could see was a dress that she would never be able to afford for her own daughter, a dress fit for a princess.

'Just think, Juliana,' she had said excitedly. 'You'll be able to use the money I was going to spend on your dress to have your hair done and to buy a really good pair of shoes. Maybe an evening bag as well. Oh, you're going to look so beautiful!'

Lily would never have understood the fact that, at the fancy school she took such pride sending her daughter to, no girl would be seen *dead* in a dress another graduate had worn before, no matter how beautiful it was. Though not of this snobbish ilk, Juliana nevertheless shrank from the thought of turning up in Barbara's dress, for Barbara would make sure every girl in her class, as well as their partners, knew whose dress it really was. Blake's sister had already gone to great pains to make sure Juliana was treated like a leper by most of the other girls at school.

But Juliana wouldn't have hurt her mother for the world. So she staunchly wore the dress, ignored the other girls' snide remarks, holding her head high and looking as though she didn't give a damn what anyone said about her. Her cool, even haughty demeanour gave the impression that their snide remarks and sniggering whispers rolled off her like water off a duck's back.

Behind the cool façade, however, lay a deep well of hurt and anger. What right did they have to treat her like this, just because she hadn't been born into money? It wasn't fair! One day, she vowed, she would spit in their eyes, *all* of them—especially Barbara!

She left the ball as early as she could, but she couldn't go home. Her mother would be waiting up for her, anxious to hear the details of the night. So Juliana slipped quietly round the back of the main house instead of going straight up to bed, intent on filling in an hour or two just licking her wounds in private. Barbara and Mrs Preston were away for the night at relatives'. Mr Preston would be ensconced in his study at the front of the house. The pool area would be deserted.

So she was startled to find Blake sprawled in one of the deckchairs, for he wasn't expected home for the summer holidays till the following day.

Juliana quickly noted the whisky glass in his hand and the half-empty bottle of Jack Daniels on the cement beside the chair. This was another of his new habits. Drinking. Though it was usually only beer.

'Well, well, well,' he drawled, his eyes raking over her. 'Is this Cinderella home from the ball? And what a lovely Cinderella she is,' he went on in his now habitually droll fashion. University—or maybe life— had turned Blake into something of a cynic.

For once, Juliana found a retort just as cynical. 'I have no doubt the role of Cinderella fits me very well. But I can't see your sister as my Fairy Godmother, can you?'

Blake's eyebrows shot up in surprise at her acid tone. 'Meaning?'

'Barbara kindly presented my mother with her old graduation dress for me to wear tonight.'

'Aah… I see…'

'Do you, Blake? Have you any idea what it's like being treated like a charity case? No, of course not! You were born with a silver spoon in your mouth.'

'Sometimes one can choke on a silver spoon,' he said darkly, and quaffed back a huge mouthful of drink.

'I haven't noticed you choking. Not unless it's on grog,' she added, sweeping over to stand at the foot of the deckchair with her hands on her hips. 'What on earth are you doing, swallowing that whisky like water? Haven't you any respect for your kidneys and liver?'

He swung his legs over the side of the chair and stood up, tall and macho in tight, stone-washed jeans and a chest-hugging blue T-shirt. 'I'm not large on respect tonight,' he muttered.

'And what is *that* supposed to mean?'

'Nothing I can tell you, gorgeous.'

She drew in a sharp breath as his blue eyes moved hotly down her body to where the deep sweetheart neckline of the dress showed an expanse of creamy cleavage. Not a busty girl, Juliana's breasts were nevertheless high-set and nicely shaped. Blake's gaze was certainly admiring them at that moment. His narrowed gaze eventually moved on, travelling down to where the ivory silk ballgown hugged her tiny waist before flaring out into a romantically full, ankle-length skirt.

'That dress looks a damn sight better on you than Barbara,' he said thickly.

His gaze lifted to her face, shocking her with the stark desire she saw in their depths. No boy—or man—had ever looked at her like that before. Blake certainly hadn't.

'Juliana,' he said hoarsely, before doing something that both shocked and fascinated her. Dipping his finger into the glass he was still holding, he reached out to trace a wet trail around the neckline of her dress. This alone made her stand stock-still with eyes wide and heart suddenly pounding. But when he bent his head to start licking the liquid from her by now shivering flesh, a dizzying sensation made her sway backwards. He caught her to him, releasing the glass for it to smash into smithereens on to the concrete around their feet.

His head bent to kiss her with such deceptive gentleness that Juliana was momentarily disarmed. He sipped at her lips, over and over, his hands lifting to slide up into her hair, to lift its heaviness from her skull, his fingertips massaging her head with an almost hypnotically erotic action.

'Juliana,' he whispered against the melting softness of her lips.

'Yes?' came her dazed query.

'Yes,' he repeated huskily. 'That's all you need to say. Yes. I think you could be very good at yes...'

His mouth turned hungry, his lips prising hers apart. But when his tongue slid inside, the strong taste of whisky blasted her back to reality.

She wrenched her mouth away and glared up at Blake, furious with both herself and him.

His eyes were glazed as they opened to look down at her. 'What is it, honey? What's wrong?'

'You're drunk, Blake Preston! That's what's wrong.'

His eyes cleared to an expression of dry amusement. 'So if I weren't drunk, it would be all right? You'd let me kiss you?'

'Yes...no... Oh, don't be silly, Blake. You know we can never be anything but friends. Rich men don't become involved with the daughter of their cook! At least, not seriously!'

A black cloud darkened his face. He looked angry about something for a moment, then wearily resigned. 'I guess you're right.' A sardonic smile pulled at his mouth. 'So what's happened to your plan to marry a millionaire?'

'I know now that the only way I'll ever be rich is to earn it myself.'

'Oh? And how, pray tell? Your school marks have hardly been encouraging.'

'I'm going to study like a lunatic from now on. I can do it. I know I can!'

He cocked his head slightly on one side, staring at her for a few moments before giving a wry nod. 'Yes. I do believe you can. Come on, I'll walk you home…'

Juliana lay awake for ages that night, no longer thinking about the terrible time she'd had at the ball, or the white lies she'd told her mother when Blake delivered her to the door. Her mind was filled with memories of Blake's mouth moving over her cleavage, his strong arms pulling her hard against him, his tongue plunging between her lips.

Had it been the realisation of his drunkness that had made her stop him, or panic at the bewildering responses his actions had evoked in her body? She'd never felt anything like it before. There had been a rush of heat and excitement, combined with a momentary compulsive urge to let go every vestige of thought, to just let Blake do as he willed with her.

What bothered her most was that she seemed to

have been responding to *Blake's* need, not her own. Why, she'd never looked upon him as anything more than a good friend before. She'd certainly never had any sexual fantasies over him as she had had over a few television and pop stars she liked. Yet all he'd had to do was look at her with desire in his eyes and she'd instinctively responded to that desire.

Juliana was stricken by the thought that maybe she was beginning to turn out like her mother, whose sexual vulnerability to men who *needed* her was quite pathetic in Juliana's opinion. She didn't want to be like that. She wanted always to be in control of her own actions, her own life. When and if she made love, she wanted it to be because *she* wanted and needed it, not the other way around. Anything else went against the grain!

By the time Juliana felt sleep snatching at her mind, she'd vowed to be on her guard against any repeats of tonight's incident. She would make sure she was never alone with Blake. She would keep other boys at arm's length as well, till she was older, and more in control of her silly self! She also vowed to do what she had boasted to Blake she would do—get a good pass in the Higher School Certificate, go to university and become a success, all by her own efforts!

Over the next two years she astounded both her mother and her teachers with her application. The boys did start hanging around, and even though she did find several of them quite attractive Juliana spurned their attentions, devoting all her time to study, and a smattering of modelling. Though she had not grown up into a classical beauty, her long, silky brown hair, tall, elegant body and exotically sculptured face gave her admission into a good modelling agency who found occasional work for her on the catwalk and behind the fashion photographer's lens.

After an excellent pass in her Higher School Certificate, Juliana began a marketing course at university, while still earning money from modelling on the side. Though not enough to live away from home. Blake, however, was doing well enough as a foreign exchange dealer to move out into a luxurious bayside unit. From gossip she had gleaned he'd quickly become quite the young man-about-town, working hard and playing hard.

It was while Juliana was doing her last year at university that tragedy struck the Preston household. Noreen Preston committed suicide with an overdose of sleeping tablets. Shortly afterwards, her husband Matthew succumbed to a heart attack, leaving behind a plethora of debts and a badly managed, almost bankrupt business.

Suddenly Blake and Barbara were parentless, and without any sizeable inheritance. Even the house carried a second mortgage. Barbara responded by marrying a middle-aged but very wealthy widower. Blake shocked everyone by chucking in his job, selling his flat and returning home to take up the flagging reins of the family company. With new ideas and a lot of hard work he eventually turned Preston's Games and Toys from an old-fashioned, non-profitable organisation into a modern, go-ahead concern whose stock was to become highly sought-after by investors and brokers all over the world.

By the age of thirty Blake Preston had become the toast of Melbourne's business and social worlds. Two years in a row he was voted Victoria's most eligible bachelor by a high-profile women's magazine.

He seemed to crown his worldly successes when he became engaged to Miss Virginia Blakenthorp, one of the débutante darlings of Melbourne's old-money families. It was around this time that Juliana herself—now gainfully employed in the marketing division of a chain of retail stores and living in a small but neat flat near the city—became engaged. To the younger son of the owner of the stores.

His name was Owen Hawthorne. He was twenty-eight and everything any woman could possibly want. Handsome. Polished. Rich.

It would have seemed that both Blake's and Juliana's futures were assured.

Yet one fateful night, the day before Juliana's twenty-sixth birthday and only a few weeks after her mother died, two engagements were broken and a third one entered into. Blake and Juliana were married a month later.

CHAPTER THREE

JULIANA was lying back in the bath, thinking about that strange night, when she heard Blake call out.

'Juliana! Where are you?'

She sat bolt upright, the abrupt action sending bubbles and water spilling over the edge on to the floor.

'I…I'm in here,' came her shaky reply. 'In the bathroom.'

Good God! she thought. Stewart must have driven like a lunatic to have dropped Blake off this early. Or had she been mulling over the past for longer than she realised? Since her wristwatch was out in the bedroom she had no idea of the exact time.

Juliana had just stood up to climb out of the bath when Blake opened the door and walked in.

'Julianna, I wish you'd…' His voice died when she swung round, giving him a full-frontal view of her nude body.

Wide-open hazel eyes found his startled blue ones. Juliana had never ever appeared naked like this before him. Not standing up. And certainly not with bubbles dripping from suddenly hard nipples. A fierce blush zoomed into her cheeks, her embarrassment finding voice in sharp words.

'For goodness' sake, Blake, haven't you ever heard of knocking?' In her haste to get out of the bath to wrap a towel around herself Juliana forgot about the water on the floor. As she hurriedly put one foot down on to the slippery tiles, it shot out from under her.

'Watch it!' Blake cried, racing forward to grab her. When she felt his hands close around her soap-slicked flesh she panicked, and tried to ward him off.

'Don't! I'm all right!'

But he already had a firm hold around her waist, lifting her right out of the water and setting her safely down on the mat in front of the vanity unit.

Did Blake deliberately slide his hands down over her bare buttocks before letting her go?

Juliana knew he probably didn't. Even so, her immediate sexual awareness produced further panic and every muscle in her body snapped tight as a drum.

'A towel,' she choked out. 'Get me a towel.'

Practically snatching the thing from his outstretched hand, she wrapped it quickly around herself sarong-style. Only then did she appreciate that Blake was staring at her in puzzlement.

Juliana knew she was acting exactly the opposite of how she'd vowed to act.

Her covering smile was not as sweetly soothing as she would have liked. 'Thank you. I—er—hope I haven't ruined your lovely suit. It's all damp down the front.'

Blake glanced down at the pale grey three-piecer which he wore most often when travelling, brushing at the waistcoat lightly. 'It'd take more than a few drops of water to ruin this little number.'

Which was true. Worth a small fortune, the mohair-

and silk-blend suit fitted his broad-shouldered, slim-hipped body like a glove and never creased, even after the longest flight. Matched as it was at the moment with a crisp white shirt and a darker grey tie, in it Blake looked both coolly suave and utterly in command of himself.

Not so Juliana. She felt a mess, both inside and out. All she could hope for was that Blake would get out of here shortly and give her some breathing space. Meanwhile…

'You must have had a good run from the airport,' she said brightly, 'to get here so quickly.'

'We did. Caught every green light.'

'I thought for a moment I might have lost track of the time.'

When Blake made no attempt to leave the room, simply moving over to lean casually against the white-tiled wall, Juliana turned to face the vanity unit, though still made uncomfortably aware of his presence by his reflection in the mirror. Since they didn't share a bathroom, each having their own, Juliana was not used to being watched going about her everyday ablutions. To have Blake do so at this particular moment in time was unnerving in the extreme.

'Wouldn't you like to go and have a drink while I clean my teeth and stuff?' she asked with another pained smile.

'No. I'd rather stay here and talk to you.'

'Oh…oh, all right.' She shrugged nonchalantly, fully aware that this was to be her first real test. What would the Juliana of a few hours ago have done in the circumstances?

She had no idea. This particular circumstance had not even been in *that* Juliana's repertoire.

So what would a woman desperate to hide her love for her husband do?

Pretend he's not in the room at all, she told herself. Pretend you're quite alone. Pretend you're talking to him on an intercom.

Taking another of the fluffy cream towels from the nearby railing, she proceeded to dry her arms, then turned to lift one foot up on to the side of the bath. 'So tell me all about your little adventure,' she invited casually while she towelled down first one long, shapely leg then the other.

'Nothing much to tell, really. It—er— Where on earth did you get those bruises?' he interrupted, straightening to frown down at three black and blue smudges on her thigh.

Juliana stared down at them as well, not having noticed them herself till now. 'I have no idea,' she said truthfully. 'Probably knocked into the side of a desk at work. You know how easily I bruise.'

'No,' he returned slowly. 'I don't, actually.'

Juliana was taken aback by the dark suspicion in his voice. Her surprise expressed itself in an edgy laugh. 'What on earth are you implying?'

She stared up at him, seeing a Blake she had never seen before. His face had an awful stillness about it, his normally lazy blue eyes narrowed and darkened till they were slits of cold steel.

Just as suddenly, however, his distrustful expression cleared, a sardonic smile dispelling the tightness around his mouth. He was his old self once more: coolly relaxed and casually indifferent.

'For a moment there I had a picture of you having a rather different encounter with a desk,' he drawled. 'I should have known better. You're not into that type of sex, are you?'

Juliana's face flamed.

Blake's pat on her cheek was both indulgent and quite patronising. 'My sweet, innocent Juliana. Who would ever have believed it? But I rather like you as you are. It's most…reassuring. Still…'

For a long moment, he just stared into her startled eyes, his hand lingering on her jawline. Juliana could have sworn that he was going to kiss her, the prospect filling her with both dread and the most appalling excitement.

Yes, kiss me, her pounding heart urged him. Kiss me, touch me, take me…

Suddenly, his hand dropped away, his shoulders squaring. 'I think I *will* go down for a drink after all,' he said curtly. 'Join me when you're ready, if you like. If not…I'll join you later.' And, turning abruptly, he strode from the room, leaving Juliana to lean weakly against the vanity unit. When she glanced up into the mirror it was to see wide, glittering eyes, and lips already apart.

She groaned, leaning forward on to curled fists, shutting her eyes against the evidence of her own arousal. God! Whatever was she going to do?

Fifteen minutes later, she was going downstairs, dressed in her favourite dressing-gown, a rather ancient dusky pink velour robe that crossed over the bodice and sashed around the waist. It had deep pockets that one could slide one's hands into and feel very cosy.

Juliana's hands were indeed slid into the pockets as she moved across the entrance hall and towards the main living-room, but she felt far from cosy. Petrified would be closer to the mark. Still, she *looked* relaxed. And that was the primary requisite at the moment.

When she moved through the archway and on to the plush grey carpet that covered the expansive living-room floor, Blake glanced up from where he was stretched out on one of the chesterfields, giving her a small smile of approval.

'It always amazes me how good you look without having to try. There you are, with your face scrubbed clean and your hair pinned haphazardly on top of your head, garbed in a robe that's seen better days, and you still look fantastic. Of course you do move very well,' he remarked, watching her walk into the room.

'And you do flatter very well,' was her cool rejoinder.

'I have no reason to flatter you, Juliana. You're my wife.'

'Oh, charming.'

His chuckle was as droll as her tone. 'So!' Placing his own generous drink on the glass coffee-table in front of him, Blake stood up. 'What will you have to drink?'

'Something strong,' she answered, not without a touch of self-mockery.

'That's not like you.'

A nonchalant shrug disguised her inner tension. 'It's been one hell of a day.'

Blake laughed. 'That's usually *my* line.'

Moving over to the antique rosewood sideboard they used as a drinks cabinet, he picked up the decanter of whisky and filled a clean crystal tumbler to halfway. Then came several ice-cubes from the silver bucket, cracking as Blake plopped them into the drink.

'This should soothe any frayed nerves you have.' He walked over to where Juliana was standing with her back to the empty fireplace. 'Here…'

She had to take both of her hands out of the shelter of the robe's pockets to accept the glass safely, cupping it firmly so that the drink wouldn't rattle. 'Thank you.'

'That's OK. Come and sit down.'

'I'd rather stand.'

Again, he darted her a sharp look. 'You *are* feeling out of sorts, aren't you? Anything I can help you with?' he asked as he retrieved his drink and joined her by the fireplace.

'Not really. Things didn't go as smoothly as I would have liked with a new product launch this week, that's all,' she exaggerated.

'What went wrong?'

'Oh, nothing major,' she hedged. 'Certainly nothing as dramatic as what happened to you yesterday. Want to fill me in on the details? You weren't in any real danger, were you?'

His lop-sided smile was rueful. 'Let's just say there were a few moments when I thought I might have to change my underwear.'

Juliana's stomach contracted. For Blake to admit as much meant he'd been very close to death and disaster. Very close, indeed.

'I...I'm glad you're home safe and sound.'

Blake's shoulders lifted and fell in a dismissive gesture.

'You *believe* me, don't you?' she urged with a weird flash of fear.

He surveyed her anxious face with a measure of surprise. 'Don't sound so serious, Juliana. Of course I believe you. Is there any reason I shouldn't?'

'Well, I...well, you...I mean...I wouldn't like you to think I would ever want you dead.'

'Of course I don't think that!' He chuckled, though a little darkly. 'You could get everything you want by simply divorcing me.'

She stared as he lifted his glass and quaffed a huge swallow. If she'd wanted evidence of Blake's current attitude to their marriage, she'd just got it. Nothing had changed since the night he'd proposed. Not a thing!

Her sigh was heavy as she lifted her own glass to her lips and drank.

'Tired?' he asked.

'A little.'

'Not *too* tired, I hope.'

'No...' There was a decided lack of conviction in that word.

A sudden strained silence pervaded the room, the only noise the clink of Blake's ice as he drained his glass.

'I think I'll go upstairs and have a shower, then,' he announced, depositing his empty glass on the mantelpiece behind them and striding from the room.

Several seconds later Juliana realised she was holding her breath. She also realised that, no matter how iron-clad her resolve to carry on as though nothing had changed in their relationship, there was one aspect where that was not possible. When Blake came to her bed tonight, it wasn't going to be the same. Not at all.

Would it be agony or ecstasy?

Either outcome worried the life out of her. For while Blake's lovemaking had always pleasured her, she'd never wanted it with this intensity before; had never been *afraid* of what her responses might be. She'd always been content to let Blake make the running, to just be swept along on *his* tide, never her own. Now, she'd discovered that love had its own tide.

Already, waves of desire were racing through her veins, their current strong and relentless. Never again would Juliana want to lie submissive beneath Blake, waiting resignedly for him to rouse her senses to an almost reluctant passion. She suspected that in future she would have to struggle to control a wildly escalating need for all sorts of intimacies, to hold herself in check lest she actually devour the man.

Common sense told her this was the last thing she should do.

Expelling the air from her lungs in a ragged rush, Juliana looked for fortification—and intoxication—in the glass her quivering hands were holding. A few swift swallows and it was empty, save some small bits of unmelted ice.

Whisky had always hit her system hard and fast, making her mellow. And yes…sometimes quite sleepy. Juliana hoped tonight would be no exception.

No such luck. The whisky, if anything, seemed to spark a recklessness in her.

Why shouldn't I devour Blake if I want to? came the rebellious thought as she swept up the stairs. He's my husband, after all. Why should I hold back, pretend, fake being *less* passionate than I feel like being? It's crazy! Blake would probably be thrilled if I became more adventurous and aggressive in bed. A man of his experience and sophistication couldn't possibly be totally satisfied with our rather bland sex-life.

But no sooner had she decided this than another more sensible and quite insistent voice whispered to Juliana that Blake *was* satisfied; that he would look upon any change in her sexual behaviour with definite disapproval.

Juliana hesitated at her open bedroom door, her gaze ignoring the rest of the exquisitely furnished room to focus on the brass bed that sat proudly against the far wall. Queen-sized and fit for a queen, with its superb antique cream lace bedspread and hand-painted ceramic postknobs, Juliana's bed had once been Noreen Preston's bed.

Thank the lord she hadn't died in it, came the unexpected thought. Noreen's body had been found in a seedy motel on the other side of Melbourne. Still, Juliana suspected that a lot of wretchedness had been fostered between those sheets. If she closed her eyes she could almost hear the poor woman crying; *see* her clinging.

Odd. Juliana had never felt any real sympathy for Noreen Preston before, the woman having always come across as a neurotic wife and simply dreadful mother. But one never knew the hidden secrets in a marriage, the whys and wherefores behind people's behaviour.

Had the handsome and selfish Matthew Preston enjoyed putting his wife through mental hell? Had he taken advantage of her obsessive love for him by greedily accepting all her attentions while callously dallying behind her back? Had he laughed at her insecurities, telling outrageous lies? Or had he thrown his infidelities in her face, till she couldn't bear any more?

'Juliana…'

She swung round at Blake's voice behind her, a nervous hand fluttering up to her throat. 'You startled me.'

'I didn't mean to.'

Her eyes flicked down over him, trying not to stare.

Some men might have looked funny in the fluffy white towelling robe Blake always wore after showering. He didn't, however. He looked gorgeous, the white colour emphasising the warm golden tan of his satin-smooth skin. If he'd been dark and hairy, the knee-length, open-necked style might not have been quite so flattering. But the adult Blake was no more dark and hairy than the adolescent Blake had been. He still looked like a young golden god, Juliana thought wryly. Her own private Adonis.

'What's the matter, Juliana?'

Blake's unexpected question snapped her eyes up to his. Had she been staring too much? Frowning, perhaps? Grimacing, even?

Juliana recognised that her heart was pounding madly in her chest. There was no doubt about it. She *would* devour him. The realisation forced her to a decision.

'Actually, Blake, I'm not feeling the best. I really *do* have a headache.'

His steady gaze was disturbingly unreadable.

'It's been getting worse all day,' she went on in quiet desperation. 'First with the problems at work, and then after Stewart called I...I...' She swallowed. 'I was very worried about you, Blake. For a while there I was beginning to think the worst.'

'Is that so? As you can see, though...' he spread his arms wide for a second '...I'm fine.'

'And I'm very happy and relieved you are, but the after-effect of worry is often a headache. Look, you did ask me what was wrong, and I'm telling you.'

'So you are,' he said in a curiously flat voice. 'I'll see you in the morning, then.'

'*Morning*?' she repeated, eyes blinking wide. Blake had never come to her bed in the morning.

His smile was dry. 'For breakfast, Juliana. We usually breakfast together on a Saturday morning, remember?'

Her face flushed with an embarrassed heat. 'Yes, of course. I…I forgot. Tomorrow's Saturday…'

'Don't forget to take some pain-killers before you go to bed,' he advised curtly.

'I won't.' His message was quite clear. Don't have a headache tomorrow night…

Taking her by the shoulders, he planted a cold kiss on her forehead. 'Goodnight, Juliana. Sleep well.'

Again she heard the hidden message. You sleep well, wife, because I certainly won't. I wanted some sex tonight and you turned me away.

Juliana felt rotten. Yet she hadn't really lied. She did have the beginnings of a headache. Probably from drinking that whisky so quickly. She also realised that by tomorrow night her tension would be beyond a joke after spending all day in Blake's company. He would expect her to have breakfast with him, swim with him, go to the races with him, possibly go out to dinner afterwards with friends, then come home and sleep with him. Better she get over the sex hurdle tonight or it might grow too daunting for her to handle.

'Blake…'

'Yes?'

'Just because I have a headache it doesn't mean you can't—um—I wouldn't mind. Really I wouldn't.'

The curl of his top lip showed distaste at her offer.

'Well, *I* would. I'm not so desperate as to force myself on my wife when she's unwell.'

'You wouldn't be forcing yourself on me, Blake,' she said huskily.

'Wouldn't I?' His eyes narrowed as they scanned her strained face.

She couldn't help it. She looked away, for fear of all he might see.

'For pity's sake, let's not make a song and dance about a bit of sex,' he said with offhand brusqueness. 'Tomorrow night will serve just as well. I'm probably more tired than I thought tonight, anyway.'

Whirling away, he was in the process of stalking off down the hallway towards his own room when he stopped abruptly and turned to face a still frozen Juliana.

'One thing before I forget,' he said sharply. 'The door leading in from the garages was unlocked when I got home. That's being a little careless, considering the level of break-ins in this neighbourhood.'

His accusatory tone flustered her. 'I don't usually forget,' she defended, 'but the telephone was ringing as I was letting myself in and it distracted me.'

'I see. Well, try to remember in future. A woman alone is very vulnerable. I would hate to see anything happen to you, Juliana. You're very important to me, you know. Well, goodnight again.'

Juliana stared after his departing figure.

No, I *don't* know! she thought with sudden venom.

I must have been mad to go into a marriage like this, she agonised. Simply mad! Whatever possessed me to accept Blake's cold-blooded proposal that night?

It couldn't have really been his money. Money would never have induced me to put my self-respect on the line like this. It must have been love. I must have been in love with Blake all along!

CHAPTER FOUR

JULIANA blinked amazement at this new line of thought. Shaking her head, she moved slowly into the bedroom, shutting the door behind her. How could she have loved Blake all along without knowing it? It seemed impossible.

Sighing her frustration, she moved over to the brass bed, tossed off her dressing-gown and climbed in between the cool crisp sheets. The pillows welcomed her by now woolly head. Maybe if she could just sleep, things would be clearer in the morning.

Sleep, however, eluded her. It was as though, once this idea had implanted itself in her mind, it refused to let go. She found herself reliving key events in her relationship with Blake, trying to see them through more mature and less emotion-charged eyes.

Finally, Juliana had to accept that a romantic love, as opposed to a platonic love, *might* have lain dormant within her without her knowing it. Blake had come along in her life when she'd been only a little girl, a very lonely little girl. In the beginning, he'd been the father she'd never known; the big brother she'd never had; the close friend she'd always craved.

These roles had clouded the main role a handsome young man might have eventually played for a young girl once she reached puberty: that of boyfriend and lover. But by then the difference in their backgrounds had erected other barriers that made such a relationship undesirable and unwise.

Appreciating these barriers far better than her younger self, Blake kept his distance once Juliana started to grow up, thereby stunting the growth of any unconscious hopes and dreams she had probably been harbouring about him. After all, if she hadn't been secretly attracted to Blake, why had she been so fiercely jealous of his many girlfriends?

Juliana only had to look at the incident after her graduation ball to realise something could easily have flared between them that night if she'd allowed it to. *She* had called a halt to Blake's attempted seduction, put off by the fact that his interest in her was only alcohol-inspired lust. Which it undoubtedly was.

Her own sexual responses that night could not be so easily explained away.

Looking back, Juliana suspected that if she'd given in to those responses back then her love for Blake might have exploded from its platonic-coated shell. But where would that have got her at sixteen? Blake certainly wouldn't have felt impelled to marry her. He simply would have toyed with her, as he'd toyed with all his other girlfriends. She would have been dropped eventually. No doubt about it.

Other questions popped into her mind as she mused about her past behaviour. Why had she guarded her virginity so maniacally all those years, only to throw it away with a kind of despairing indifference the night she heard Blake had become engaged to another woman? And why choose that particular night finally to say yes to Owen's repeated proposals of marriage, if not because she subconsciously accepted that Blake was no longer a possible husband?

Blake…

Her secret hero. Her dream man. Her Prince Charming.

Yet he was hardly a Prince Charming.

Oh, maybe he had been once, before life tainted and warped his judgement of people and relationships. There'd been a kindness, an open-hearted generosity in the adolescent Blake that had drawn Juliana to him. The adult Blake, however, was ruled by a world-weary cynicism, not to mention a wariness of love, that made him capable of all sorts of things.

Juliana could still recall her shock when he'd proposed to her that night. There again, it had been a night of many shocks…

Owen had been the instigator of the first. They'd been about to go out on a dinner-date on the eve of her twenty-sixth birthday. She'd been running late because she'd been kept back at work to finish some problem or other. She remembered she had been putting the last touches to her appearance when Owen had come into her bedroom, watching her in silence while she applied some burgundy lip-gloss that exactly matched her burgundy crêpe dress.

She'd smiled at him over her shoulder as she put in her long dangling gold earrings. It was then that he'd come out with it.

'You do realise you won't be working after we're married, Juliana.'

Her hand froze on the last earring. She hoped she'd heard wrong. Frowning, she forced the last earring in then turned slowly to face her fiancé. 'I do realise I can't stay on at Hawthorne Bros once I'm your wife, Owen,' she agreed. 'That's company policy. But I intend finding another job.'

'No.'

'What do you mean, no?'

'I mean no, you won't be getting another job.'

She could not believe her ears. Owen, playing the controlling husband? If he knew her at all, he would know that was anathema to her.

His handsome face carried an appeasing smile as he came forward to take her in his arms. 'I want you free to travel with me, Juliana,' he said silkily. 'How can we just pack up and go off at will if you're tied down to a job?'

Juliana immediately felt a sense of panic take hold deep within her. She struggled against the awful suspicion that her engagement to this man was one big mistake. 'I have no objection to an extended honeymoon,' she compromised, 'but I can't envisage my life without my own job and my own money.'

'But you'll have all the money you want,' he argued softly. 'I'll open a special bank account for you to cover all your needs. You won't find me lacking in generosity, Juliana. You'll be kept in the manner to which I'm sure you'll quickly become accustomed.'

Juliana only heard one word. *Kept*.

She drew back to stare up at the man she'd thought she loved, thought she wanted to marry.

'I doubt I'd ever get accustomed to being *kept*,' she said shakily.

His laughter was dry. 'Come now, Juliana. You can't tell me you want to go on working in a dreary office when you can live the high life. Just think! You won't have to get up till lunchtime if you don't want to.'

'But I *hate* sleeping in!' she protested, further warning bells going off in her brain.

'That's because you're not used to it. Poor darling, you've had to work so hard just to make ends meet. It will be my pleasure to spoil you. All you have to do in return is be my loving wife. Now that won't be so hard, will it?'

He kissed her full on the mouth, his wet tongue demanding entry. Normally, Juliana didn't mind Owen's kisses. She usually found his ardour comforting, the body contact soothing the deep loneliness within her. Suddenly she found him cloying in the extreme.

Suppressing a shudder, she allowed him a few brief moments before pulling her mouth away, horrified at the growing repulsion within her heart and body. With an apologetic grimace, she eased herself out of his hold. 'Please, Owen, I can't think when you're doing that, and I need to talk to you.'

'I can't think when I'm doing that either,' came his desire-thickened reply. 'I'm mad about you, Juliana. You must know that.'

She stared at him. Yes, she did. But was madness love? And what of her own feelings? It was hard to keep telling herself she was in love with the man when his kiss just now had repelled her so. Just thinking about going to bed with him again made her feel sick to the stomach.

There was no doubt about it. She could not go through with this marriage.

'I won't ever give up working,' she said firmly. 'It's who I am.'

Owen's face showed exasperation. 'Who you are? What kind of crap is that? You're Juliana, my fiancée, soon to be my wife!'

'I don't think so…' Looking down, she began removing the diamond engagement-ring from her finger. 'I…I'm sorry, Owen,' she said as she held it out to him.

He stared down at her outstretched hand. 'You must be joking.'

'Unfortunately, no. But surely you can see that marriage between us wouldn't work. We just don't want the same things in life. It's best we found that out now, before it was too late. Please, Owen…take the ring.'

He backhanded her fingers with a vicious slap, sending the ring flying across the room. 'Keep the bloody thing!' he snarled. 'You might need it to pawn when you're starving. And you will be, honey, if you stay in this town. Come Monday you won't have a job, a reference, or a reputation. You'll find life can be pretty tough on the bastard daughter of a crummy cook who hasn't the brains to know what side her bread's buttered on. You stupid bitch! You could have had it all! But what can you expect from the gutter class? I should have listened to my friends.'

He stormed out of the flat, leaving Juliana to stare, pale-faced and wide-eyed, after him. Shock was her first reaction, for she had never seen that side of Owen before, never dreamt he could be so violent and vengeful.

But shock was soon replaced by a crippling anxiety. Owen had the wealth and power to do what he threatened. She was a woman alone in the world with no one to turn to, no one to help her. No one except…

'Blake,' she whispered aloud.

She didn't stop to think if he would be home. She simply called a taxi and went over to the Preston house and rang the front doorbell. Blake's new cook-housekeeper answered, a dour widow named Mrs Dawson.

'Yes?' the woman asked suspiciously before recognising Juliana. 'Oh, it's you, Miss Mason.' Juliana had met Mrs Dawson when she'd come over to remove her mother's effects a few weeks before. Not that there had been a lot. Some clothes and jewellery. A few ornaments and photographs. Not much to represent a whole life. When Juliana had expressed as much to Blake that weekend, he'd said that *she* was her mother's legacy to the world.

'Lily was very proud of you, Juliana,' were his parting words that day.

Juliana closed her eyes for a second. Oh, Mum, I

wish you were still alive. I need you, need your love and support. I'm frightened.

'Is there something I can do for you, Miss Mason?' the housekeeper asked.

'I have to speak to Blake. Is he home?'

'I'm afraid not. Would you like to leave a message?'

What possible message could she leave? Blake, I've jilted Owen and he's going to take revenge by blackening my name and making sure I can't get a decent job in Melbourne?

You didn't put such a message in the hands of a stranger.

'I need to see him personally. Can I wait, do you think? Will he be coming home tonight?'

Mrs Dawson looked dubious. 'He might be very late…'

'I don't mind. I really need to see him. It's a matter of life and death.'

Mrs Dawson sniffed down her not inconsiderable nose. 'Well, I suppose you can wait, if you must.'

'I must.'

'Come into the family-room then. There's a television there. I was about to watch the Friday night movie.'

Mrs Dawson retired at ten-thirty after the movie finished, an incomprehensible thriller that had about as much suspense as a parliamentary sitting. Not that Juliana was in a fit state to view television. Still, she had to do something while she awaited Blake's return. She was sitting there blankly watching the screen around eleven-thirty when she heard a car rumble into the garages.

Blake was home.

Jumping to her feet, she raced into the kitchen, where she practically collided with him on his way through.

'Juliana!' He smiled for second when he first realised whom he'd run into. But then a frown claimed his smile. 'What on earth are you doing here at this hour?'

'Waiting for you.'

'But why?'

'I…I need help.'

'What kind of help?'

'It's hard to explain. Do you think I could make us both a cup of coffee while I tell you? This could take some time…'

'To hell with coffee. Let's have a real drink. I'm in dire need. Follow me.'

'What's wrong with *you*?' she asked as she hurried after him into what had once been his father's study. It was not a room she'd been in often, certainly not since it had been redecorated. Gone was the old-world stuffy look, replaced by sleek modern lines to match its new occupant. The colours were predominantly grey and black, the curtains a dark red. Blake's black trousers and grey silk shirt blended perfectly.

He shot her a rueful glance from behind the built-in corner bar. 'I doubt you'd be interested. You'd only say it serves me right, that rich bastards like myself deserve all we get. Or has your attitude to rich bastards changed since you got engaged to the honourable Owen Hawthorne?'

Sighing, Juliana lowered herself into a squishy black leather armchair. 'Not exactly.' Her voice reeked with an acid bitterness. 'If anything, it's got worse.'

Blake's eyebrows shot up. 'I take it all is not well in lovers' land?

'I'm going to flush his engagement-ring down the toilet when I get home! After I've found it, that is.'

Blake laughed. 'I take it you've had a little spat?'

'Hardly little. And it's not a laughing matter, Blake. The man's threatening to strip me of my job and my reputation. He says I won't ever get a decent position in Melbourne again.'

'Good God, Juliana, whatever did you do? Have you been playing around behind his back or something?'

Juliana shot Blake a savage look. 'Is that what you think of me? That I'm no better than a two-timing tramp?'

His shrug was irritatingly nonchalant. 'I think you're a very beautiful, ambitious young woman who always said she'd marry a millionaire. Can I be blamed for thinking that love might not have come into the arrangement, and that you might have become a fraction bored with Owen's performance in bed? I've heard rumours that he wouldn't get into the *Guinness Book of Records* as the world's greatest lover.'

Juliana wished she could have stopped the fierce blush coming to her cheeks. She'd often thought that Owen wasn't the most skilful of lovers. He was much too fast. But, considering her own tendency to be less than passionate in bed, she had brushed aside any concern over the matter. She'd already come to the conclusion that sex was overrated, anyway.

Still, Blake's assumption that a man's ineptness in bed excused faithlessness annoyed her. As did his assumption that she was little more than a cold-blooded gold-digger.

'I'll have you know that I am not into the casual bed-hopping your lot seem to indulge in,' she countered sharply. 'I also would not dream of being unfaithful to the man I was engaged to. To me, an engagement is as serious a commitment as marriage. When I marry, it will be for life! That's why I broke my engagement. *I*, not Owen. I knew it wouldn't work out.'

'Why wouldn't it work out?' Blake came forward with a couple of glasses filled with whisky and ice. He pressed one into her hands and sat in a chair adjacent to her, watching her face as she struggled to find the right words.

'I…I…'

'Didn't you love him?' came the probing query.

Juliana sighed. 'I *thought* I did…'

'But you realised you didn't.'

'Yes.'

'When?'

'When he demanded I give up work after we were married.'

Blake laughed. 'Stupid man. That would have been

the kiss of death with you. Clearly he doesn't know you very well.'

Juliana couldn't help it. She laughed too. But then she sobered. 'Whatever am I going to do, Blake?'

'It's quite simple, really, if you're prepared to put aside the romantic notion of marrying for love.'

She stared over at him. 'I'm not sure what you're getting at. I'm not going to change my mind and marry Owen. Even if I loved him, I wouldn't marry a man who demanded I give up everything for him. I don't believe in that type of love.'

'Believe me, neither do I,' Blake returned drily. 'But I'm not suggesting you still marry Hawthorne. I'm suggesting you marry me.'

Juliana was lost for words. For a second, a strange elation swept through her. Till she remembered one crucial factor. 'But you're already engaged!' she burst out.

'Actually, no…I'm not. I broke it off tonight. That's why I was home early.'

'But…but *why*?'

His expression was deadpan. 'Would you believe I found out tonight that Virginia was planning to do what Owen wanted you to do?'

'What? Give up her job after the wedding?'

His smile held no humour as he nodded. 'Perverse, isn't it?'

She could think of nothing to say. Knowing Blake as she did, she knew that he would shrink from having a wife staying home and devoting herself entirely to him.

'Did…did you love her?' she asked at last, the question sticking in her throat for some reason.

He shrugged. 'What's love? I enjoyed making love to her. I also thought she would make a good mother. I want children, Juliana.'

'And Virginia didn't?'

'Not for donkey's ages. That was the straw that broke this camel's back.'

'I…I see.'

'I thought you would. You know me as well as I know you. So what do you say? If you marry me, Juliana, you won't have to worry about Owen Hawthorne's threats. I'll make sure they come to nothing. I'll also make sure you get a really good job, something even more satisfying than you have at the moment.'

Juliana could only shake her head. 'Blake, this is crazy!' Yet, crazy as it was, she could not deny she felt quite excited by the idea.

'Why is it crazy? You're everything I could possibly want in a wife—beautiful, intelligent, independent. And you'd make a good mother too. You *want* children, don't you?'

'Yes, of course.'

'I thought so. You had a good example of maternal love.'

'Aren't you worried that if I said yes I might be marrying you for your money?'

He smiled. 'Not at all. In fact, it would please me if that were the case.'

'Blake!'

'You don't honestly think I want you madly in love with me, do you?' he retorted curtly. 'I need that kind of marriage like I need a hole in the head. It will be quite enough if you like and respect me as much as I've always liked and respected you.'

She flushed with pleasure at his words. But the pleasure was tinged with worry. 'But…but what about sex?'

'What about it?'

'I…I don't think I'm very good at it.'

His eyebrows shot up. 'I find that hard to believe.'

She sighed. 'Well, believe me, it's true.'

'The girl I kissed on her graduation night was not even remotely frigid. You let me worry about the sex, Juliana. So what do you say? Will you marry me?'

Her lips remained pressed tightly together, even though the temptation to just say yes was quite strong.

'Think of the alternative,' he argued softly. 'No job; no reputation; no future. As my wife, you'll hold a position of power and privilege in this town. No one will turn their nose up at you, believe me. They'll kowtow and grovel. And no daughter of ours will ever have to wear a second-hand gown to her graduation…'

Was it this last incisively timed remark that made up her mind for her?

Juliana had thought so at the time; had thought her decision to marry Blake had been one of bitter practicality.

Now she knew different.

She'd wanted to marry Blake all along, loved him

all along. But she would never have what she really wanted: his love in return.

'Oh, Blake…Blake,' she cried, and turned to bury her face into the pillow.

CHAPTER FIVE

'MORNING.' Blake breezed into the kitchen dressed far too sexily in a pair of tight stone-washed jeans and a blue windcheater the exact colour of his eyes. His thick tawny hair, Juliana noted, was still darkly damp from the shower, and trying to curl. It always did that when it was going to rain.

'Morning,' she returned crisply, and lowered her eyes again to the frying-pan, a silent groan echoing a painful acceptance that her sexual awareness of Blake had only increased overnight, as she'd feared it would. As though in readiness for this frustrating event, she herself was wearing a loosely fitting tracksuit in a very nondescript grey flannel.

Blake perched up on one of the kitchen stools. 'How are you feeling this morning?' he asked. 'Better?'

'Much better, thank you.'

Normally, Juliana liked Saturday breakfast, liked the relaxed informality of Blake chatting away to her while she performed her one cooking chore of the week. Today, she was far from relaxed.

'You don't look all that great,' he remarked.

Juliana gave him a dry look. 'I'm fine. Stop fussing. If I did that to you, you'd give me short shrift.'

He laughed. 'So I would. But maybe you should

74

have a nap this afternoon. You've got dark rings under your eyes.'

'Aren't we supposed to be going to go to the races this afternoon?'

'Nope. Rain's forecast. I can't bear the races in the rain. Besides, I thought two trips to Flemington in one week might be too much for you. I know you're not *that* keen. Or have you forgotten what next week is?'

Juliana groaned out loud as she remembered it was the first week in November, Melbourne Cup week. Usually she avoided the famous spring racing carnival, because the crowds were horrendous, but the company she worked for, Femme Fatale Cosmetics, had booked one of the promotional marquees for Oaks Day on the Thursday—Ladies' Day. In her position as public relations officer, she would be obliged to go.

'Damn,' she muttered. 'I'll have to buy a new outfit, hat and all. Are you coming with me on the Thursday? You weren't sure when I told you about it before.'

'Sorry. Can't. From what Stewart told me last night, the Sydney branch could do with a good shake-up. I'm going to fly up there on Monday and stay the week.'

The news that Blake was going away so soon after his return did not depress Juliana as much as it would have done a day ago. She almost felt relieved. She certainly looked up at her husband with a brightening smile on her face. 'That's all right. I'll find someone else to go with me.'

She was startled by Blake's answering scowl. 'Well, you don't have to sound so happy about it. I thought you liked my company.'

'I *do*!'

'Do you? I'm beginning to wonder after last night.'

Juliana was taken aback—and somewhat annoyed—by his nasty tone. It was so unjustified. 'Blake, I had a headache. And, if you remember correctly, I didn't refuse to sleep with you. You *chose* not to.'

'Out of consideration for you,' he pointed out testily.

'Out of deference to your male ego, more likely!' she shot back. 'You don't consider *me*, Blake. You only ever consider *yourself*!'

For a long moment, they stared at each other, both angry, yet shocked as well. Blake especially. Juliana had never spoken to him like this before, had never accused him of callous selfishness.

His expression was unlike any Juliana had ever seen on Blake. He was pale. Shaken. Yet simmering with a barely held fury. 'My dear Juliana,' he said, his low monotone evidence of the difficulty he was having in containing his temper. 'You knew full well the sort of man I was when you married me. I *am* selfish, I admit it. But not in a sexual sense. If I were a selfish lover, I would have spent the night with you anyway, and to hell with your feelings!'

'You *never* spend the night with me,' she flung back resentfully. 'And it's *often* to hell with my feelings!'

He glared at her, his blue eyes getting colder by the second. The smell of burning bacon was filling the kitchen but both of them ignored it, each equally intent on venting their own anger.

'If by that remark you're saying I *don't* always satisfy you in a sexual sense, then you're the best darned faker in the business! Even on our wedding night, when you were as nervous as a kitten, I managed to do the right thing by you. If that wasn't my considering your feelings then I don't know what it was!'

Juliana flushed guiltily as she recalled her wedding night. Blake was right. That could have been a disaster, she'd been so nervous and uptight.

They hadn't gone away for a honeymoon after their simple register office ceremony; Blake had not wanted a big white wedding or any fuss. She had agreed at the time, since she had still been somewhat embarrassed over the speed of their marriage, a mere month after Blake had proposed.

Yet during that month not once had Blake touched her in an intimate or sexual manner, except for a couple of quick goodnight kisses. Juliana found herself on her wedding-day wishing that he had, so that the night ahead didn't loom as such unknown territory. Questions kept flashing through her mind all day. Would she be as hopeless as she had been with Owen in bed? Would she find herself tensing up as she always did once her clothes were removed? Would she always be left feeling inadequate and guilty?

She was an intelligent woman and knew that all the blame could not be put on Owen for her failure to find fulfilment on the occasions when she'd had sex with him. When she'd told Blake she wasn't any good at sex, she had meant it.

So when the time had come to undress, that first night, she'd been almost in a state of frozen panic.

Blake had recognised that she was a cot-case, and in deference to her nerves—or so she had thought at the time—had told her to shower and pop into her own bed and turn out the light.

She had done what he suggested, but had still been literally shaking when he'd finally come into the room and slipped between the sheets.

'You're naked!' she gasped.

'And you're not,' was his dry reply.

'Yes, well, I...I...'

'Hush,' he said, and gathered her close. 'We'll just talk till you stop shaking.'

'T-talk?'

'Yes, talk. You were always pretty good at talking. Maybe if we start with something you *are* good at we'll get your confidence up and things can progress from there.'

'I wouldn't b-bet on it if I w-were you,' she returned, her teeth chattering.

'We'll see, honey, we'll see. So tell me about your new job. Do you like working in public relations rather than marketing?'

And that was how he went on, asking her question after question till her mind was totally distracted from the sex that was to come. It was only later that she realised that somewhere along the line he had subtly started touching her, stroking her, kissing her. First on her shoulder, then her neck, her ear, her cheek, her forehead, her nose, and finally...her mouth.

It was at that point that the question-and-answer technique had given way to a more direct line of action. Not that Blake had turned animal or anything. He'd remained patient and gentle, skilfully removing her nightwear without frightening her, after which he'd showed her that passion did not necessarily have to be either savage or wild. It could be slow-building and sweet. Blake whispered soft, tender endearments to her while he caressed her breasts and kissed her mouth, telling her she had a beautiful body and that he wanted to lose himself in it.

Which he eventually did. But not roughly, and certainly not quickly. She remembered how surprised she'd felt at first when it had looked as if he would never stop. Not that it wasn't pleasant. It was. No…*more* than pleasant. It was quite exciting, causing her heart to race and an alien heat to invade every corner of her body.

She'd felt vaguely embarrassed by her responses, the way her lips fell apart to let escape her rapid panting, the way her body started arching up to meet Blake's powerfully deep surges. And then… Oh, God, then she'd felt as if everything was squeezing so tightly inside her. She'd cried out in a type of startled shock, but soon her cry had turned to a sensuous gasp followed by an even, shaming moan, then finally to a long, contented, shuddering sigh.

Juliana flushed again at the memory of that night, and all the nights since when she'd moaned beneath Blake's skilful hands.

But moans could mean many different things. Physical satisfaction perhaps, but also pain, as well as emotional torment. Would she moan a different type of moan tonight?

'You can't deny that I satisfy you in bed, Juliana,' Blake reiterated with some asperity.

'There are many types of satisfaction,' she muttered, truthfully but perhaps unwisely.

His glare was harsh. 'Meaning?'

Juliana finally realised that she had crossed over into very dangerous territory with this argument.

She shook her head and turned her attention to the already charred bacon. 'I'll have to cook some more. This is ruined.'

'Don't brush me off, damn you!'

Juliana stared up at Blake's now standing figure. The muscles in his face were taut, his jaw squared angrily, his fists clenched on the counter-top. God, he looked as if he wanted to hit her.

She scooped in a deep, steadying breath, letting it out slowly. 'I'm not brushing you off. You're right and I'm wrong. You're a wonderful lover and you always satisfy me, OK?'

'No, it's not OK. You're obviously disgruntled about something but won't come out with it!'

'It's nothing, Blake.'

'So you won't tell me.'

'There's nothing to tell!' she insisted.

'You're lying, Juliana. Something's troubling you and you don't have enough confidence—or *guts*—to tell me.'

She sighed. 'Don't make a mountain out of a mole-hill, Blake. It's nothing. Honestly. I've just been out of sorts lately, that's all. Please sit back down and I'll cook us some more breakfast.'

For a few startling moments she thought he was going to stalk out of the room. It would have been a most uncharacteristic gesture on Blake's part. He was not given to violent moods, or fits of temper. A dry sarcasm was the furthest he went in expressing disapproval or anger.

Juliana watched with a measure of astonishment as he battled with his emotions. Briefly it looked as if he *was* going to act like a typically infuriated spouse.

But then the old Blake resurfaced and he shrugged offhandedly, the tense lines in his face melting away. 'I guess I'm not used to your being temperamental,' he said with wry relief in his voice.

Juliana's fingers tightened around the plastic scoop she was holding, lest she lash out at him with it. If only he would show her for once that he really cared about her. If only he *would* storm out of the room, or just lose his temper. Anything would be better than this detached persona he hid behind all the time.

But she said nothing, did nothing, merely went on with cooking some more breakfast, letting Blake move the conversation round to less threatening topics. Yet all the while, underneath, she remained troubled. Where would all this end? How soon before she blew up again over some inconsequential matter, simply because she wanted more than Blake could give?

The problem seemed insurmountable. As much as she'd thought last night that she would do anything to save her marriage, Juliana now wasn't so sure. Maybe trying to save this marriage would prove too costly…

The telephone ringing towards the end of breakfast startled Juliana, making her jump up from her stool. Her nerves were obviously still on edge. Blake darted her an odd glance before reaching up to lift the receiver down from the wall. 'Yes?' he answered nondescriptly.

Nothing could be gleaned from Blake's end of the conversation, either who was calling or what it was all about.

'Hi, there… Really? That's thoughtful of you… Yes, we would… Send them over in a taxi… I'll pay for it… Thanks again… Yes, we will… Bye.'

'What was that all about?' she asked as he hung up.

'Jack Marsden had tickets for himself and Gloria to see *Phantom of the Opera* tonight but they can't go. Gloria's mother's ill and they have to visit her this weekend. He knows how much you like the show so he immediately thought we might like to go. He's sending the tickets over in a taxi.'

'Oh, how marvellous!' Juliana exclaimed, instantly excited despite the events of the morning. She'd seen the show for the first time earlier that year and had been dying to go again, but all the good seats were booked out months in advance. 'But how did he know I liked the show?' she asked, and started to clear up.

'I guess I must have mentioned it to him after we went last time, and, being the canny businessman that he is, he remembered. Jack wants me to invest some money in his construction firm. He'd go and buy tickets on the black market if he thought it would get him in my good books.'

Juliana could not help a sad little sigh. 'Why do you have to be such a cynic?'

'A realist, Juliana, not a cynic.'

'I can't see the difference.'

A dark cloud marred his beautiful blue eyes as he looked at her. 'You know, Juliana, I always thought you liked me.'

'Don't be silly, Blake, I *do* like you.'

'But not my so-called cynicism.'

'That's right.'

There was a short, sharp silence. Juliana bent to the task of clearing up.

'It will be our first anniversary in two months,' he resumed abruptly.

She looked up, forcing a smile to her lips. 'Yes, it will be. Why do you mention it?'

'I thought I might remind you of the agreement we made before we were married that if after the first year we thought our marriage wasn't working out, or if either of us did something foolish like fall in love with someone else, then we would call it quits.'

Juliana swallowed. She hoped she didn't look as sick as she felt. 'What…what are you trying to say? *Have* you fallen in love with someone else?'

His expression was startled. 'Don't be ridiculous. Love and I had a parting of the ways years ago. Good God, what a ghastly idea!'

'Then what *are* you trying to say?'

'I'm not exactly sure. I did think you were happy.

But last night, and this morning…' He shrugged, clearly confused by the situation.

Yet his confusion touched Juliana. She wanted to stop what she was doing, take him in her arms, hug him, tell him she would never leave him.

Of course she couldn't do that. All she could do was try to verbally reassure him that she *was* happy, that she would *never* leave him. But before she could say a single word, he swept on, mocking in his self-reproach.

'Hell, what am I doing, asking you for reassurance like an insecure child, just because you're in a bit of a mood? I'm quite sure that if you wanted out of this marriage you'd tell me. You've always been as straight as a die.' His wry grin dismissed any lingering irritation. 'So! What are we going to do for the rest of the day?'

Juliana felt quite annoyed with him. There he'd been, about to lock horns with real emotions, real feelings, however confusing they might be. And what had he done? Once again darted behind that impenetrable shield, the one that closed tight around his heart, the one that shut out anything that could make him seem vulnerable in any way.

'I don't know about you,' she returned sharply, 'but I have to go shopping for clothes. Then I have to get my hair trimmed, after which I've been ordered to take a nap, since I have horrible dark rings under my eyes. But, since *you* have nothing to do, you can start by putting these dishes in the dishwasher!'

And with that she dropped everything, spun round

and stalked from the kitchen, uncaring that Blake was gaping after her with his mouth open and blue eyes blinking wide.

CHAPTER SIX

JULIANA returned to the house from her shopping and hairdressing expedition as late as she possibly could, informing Mrs Dawson on the way through that she would have a small tray of toasted sandwiches in her room rather than a sit-down meal that night.

'What about Mr Preston?' the housekeeper asked. 'What will he be having?'

Juliana stopped and frowned. 'Hasn't he said anything to you about our going out to see *The Phantom of the Opera* tonight?'

'Not a word,' the woman sniffed. 'He left shortly after I arrived back this morning. I think he went out to play golf, since he took his golf-clubs with him.'

'Golf? In the rain?'

'Rain doesn't bother a man if he wants to play golf,' Mrs Dawson humphed. 'My Fred used to play all weekend, come rain, hail or shine. Can't see the attraction myself. A lot of walking and very little playing.'

'I couldn't agree more,' Juliana said with a small smile. She imagined poor Fred was only too glad to be out of the house and away from his bossy wife.

Suddenly, and quite unexpectedly, the other woman smiled too, showing good teeth behind her thin lips and quite attractive dimples in her cheeks. For once

Mrs Dawson looked the fifty-five she was rather than a sour sixty-five. Then she did something else that astounded Juliana. She gave her a compliment. 'Your hair looks good that length, Mrs Preston.'

'Oh, do you think so?'

Juliana hadn't been too pleased with the hairdresser when she'd cut off much more than her usual one-inch trim, leaving it swinging just on her shoulders rather than resting down on her shoulder-blades. It wouldn't have happened if she hadn't been so distracted over Blake, and while all the girls in the salon had said it suited her she hadn't been too sure. Yet here was Mrs Dawson actually smiling at her and agreeing with them. In that case, it had to be true.

'It's still long enough to put up if you want to,' the housekeeper advised her with her usual practicality.

'Yes, I suppose so. I hope Blake likes it.'

'I doubt Mr Preston will even notice. Men don't notice such things about their wives. They only notice on *other* ladies.'

Juliana was inclined to agree with her. Still, the caustic comment underlined the fact that maybe dear old Fred had been doing a little more than playing golf during his lifetime. 'He certainly won't notice tonight, since I'm going to put it up.'

'When would you like me to bring up your tray, Mrs Preston?' the housekeeper asked with yet another astonishing smile.

Juliana found it hard to get used to the house-keeper's unexpected warmth, but she was not about to lose the opportunity to become friendly. The woman's stiff attitude towards her had been hard to live with.

'Not till six,' Juliana said. 'Oh, and Mrs Dawson...'

'Yes?'

'Please call me Juliana.'

The housekeeper was taken aback, yet clearly pleased. Perhaps she never disliked me at all, Juliana decided. Maybe Blake insisted when he employed her that she keep her distance. That would be just like him.

This last idea was almost confirmed by the woman's saying warily, 'But...but what about Mr Preston?'

'You can call *him* anything you darned well like,' Juliana said firmly. 'But in future *I* will only answer to Juliana.'

'In that case, you'd better call me Susanne.'

'Susanne. What a lovely name!' Juliana beamed. 'But enough of this girl-talk; I'd better get a move on if I'm to be ready on time.'

'Anything I can do to help? Any ironing?' Susanne Dawson nodded towards the parcels Juliana was carrying.

'No, these aren't for tonight. They're for Ladies' Day at the races next Thursday. I'm going to wear my green velvet tonight.'

'Ah, that's a lovely dress. But you're right, it would look better with your hair up. Then everyone can see the pretty sweetheart neckline. Better shake a leg then, Mrs—' She broke off with a wry chuckle. 'Better hurry, Juliana. I'll be up on the dot of six with a tray.'

Juliana laughed as she raced up the stairs. But, as she swept into her bedroom and looked at that bed again, any feelings of buoyancy faded. Not even the prospect of seeing her favourite musical in a couple of hours could revive her spirits. All she could think about was afterwards…

'You're looking lovely tonight, Juliana,' Blake said blandly on the way to the theatre in a taxi.

She slanted a long, thoughtful look his way. He was sitting there, staring away from her through the passenger window to his right, casually resplendent in pale cream trousers and a shirt, a blue-grey blazer lending the outfit a slightly nautical look.

'Thank you,' she returned just as non-committally, thinking to herself how like Blake it was to come home shortly after she had that afternoon and not say a word about the morning's altercation; how like him not to question her arrangements about that night's meal; how *very* like him to compliment her appearance without really looking at her.

'Susanne thinks this colour looks well on me,' she added with a perversely mischievous smile. For she knew her remark would draw a reaction.

His head turned, his fair hair glinting as they passed under a bright street-light. 'Susanne? Who's Susanne?'

'Our housekeeper.'

He lifted a single eyebrow. 'Since when have you two been on first-name basis?'

'Since today.'

'And what brought that on? You know I like to keep my employees at arm's length.'

'Yes. But I don't.'

He stared at her for a few seconds. 'What in God's name is bugging you, Juliana? This can hardly be some sort of women's liberation kick, since you'd have to be the most liberated woman I know. I don't make you answer to me for anything.'

'Good,' she snapped. 'Then I don't have to explain why I've chosen to call Mrs Dawson by her first name, do I?'

She saw the anger well up in his eyes and revelled in it. Go on, she urged in silent desperation. Lose your temper with me, right here in this taxi, in front of a stranger. *Do it*!

He sucked in a ragged breath. His blue eyes glittered dangerously. His fists were clenched tightly by his side.

But, in the end, he didn't lose his temper. Taking a few moments to control himself, he eventually presented to her a totally composed face. Or was it a façade? Juliana had to admit that a muscle still twitched in his cheek. Was that evidence of the intensity of the struggle that was going on inside him? Or simply a sign of male anger that she should have put him in such an invidious position? Juliana knew Blake would be hating this.

'No,' he said in a low, deadly voice. 'You don't. Now if you don't mind I would like to terminate this conversation. *Right now*,' he bit out under his breath. 'I can't abide couples who make scenes in public.'

Juliana knew when she had pushed an issue as far as she could. Besides, what had she hoped to achieve? Was this how her love for Blake was going to take voice from now on, by her trying to goad him into an emotional response, no matter what it was?

She sighed her depression at living life on such a tightrope.

'They're still working on the road outside the theatre,' the taxi driver said just then over his shoulder. 'But I'll get you as close as I can.'

There was an atmosphere of excitement before each performance of *Phantom of the Opera*, the musical that had already become legendary, and in a way the traffic bedlam outside the old Princess Theatre only added to that air of excitement. Juliana found herself caught up in it the moment she climbed out of the taxi. People were pouring out of tour buses; others were being dropped off by car and taxi; still more simply walked up from where they'd either parked or alighted from trams.

'Do you want to fight your way through for a drink at the bar,' Blake asked as they made their way slowly towards the crowded entrance, 'or shall we go straight to our seats?'

'I suppose we might as well head for our seats,' she said with a frowning glance at the even more crowded bar on the left. Really, both the foyer and the bar were far too small, but it was the only theatre in Melbourne—in Australia for that matter—that had the kind of stage that could accommodate such a show as *Phantom*. It also brought an enormous amount of tourist trade to Melbourne, so Juliana supposed the locals couldn't complain. Still, she would have liked a drink, a fact which Blake must have noted.

'I'll get you a glass of champagne at half-time,' he promised.

The show was as marvellous as it had been the first time Juliana had seen it, even though there had been some changes of cast since then. When the lights came on for the interval she gave a huge sigh of ragged pleasure.

'Isn't it a wonderful show?' she said. 'Spectacular and stirring and oh, so emotional. You can't help feeling sorry for the Phantom; he does love Christine so…'

Blake turned to her with a sardonic smile on his face. 'I didn't realise you were such a romantic, Juliana. The man's a maniac and a murderer. My sympathies go to Raoul, not to mention the theatre owners.'

'Yours would,' she muttered.

His chuckle was dark. 'Because I'm an unfeeling bastard, or a businessman?'

'Aren't they one and the same?'

Juliana saw his eyes narrow with a flash of anger, but then he stood up to glance around the rapidly emptying seats. 'If I don't head for the bar post-haste I won't be back before the curtain goes up for the second half. Do you want to go to the Ladies'?'

'No. I'll just sit here.'

'OK.'

Juliana sighed as she watched him slip lithely through the groups of departing people. No doubt he would still get served fairly quickly. Blake had that effect on waiters and barmen.

She was sitting there, feeling unhappy with herself for the way she kept making inflammatory remarks to Blake, when the sounds of merriment behind her drew her attention. Looking back over her shoulder, she saw that a group of young people several rows back were laughing and joking in that rather loud manner young gentlemen and ladies often engaged in when they got together. Not that they were being loud enough to be offensive. The theatre was practically empty, anyway.

Juliana was simply amazed, however, to see that one of the young men was none other than Stewart Margin. She stared as Blake's normally prim and proper secretary began acting the goat with his friends, pulling faces and puffing out a non-existent bosom, clearly taking off the role of Carlotta in the show. When he suddenly noticed her staring back up at him, a dark flush of embarrassment stained his cheeks.

For a moment he didn't seem to know what to do. She too felt embarrassed for him, so she swung round and stared blankly ahead, doing her best to hide her slowly spreading smile. Who would have believed it? Stewart Margin was human after all! In a way it reminded Juliana of what happened that afternoon with Mrs Dawson. You could have knocked her over with a feather when Blake's housekeeper had smiled at her.

An unexpected tap on her shoulder had her spinning round in the narrow seat. Stewart was sitting in one of the empty seats behind her, looking worried but not altogether remorseful.

'Good evening, Mrs Preston,' he said somewhat

stiffly, and somewhat in contrast to his performance
of a few moments ago.

'Stewart…' Juliana could feel her lips twitching.
Dear heaven, she was going to burst out laughing. She
could feel it. In an effort to stop such a catastrophe,
she bit her bottom lip.

'Is—um—Mr Preston with you?'

She nodded. It seemed the safest course.

'You—er—I mean…I'm sorry if we were annoying
you just then, Mrs Preston. I know we were a touch
loud but we were only having a little bit of fun. I
mean…you won't tell Mr Preston, will you? He thinks
that I'm—er—' He sighed his frustration. 'The fact is,
one must act in a certain manner in front of Mr Preston, or one doesn't get along with him, if you know
what I mean…'

Suddenly, any wish Juliana had to laugh dissolved
into a longing to cry instead. She knew very well what
Stewart meant. Very well indeed.

A sad little smile touched her lips as she reached
out and patted the young man's hand. 'It's all right,
Stewart. I fully understand. You weren't annoying me
just now and I have no intention of telling Mr Preston.
I suppose I was merely taken aback to see you—er—
enjoying yourself so much.'

Now Stewart smiled. Grinned, actually. Juliana was
surprised to see how attractive he was with his usually
bland grey eyes twinkling. It came to her then that
Blake's secretary would not be unpopular with
women. 'You thought I was a stuffed shirt, I suppose,'
he chuckled.

'You certainly give a good impression of one.'

His eyes flicked over her with such direct male appreciation that she was startled for a moment. 'And you, Mrs Preston, give a very good impression of a society wife. But I found out differently yesterday. You've got a heart, lady. Mr Preston is one lucky guy.'

Juliana flushed under the compliment. But along with the warm rush of pleasure came that longing to cry again. If only Blake *wanted* her heart...

'I'd better get back to my seat,' Stewart said when people started filing back into the row he was occupying. 'Thanks again, Mrs Preston. Look after yourself.'

She watched him make his way slowly along the row, wondering exactly how old he was. Twenty-six or -seven, perhaps? Younger than she'd always imagined. Before seeing him here tonight, she would have said thirty at least.

'Was that Stewart you were just talking to?'

Juliana swung back round to find Blake standing next to her, a tall glass of champagne in his hand.

'Er—um—yes—yes it was actually.' Dear lord, why did she have to sound so darned guilty?

As Blake handed the glass over to her she was stung by the coldness in his eyes. 'You two seemed to be having a very confidential little tête-à-tête. I had no idea you were so chummy.' He sat down, at last giving her some peace from the chill of his gaze. 'I also had no idea he would be here tonight. He certainly never mentioned it to me.'

'Well, why would he?' she defended. 'If you keep

your employees at arm's length, they're not going to tell you about their private life, are they?'

'I suppose he tells *you* all about his private life, though,' he said silkily. 'Does he call you Juliana as well?'

'Don't be so ridiculous, Blake. You know he wouldn't dare.'

'Not in front of me, he wouldn't. But I've no idea what he might dare when I'm halfway across the world.'

Juliana's mouth dropped open as she turned to stare across at her stony-faced husband. 'My God, you're jealous!'

His top lip curled in open contempt of this suggestion, 'Now *you're* being ridiculous! I am not, however, a fool. And a fool I would be if I ever took a beautiful woman like you for granted. Now close your mouth and drink your champagne, Juliana. The curtain's about to go back up.'

It was to the credit of the show that within minutes Juliana forgot her emotional turmoil and became involved in the world of magical fantasy being played out on the stage. Though she would have been blind not to have seen the faint echo of her own situation in the storyline. The Phantom loved Christine to distraction, but it was to remain an unrequited love. Christine's heart belonged to another.

Blake's heart did not belong to another, Juliana conceded. It was simply incapable of loving her the way she wanted to be loved. Still…she shouldn't complain.

He *did* care for her, in his own peculiar way. It would have to be enough.

They didn't spot Stewart in the crush of people after the show. Which was just as well, Juliana thought. Blake had been peeved by her chatting to his secretary. She didn't seriously believe he envisaged an affair between her and his secretary, but *nothing* was supposed to undermine the distance he liked to keep from those who worked for him. No doubt she'd already irritated the life out of him tonight by calling Mrs Dawson Susanne. Juliana was by nature a reserved person, but even she could see that Blake carried this obsession for insulation too far. Maybe it was time to quietly challenge it, to try to break it down somewhat. It wasn't a healthy attitude, she was sure of that.

Not tonight, however, she decided as they travelled home in a taxi in dead silence. She had done quite enough challenging for one night. Besides, she had other things on her mind.

'I think I'll go straight up to bed,' she said immediately they were inside the house.

'I'm having a nightcap first,' Blake returned. 'I'll join you shortly.'

Juliana did her best to keep her mind totally blank as she went through her night-time routine. She took off and hung up her clothes in the large Italian-designed walnut wardrobe; showered in her white-tiled gold-tapped bathroom; dried and powdered her body with a fragrant talc; cleaned her teeth; rubbed a light moisturiser into her face; took down and brushed out her hair.

This she stared at for a moment, thinking of Susanne's earlier comment about men not noticing changes their wives made to their appearance. It would be interesting, in a way, to see if Blake did notice. Hard not to. Several inches had been chopped off, leaving it to swing round her shoulders in a thick glossy curtain, the straight fringe lending mystery to her already exotic eyes.

Juliana never wore a nightie these days if she knew Blake was going to join her. It seemed coy to do so. Coyness was something she didn't like in women. If a wife was going to let her husband make love to her then why put clothes in the way? Maybe if he made love to her elsewhere in the house then it might be interesting to start with clothes on. But Blake had never done that.

What would she do if he ever did? How would she react?

Juliana's fingers tightened around her hairbrush as the most amazing fantasy started drifting into her mind. Agitated by it, she started vigorously brushing her hair, but soon her hand slowed to a stop and, while her eyes were wide open, it was not her reflection in the mirror that Juliana kept seeing, but another, heart-stopping vision…

Blake coming up behind her in the kitchen when she was cooking breakfast on a Saturday morning, wrapping his arms around her, pressing close so that she could feel his arousal through his bathrobe. She was also wearing a bathrobe under which she was similarly naked. He undid the sash, parting her robe to start playing with her breasts. Her breathing became very rapid, but she kept pretending to cook even though she was becoming uncontrollably excited inside. Only when his hands slid down between her thighs did she stop what she was doing. Whirling, she pulled his mouth down to hers in a savage kiss. Soon they sank down on to the kitchen floor, oblivious of the cold tiles, oblivious of everything but their passion for each other…

Suddenly, Juliana snapped back to reality, but the fantasy had left her with her heart pounding and her skin burning. She shook her head violently, trying to dispel more erotic thoughts from flooding her mind. Agitated by the effect they were having on her, she fled back into the bedroom, where she dived quickly in between the cool sheets.

Her mind, however, was relentless.

There followed the pool scenario…the dining-room…the sofa…

She squeezed her eyes tightly shut and huddled down under the quilt, but there was to be no peace in that either.

The shower…the stairs…

'Not asleep, are you?'

Her eyes flew open to encounter Blake closing the door, unsashing his robe as he walked towards the bed.

'No,' she gulped.

He smiled. God, but he was heart-stoppingly handsome when he smiled.

'And no headache?'

She shook her head.

He stared down at her. 'You've had your hair cut.'

Any satisfaction that he had noticed was over-shadowed by the tumultuous feelings racing through her at that moment. Half of her wanted him to part that robe, to let her see him in all his glorious naked-ness. The other half was petrified at what she might do if this madness inside her got out of control.

'It suits you,' he said.

Her smile was jittery.

He stared down at her some more, his eyes trav-elling down her face and over her bare shoulders. The quilt was pulled up tightly over her breasts, which was just as well for Juliana knew full well that they were swollen, the nipples hard peaks of arousal.

'You looked lovely in your green velvet tonight, Juliana,' he said thickly, 'but you look even lovelier without anything on. I didn't realise till I saw you getting out of your bath last night what a truly perfect body you had. Don't hide it away from me, honey. Let me see you…'

Juliana panicked when he tried to extract the blanket from her suddenly clenched hands, her eyes widening into large frightened pools as she gazed up at him in panic-stricken alarm.

'I…I don't want you to.'

He stopped, a dark frown instantly marring his handsome features. 'Don't want me to do what? *Look* at you, or make love to you?'

'L-look at me.'

His sigh was definitely disgruntled. 'Why are you so damned shy?' he said, shrugging out of his robe and climbing in beside her. 'I'd understand if you were ugly perhaps, but by God, Juliana, you're gorgeous!'

Juliana said nothing, her heart pounding wildly as she felt his arousal brushing against her. Dear God, if he only knew! Her fantasies had just shown her her secret longings. She was simply dying to touch him, to show him the extent of her passion.

Shy? She could see now that her so-called shyness had been nothing but a blind, hiding her true self. Now, she wanted to snap that blind up, throw open the windows, let the light shine in. She wanted Blake to see her for the sensual woman she really was, to take that sensuality and explore it to the fullest.

But wanting and doing were two entirely different things. She had no real experience to fall back on. Besides, how could she suddenly start acting differently? Blake would think it strange. Still, he *had* just given her the opportunity to be a little bolder...

'I'm not *that* shy,' she said huskily, and trickled a tentative hand down his bare chest and over his stomach.

His muscles flinched beneath her fingers, his stomach tightening as he sucked in a startled breath.

'Don't...don't you want me to touch you?' she whispered shakily. Oh, how quickly could one's confidence be shattered! Juliana suddenly felt stupid and clumsy and totally inadequate.

Steely fingers tightened around hers. 'God, yes,' he groaned, and carried her hand to his eager flesh, showing her what he liked. 'Yes,' he urged. 'Just like that.'

When he left her to it, Juliana continued for several

minutes, fascinated by the thrill of power she felt every time she made him groan or shudder. She was beginning to contemplate a more intimate foreplay when he suddenly loomed up to throw her back against the pillows, kissing her with such savagery that she thought she might suffocate. But it would have been a glorious suffocation!

'You don't know what you've started,' he growled at last, capturing her wrists and holding them wide on the bed. 'By God, woman, you should have let the devils lie. Now I won't be content with less than everything. Do you understand me?'

She merely stared up at him, eyes wide, heart thudding.

'*Do you understand me*?' he repeated, and shook her.

'Yes,' she rasped.

'Don't stop me this time,' he ground out, and, discarding her wrists, he threw back the blanket and began sliding down her exposed body, his mouth hot and merciless on her shivering, quivering flesh.

There was no question of stopping him. He was unstoppable anyway. But it soon became obvious to Juliana that there was so much she didn't know about sex, and so much that Blake did.

He sent her over the edge within seconds of reaching his goal. But instead of it being the end, it was only the beginning. Sometimes she felt like a rag-doll, pushed this way and that, a mindless receptacle for his almost insatiable passion. He wanted her every way he'd never had her before.

Even after he'd seemingly spilled every drop of seed into her, and they were collapsed together on the bed, Blake did not leave her alone, trailing his nails lightly over her swollen nipples, making sure he never let her come down from that plateau of sexual sensitivity and abandonment he seemed to have taken her to. Soon the desire to touch him back took possession of her. But her hands were not enough for him. He wanted her mouth as well. He *insisted*.

Dazedly, she complied, finding it a surprisingly arousing experience. And this was the way she achieved the unachievable, stirring him again till he could stand it no longer. It was then that he lifted her on to him, kneading her breasts quite roughly while he urged her to ride them both to another exhausting climax.

Hours passed. Dawn came. And they finally slept.

Yet when Juliana awoke, Blake was not in bed with her. She lay alone and naked on top of the sheets, a picture of decadent disarray. Her hair was tangled, her lips puffy, her thighs and breasts faintly bruised.

'Will an apology do? Or do you want a divorce?'

Juliana's legs shot up under her as she scrambled into a semi-sitting position, swivelling round on the bed in the direction of Blake's voice.

He was in the window-seat, his back against the frame, his knees up, still as stark naked as she was.

Juliana swallowed, reaching for a pillow to hug against herself. 'Why…why would I want either?'

His head turned slowly till their eyes met. Juliana was truly shocked. He looked almost haunted as though he'd just committed the most dreadful crime, when all he'd done was make love to his wife as he perhaps should have all along. OK, so he'd managed to put ten months' worth into one night. And he had been a touch brutal at times. But she'd never been in any real pain. At least, not any that she hadn't enjoyed.

There was a fine line, Juliana had discovered the previous night, between pleasure and pain. She licked dry lips at the thought of some of those razor-edged moments.

Blake was staring at her.

'Are you saying that you didn't mind the things I made you do last night?'

Juliana flushed fiercely, for she could not deny that daylight had a tendency to make some of their love-making seem incredibly uninhibited. But she wasn't ashamed of it. She loved Blake. She was his wife. Nothing they did together was wrong. If he was a little forceful then maybe she had needed him to be. She certainly hadn't wanted to go on enduring the sort of antiseptic, clinical sex they'd been having. Her love demanded more than that now. At least she might find some peace in carnal passion, if that was all Blake was capable of.

'No,' she said simply. 'I didn't mind. We're married, aren't we?'

'Might I remind you that married men have been charged with rape before today?' he returned drily.

'But you didn't rape me last night!'

'It felt as if I did.'

'Did it?' She was totally astounded at his undoubted sincerity. 'But why?'

He glared at her. 'You ask me that? You, who shook with fear on our wedding night, who shuddered whenever I tried to go past the most basic foreplay and intercourse, who even last night didn't want me to *look* at her. For God's sake, Juliana! What do you expect to think—that you suddenly went from prudish innocent to wanton whore in one night? Of course I forced you! If I didn't then…then—' He broke off and looked at her as though he were seeing a ghost.

Oh, my God, she panicked. He's realised I've fallen in love with him.

Apparently not, however. For suddenly he swung his feet down from the window-seat and stood up, hands clenched by his side, uncaring if she saw that in his anger he had become sexually aroused. He glared at her across the room, and if looks could kill she would have shrivelled up on that bed right then and there.

Juliana cringed when he strode menacingly across the room, but he did not touch her, merely swept up his bathrobe from the floor and pulled it on, sashing it round his waist with angry movements. By the time he looked at her again, however, his face was a stony mask, all emotions carefully hidden away.

'If I thought for one moment,' he said in a tightly controlled voice, 'that it was my loyal assistant who'd corrupted you over this last three weeks then I would tear him limb from limb. Only my knowledge of Stewart Margin's ambition puts my mind at rest on that regard. He might fancy you—after all, what man wouldn't? But he would not dare put any secret desires of his into action. He knows what the penalty would be. The same goes for my business friends and acquaintances. That only leaves someone you work with. Your resignation goes in first thing Monday morning, Juliana. If not, I'll start divorce proceedings immediately.'

CHAPTER SEVEN

JULIANA gaped up at him while the import of his words sank in.

'I take it by your silence that you will do as I say,' he drawled. 'After all, I'm sure you want to continue as Mrs Blake Preston, don't you, Juliana?'

Did she?

'In that case we won't mention the matter of your little indiscretion again,' he finished coldly, and, turning, strode from the room, leaving the door open behind him.

Juliana stared at the empty doorway for a few seconds before throwing the pillow away and dashing after Blake.

His bedroom was empty. Where had he gone? The sound of the shower running sent her hurtling into his bathroom, uncaring of his privacy, uncaring of her own nudity, uncaring of anything but the need to give voice to the fury welling up within her. She banged back the sliding glass door to reveal a naked Blake standing there under a steaming jet of hot water, his face upturned, his eyes shut. He didn't flinch an inch, or open his eyes, or turn her way.

'How dare you?' she spat. 'How *dare* you? I have not even *looked* at another man during our marriage, let alone slept with one. For you to imply...no, not imply, *accuse* me of being unfaithful while you were away, of doing with some other man the sort of things we did last night, why I…I…words fail me!'

She scooped in some much needed air. Her whole body was shaking uncontrollably. But even in her rage some inner instinct warned her to be careful with what she said, what she admitted. 'Has it ever occurred to you I might have become a little bored with our sex-life?' she ranted on. 'For it had become boring, Blake. Even you must recognise that. Boring and predictable. And maybe I've become dissatisfied with the way you never touch me unless it's in bed. A wife likes her husband to show outward signs of affection occasion-ally.'

Now Blake opened his eyes to look at her. They were hard and disbelieving. Juliana put her hands on her hips in a gesture of defiance and outrage. 'I have *not* taken a lover, either at work or any other place. And I will *not* resign on Monday! If that means you are going to divorce me, then so be it! Nothing, not being your wife or all the money in the world, is worth having to give up my independence and self-respect! To tell the truth, I can't imagine why I agreed to marry you in the first place, Blake Preston. You'd have to be the most selfish, cold-blooded, monstrous man in the entire world!'

The hands that shot out to grab her came so fast that she'd been yanked into the shower before she could say Jack Robinson. Blake slammed her hard against the wet tiles, holding her hands captive on ei-ther side of her, jamming one solid thigh between hers.

'Is that so?' he ground out, his sneering mouth only inches from hers. 'Well, in that case you won't be surprised to hear I don't believe a word you've just said. But you've got guts, Juliana, I'll give you that. *And* imagination. Bored, were you? Dissatisfied, were you? Then why didn't you say something? You're an intelligent woman. You must have known any man would have wanted more than what you were giving me.'

His water-slicked knee lifted to start rubbing between her legs, making her breath catch and her stomach tighten. She knew she shouldn't respond beneath such an outrageous caress, but she did. Dear God, she did! His mouth curved into a cynical smile.

'You've suddenly discovered sex, Juliana,' he mocked. 'And you didn't discover it with me. That's the truth of it, my treacherous little wife. But I've always been a man to try to turn disadvantage to advantage. If it's imaginative sex you want, then I'm sure I can keep this new appetite of yours well satisfied.'

She gasped as he moved his other leg between hers, holding her there against the wall while he manoeuvred his impassioned flesh into her shockingly ready body. She turned her face away in appalled horror at the pleasure she felt, the mad excitement that took possession of her as he set up a relentlessly erotic rhythm. The water cascaded down over his head, splashing into her parted lips, trickling down over her distended nipples.

'Is this what you want?' he said, his voice slurred.

She wanted to scream her denial but no words came from her panting mouth. And then she was shuddering against the wall, her knees going from under her. He lifted her then, carrying her limp, wet body back into his bedroom, spreading her out across his bed where he continued quite mercilessly till he too spasmed with a violent release.

Almost immediately, he levered himself up from her shattered body, staring down into her utterly drained face with eyes like hell.

'Keep your job,' he grated. 'But God help you if I ever catch you with another man again.'

He turned and went back into the still running shower, this time locking the door behind him.

If she'd been in her own room, Juliana would have curled up where she was and cried her eyes out. But the possibility that Mrs Dawson might come upstairs at any moment to do the bedrooms sent her stumbling back to her own room and her own bathroom. She too locked the door, leaning against it and letting the tears run unashamedly down her face.

She spent ages in the bathroom, bathing at length. And thinking long and hard.

The marriage was doomed, she finally decided. Doomed...

Yet to simply throw in the towel when she loved the man so much seemed a cowardly thing to do. More than cowardly—extremely difficult, considering the changed nature of their sexual relationship.

Who would have believed she could be so easily and devastatingly satisfied as Blake had satisfied her in that shower? How did you turn your back on such pleasure?

But she had to if she was going to live with herself. Life was more than the physical. And so was a marriage.

When she finally came out of the bathroom, the bed had been made with fresh sheets, the room tidied and dusted. Juliana blushed to think of what Susanne might have thought about the state of the bed. She pulled on jeans and a top, and was standing there, trying to decide what to do next, when there was a knock on the door.

'Juliana… It's Blake…'

'C-come in,' she stammered, instantly nervous. Now was the moment to tell him she could not go on if he really believed she was an unfaithful wife; if he was going to continue to treat her with contempt.

Surprised to find him dressed as though for work in a business suit, Juliana was at a loss for words for a moment. Blake, however, was not similarly indisposed.

'I've decided to fly to Sydney this afternoon,' he began straight away, standing with his hand still on the doorknob. 'I'll be back on Wednesday evening in time to take you to the races on Thursday. Before you say anything, I want to apologise, not for my behaviour—since you undoubtedly enjoyed what I did,' he inserted drily, 'but for my accusations of adultery, and my rather lack-lustre performance during this marriage so far. I mistakenly thought the type of sex-life we had was all you could handle. Obviously I didn't see the signs of change. Maybe I've also left you alone too much, a factor which will-be remedied.'

He sighed then. It was a weary, troubled sigh. 'I don't want to lose you, Juliana. I value our marriage and I want it to last. Maybe it's time we started trying for a child.'

A *child*? A child would bind her to him forever. There would be no escape. Juliana needed that escape for a while. Much as Blake's words just now had soothed most of her doubts and fears, she still wasn't entirely convinced their marriage would last.

'I...I think we should wait a while for that, Blake,' she returned hesitantly. 'At least till the New Year, the way we planned.'

His gaze locked on to hers, his eyes intent. What was he trying to see?

'Very well, Juliana,' he conceded matter-of-factly. 'Goodbye. I'll see you on Wednesday. You can tell Mrs Dawson I should be home for dinner.'

And then he was gone.

Juliana sighed. What had changed? No goodbye kiss. No asking her to accompany him to the airport. No doubt she would not hear from him during the days he was gone, since three days would hardly warrant a phone call in Blake's opinion.

Juliana was wrong about that. He did call. Every night. At first, she was thrilled, but then not. The calls were brief and rather brusque. Clearly he was checking up her, seeing if she came home every evening. When he called her again at work on Wednesday morning she was quite sharp with him, even though he was only telling her that he would be taking her out for dinner that night and that she was to inform Mrs Dawson not to cook for them. After she'd hung up, she regretted her sharpness, but she couldn't help suspecting that Blake had been trying to catch her out at something at work.

As luck would have it, she was kept late at work that day. Blake was already home when she turned into the driveway for there was a light on in his bedroom. As Juliana used the remote control to open the garage doors, a nervous agitation churned her stomach.

She knew why.

Not a night had gone by since Blake left that she hadn't wanted him. Quite fiercely. Yet, with the passing of the days, that mad night she'd spent with him, plus the incident in the shower, had taken on an unreal feeling. It was as though it hadn't happened to her and Blake, but to two other people. Strangers. Juliana worried that Blake would never be like that again, that *she* would never feel like that again.

The kitchen was deserted as Juliana walked through from the garage. She had given Susanne the night off in view of her not having to cook for them, and the housekeeper was happy enough to visit her sister who lived in the Dandenong Hills. She wouldn't be back till the next day.

There was only herself and Blake in the huge house. The thought excited Juliana. She hoped it would excite him.

He didn't look at all excited, standing at his dressing-table, putting his gold cuff-links into the sleeves of an ivory silk shirt. The front buttons were undone and the shirt hung open, showing an expanse of smooth golden flesh down to where his charcoal-grey trousers stopped the unconsciously sensual display. He glanced up once he became aware of her standing in the doorway, watching him. It was a very fleeting glance.

'Ah, there you are, Juliana.' Not a word of enquiry or reproach about her being late. 'I've booked a table for seven-thirty. You've only got thirty minutes. Look, why don't you leave your hair up, have a quick shower and put on that green velvet dress you had on the other night? I really liked that on you and it won't need ironing.''

He finished with his cuff-links and started buttoning up his shirt. When she continued to stand there, staring at him, he lifted an eyebrow at her. 'Is there something I can do for you?' he drawled.

She tried not to flush at the image in her mind.

'No. I was going to ask how things went in Sydney but it can wait, I suppose.' And, whirling away, she fled to her room, closing her eyes in pained humiliation as she shut the door behind her.

Twenty-five minutes later she was struggling to pull up the back zip of the emerald-green velvet when Blake materialised behind her. 'Let me...'

Her eyes flew to his in the dressing-table mirror, but he merely smiled that enigmatic smile he sometimes produced and zipped her up. Yet his hands lingered on her shoulders, his gaze admiring as it travelled slowly over the reflected dress in the mirror. Juliana found herself looking at the dress as well, trying to control the wild fluttering of her heart.

It was a simple style, cut to hug the line of a woman's body, the skirt pencil-slim and just above the knee. The sleeves were three-quarter-length and tight, emphasising the slenderness of her arms. But it was the neckline that drew the eyes, the wide sweetheart shape showing a good deal of creamy flesh and just a hint of cleavage.

Juliana had first discovered the style suited her figure when she'd worn Barbara's graduation gown, and since then she had often bought dresses with that neckline. The only drawback was that bra straps often showed, so the right underwear was required.

Juliana always wore a strapless corselette of stretch black lace with this particular dress, since such a garment also enhanced the hour-glass shape that best displayed the tightly fitted style. Her years of modelling had taught her how to show her figure off to best advantage. Such underwear pulled in her waist, giving her slender hips a fuller look, and pushing up her limited bust.

Thinking about her underwear, however, especially with Blake standing so close behind her, was making Juliana hotly aware of her body.

'I have a little present for you,' he astonished her by saying.

She went to turn around but he held her there with an iron grip. 'No, stay right where you are...'

Drawing a long green velvet case from his suit jacket pocket, he unclipped it and placed it on the

dressing-table in front of her. In it was the most beautiful emerald and gold necklace Juliana had ever seen.

'Oh, Blake! It's magnificent!' she exclaimed, reaching out to run her fingers over it. Clearly, he had had
the green dress in mind when he'd bought it.
'But…but what's it for?' She glanced up at his face
in the mirror. 'It's not my birthday for another month.'

His smile was odd as he lifted the necklace from its
velvet bed and secured it around her neck. There was
no doubt that it looked spectacular against her pale
flesh but Juliana had the strangest feeling that with this
gift Blake had just paid for services rendered. Or was
it for services still to *be* rendered?

'Does it have to be for anything?' he said suavely.
'Can't I give my beautiful wife a gift?'

'Yes, but…'

She froze when he bent to kiss her neck. 'Do shut
up, Juliana, and just let me do things to please you.
Isn't that what you said you wanted? Outward displays
of affection? From now on I will give you whatever
takes my fancy. And *do* whatever takes my fancy…'

His mouth trailed lightly back up to her right ear,
where he blew softly into the shell-like cavern. Juliana
shivered.

'Perhaps we'd better be going,' he said softly.

Dinner at the restaurant was agony.

First, Blake had booked one of those ghastly places
where people went not so much to eat, but to be seen.
Celebrities and millionaires abounded. Most of the
men had little dolly-birds on their arms: not wives—

mistresses and girlfriends. And they all dripped with expensive jewellery.

Juliana's new emerald necklace felt as if it was lit in neon around her neck, especially after one abominable woman made caustic mention of it. *Kept woman*, Juliana felt it was screaming out to everyone. Which was crazy really. Blake was her husband. How could that make her *kept* in any way?

Yet by the time they left the restaurant Juliana was very much on edge.

'I didn't like that place, Blake,' she said with a little shudder. 'I don't want to go there ever again.'

'Oh? What was wrong with it?'

'The food stinks and so does the clientele.'

He laughed. 'You don't like the rich and famous any more?'

'I never did like them, as you very well know. I merely envied the power they had.'

'So if you couldn't beat them, you joined them, is that it? After all, might I remind you that your husband is a very rich man?'

'No, you don't have to remind me...' Her hand lifted to finger the necklace.

He slanted her a dark look but said nothing. Silence was maintained till they were climbing out of the car inside the garages.

'The night's still young,' Blake said. 'Care for a swim?'

'I...I don't think so.' The pool had become the focus of Juliana's most persistent fantasy lately.

'What, then? You tell me what you want to do.'

His eyes clashed with hers over the roof of the car. Why did she get the feeling he was taunting her, trying to make her say that she wanted him to make love to her? Was this to be her punishment for changing the status quo in their relationship? Constant humiliation?

Juliana fiercely resented being put in such a position. No way was she going to beg, or grovel, or even hint.

'I don't know about you,' she said casually, 'but I have a good book to read.'

'Oh? Anything I've read?'

To be caught out in a lie made Juliana's teeth clamp down hard in her jaw. 'I doubt it,' she bit out, vowing to snatch up anything from the family room on the way through. Susanne was always reading.

'You don't want a nightcap?'

'Well…maybe a port before I go up.' To race away would seem as if she was frightened to be alone with him.

'You didn't ask me what happened in Sydney,' he remarked while he poured them both a port.

Juliana was settled in one of the three gold brocade armchairs that matched the sofa. The sofa, like the pool, had been put on her list of no-nos for a while. She took the glass with a stiff smile on her lips. 'Sorry, but I'm sure you handled things with your usual panache.'

'*Panache*? What kind of business term is that? Panache, I ask you!' He dropped down in one of the other armchairs, stretching his legs out in front of him and loosening his tie. 'I gave those lazy, inefficient idiots up there a blast that could have been heard all the way to Melbourne. I doubt they'd be telling their wives tonight that their boss has *panache*.'

'Sounds as if you were in a bad mood,' she pointed out.

'Maybe.' He shot her a knowing look. 'Maybe I had good cause…'

'Meaning?'

'Meaning I would have much rather been here, making mad, passionate love to my wife.'

Juliana's hand shook as she lifted the port to her suddenly dry lips. She sipped the drink, her gaze finding Blake's over the rim. There was self-mockery in those glittering blue eyes, but real desire as well. Her stomach lurched.

'Take off your clothes,' he said abruptly.

Some of the port spilt into her lap. 'Oh, my God, my beautiful dress!' She shot Blake a savage glance. 'You made me do that,' she accused. 'You, with your pathetic suggestions.'

He laughed and stood up. 'It's you who's pathetic, Juliana.' He came over and dabbed at the spilt port with the scarlet hankie he had in his pocket. Leaning over, he kissed her full on the mouth then fixed ruthless eyes upon her. 'You've been on fire for sex all night and what have you done? Complained. Quibbled. *Lied*. Why not come right out and say you want me to ravage you? Why not stand up and take that damned dress right off? It's what you want to do, isn't it? Or would you really prefer to go to bed with a good book?'

He lanced her stunned face with a furious glare before straightening to stride back over to the bar. 'To hell with this port. I need a real drink!'

He rattled the whisky decanter, even spilling some as he filled a fresh and very tall glass. 'Here's to a return to prudery!' he announced, and lifted the glass in a mocking toast. But when he turned around to further deride the woman who had ignited such an uncharacteristic display of temper and emotion, Blake froze.

She stood before him, the dress on the floor, her body the epitome of erotica in the black lace corselette, her long slender legs encased in sheer black stockings that ran all the way down to her black high heels. The emerald necklace around her neck looked exotic and somewhat depraved. Her breathing, he noted, was rapid, and there was a wild light blazing in her eyes. She had never looked more dangerously seductive or more breathtaking beautiful.

'You bitch,' he rasped, and, putting the glass down, moved slowly towards her, a smile on his lips.

CHAPTER EIGHT

JULIANA'S chin lifted. 'If I'm a bitch, then what are you?' she countered, well aware that she was being deliberately provocative. But, having taken up Blake's challenge, no way was she going to back down.

'Oh, I'm a bastard through and through,' her husband agreed, his smile turning rueful as he reached out to touch the emerald necklace around her throat. 'But a very rich bastard, you must admit,' he added, and, curling his fingers around the necklace, he began pulling her towards him.

The taunt over his wealth added a fiery fury to Juliana's already heated bloodstream. When her head was yanked indignantly backwards, the clasp gave way and Blake was left holding the broken necklace in his hand.

'Don't you ever throw your money in my face again!' she hissed. 'And don't you ever parade me in front of other people like some cheap whore!' Snatching the necklace from his stunned fingers, she flung it across the room. 'That's what I think of your thinking you can buy me!'

Too late Juliana realised she had finally done what she'd always thought she wanted to do to her unruffl-able husband: make him really lose his temper. But the actuality was not quite as desirable as she had once imagined. Blake looked as if he wanted to kill her.

'I don't have to buy you,' he ground out savagely. 'You're my wife! I can damned well have you any time I want you.' And, with his face flushing an angry red, he scooped her up into his arms and dumped her on to the sofa, pinning her there with a knee across her stomach while he began reefing his clothes off: first his tie, then his jacket and shirt till he was naked to the waist.

Only then did he turn his attention to *her* attire, reefing open the hooks that ran down the front of the black lace corselette and wrenching both flaps aside, exposing her body to his glittering gaze. Holding her shoulders down, he sat on the edge of the sofa, effectively stopping her from escaping. When his mouth started to descend towards one of her hard-tipped breasts Juliana lashed out with closed fists, striking the side of his head, his shoulders, his chest.

'No you can't damned well have me any time you want me!' she screamed at him. 'Not unless I agree.'

His smile was frightening as he gripped her flailing hands in an iron grasp. 'You'll agree all right, my sexy Juliana. You'll agree…' And, pinioning both her wrists within one large male hand, his free hand set out to make his prophecy come true, sliding down over her flat stomach and under the elastic of her tiny black lace bikini briefs.

'No,' she groaned once he found his target.

'Yes,' he bit out, and ruthlessly continued.

'You're a bastard.'

'We've already established that.'

'I...I won't give in,' she cried, but her voice was already unsteady, her heart hammering away like mad.

Gritting her teeth, she tried to ignore the sensations his knowing hand was evoking, tried not to let her thighs fall evocatively apart to give him easier access to her body. But she was fighting a losing battle. In the end, pride demanded she not let him win, even as she lost.

Catching his heavy-lidded gaze with a desire-charged look of her own, she smiled a smile as perversely wicked as his had been. His eyes widened, that tormenting hand stilling for a moment.

'Don't stop,' she husked, and arched her back in voluptuous surrender.

His hand withdrew as he stood up, his breathing as ragged as her own. 'No,' he said thickly. 'You won't get what you want that easily. You'll earn your pleasure, wife.'

'What makes you think I won't enjoy earning it?' she rasped, and levered herself up into a sitting position, her hands going to the belt on his trousers.

His fingers closed over hers, then tightened. Her eyes flew upwards, locking with his. The pain of the buckle digging into her palm was intense but she refused to make a sound. Finally, he laughed and drew her upwards till she was standing, trembling, before him. A few violent movements and he had stripped her totally naked, except for the long black stockings and her high heels.

For an interminable time he simply stared at her, his

torrid gaze roving over her softly parted lips, her swollen breasts, the triangle of damp curls that so ineffectually guarded her desire. When he reached out to touch her there, she sucked in a shuddering breath.

'Juliana,' he said, and with a groan of raw need moved to crush her against him, grabbing the back of her head and covering her mouth with his till she was weak and pliant in his arms.

'And now, my incredibly beautiful wife,' he muttered at last against her panting mouth, 'let's see just how far you'll let your bastard of a husband go…'

'Wake up, sleepyhead.'

Juliana yawned and stretched, then buried her face back in the pillow. 'Can't,' she mumbled. 'Too tired.'

'I don't doubt it,' Blake muttered drily. 'But we have to get going. If we're not at Flemington by eleven we won't get a parking spot, even in the members' area. It's nine already.'

'Nine!' Juliana shot upright, pushing her hair out of her face. 'My God!' she exclaimed, looking around her. 'I'm in *your* room. When did we…?' Her frown was puzzled, for the last thing she recalled was falling asleep in Blake's arms on the sofa.

'I carried you up,' he told her on a sardonic note. 'And believe me, I won't do it again in a hurry. Either you weigh a ton or I was a little—er—done in at the time.'

Laughter bubbled from her lips. Some time during their crazed lovemaking session last night all the anger and frustration associated with their changing sexual relationship had been routed. They'd mocked each other, taunted each other, dared each other. They'd even hurt each other. Juliana could remember slapping Blake once, and he'd slapped her right back.

But the final outcome had been a purging that left them both exhausted, yet at peace with each other. Afterwards, Blake had cradled Juliana in his arms and told her that there would never be another woman for him. Never.

It might not have been an avowal of love, but it was as close as he would ever come to it. Juliana had drifted off into a deep sleep, happy and content.

She had woken just as happy. 'You should know better than to challenge your old diving mate, shouldn't you?' she teased.

Blake smiled from where he was lying next to her, his arms linked behind his head. 'They were great days, weren't they, Julianna?'

'Marvellous...'

'Too bad we had to grow up and become part of the world at large. It's not a very nice place.'

Juliana's heart turned over at Blake's sudden bleakness of spirit. She much preferred the man he'd been last night, the lover who'd cuddled her close and said the sweetest of things.

'No, it's not,' she agreed, 'but we can make our own little corner a nice place, can't we?'

His head turned towards her, and a small smile tugged the grimness from his mouth. 'My darling Juliana...the eternal optimist.'

'I'll settle for being just your darling Juliana,' she

whispered, and kissed him on the cheek. 'I do so love being your wife, Blake. I love everything about it. Now more than ever.'

She saw his hesitation to accept her love, despite her having skirted around saying straight out that she loved him. In the end, he couldn't help withdrawing from any open acceptance, defusing a situation he obviously found awkward with a flash of dry humour.

'I know exactly what *you* love, Mrs Preston, and I'm not going to be conned into any more. As it is, I'm going to have to take a bottle of vitamin E tablets with breakfast, plus a swag of oysters for lunch. Speaking of lunch, up you get, lazy-bones. The gee-gees await!'

He himself bounced out of bed and headed straight for the shower without looking back. Juliana noted that he carefully locked the door behind him.

She shrugged away any upsurge of dismay. Blake was not about to change in a hurry. But he *was* changing. After all, he hadn't put her in her own bed when he'd carried her up, had he? He'd put her in *his*.

'This place is madness today!' Juliana exclaimed, looking at the cars pouring into Flemington. And it was only ten-forty!

Blake had managed to squeeze his turquoise Mercedes sports car into a smallish spot near a fence, not far from the members' entrance into the track. As was the tradition during the Melbourne Cup carnival, people had set up picnics behind and between their cars, with caviare and chicken and champagne on the menu, but still more people were surging towards the gates of the course proper, anxious to soak up the atmosphere inside the grounds.

'It was worse on Tuesday, I heard,' Blake said, coming round to join her at the back of the car. 'Something like a hundred buses parked down along the Maribyrnong River, and countless limousines dropping off Arab sheikhs and their entourages all morning.'

'How would you know?' she frowned. 'You were in Sydney.'

He grinned. 'Stayed in the motel and watched it on telly. Can't miss the Melbourne Cup, you know. I'm a Melbournian!'

'I suppose you even backed the winner.'

'Of course. I had half the field.'

'Blake! You can't win punting like that.'

'Juliana, my sweet...'

She caught her breath when he put a protective arm around her to steer her safely through the milling crowd.

'...one doesn't try to win on the Melbourne Cup. One tries to end up with a ticket on the winner. That's totally different. After the race, one surreptitiously slips all the dead tickets into nearby waste-paper baskets then produces the winning one. Everyone thinks you're a genius!'

Juliana laughed and shook her head. 'I won't from now on. I'll know the truth.'

'Ah, yes, but...' he gave her an affectionate squeeze—in public! '...I don't mind *you* knowing the truth. There shouldn't be any secrets between a husband and wife, should there?'

Juliana's heart turned over. Tears hovered, but she quickly blinked them back and lifted a dazzling smile to his handsome face. 'No, Blake. No secrets. None at all.'

He stared down at her for a second, and she could have sworn a dark cloud flitted momentarily across his eyes. It worried her. Did he still think she might have had an affair? Oh, surely not.

'Blake…'

'Mmm?'

'I…' She glanced around her. People were pressing close. The words died in her throat. Which was just as well, perhaps. The more she protested her innocence, the more guilty she might sound. Best say nothing.

'Oh, nothing,' she went on with an offhand wave of her hand. 'It's going to be warm, isn't it? I'm glad I wore something reasonably cool.'

The pink linen suit she had on was very simple, with short sleeves, a straight skirt and big black buttons down the front of the jacket. Teamed with a saucy black hat that dipped over one side of her face, and other black patent accessories, Juliana thought she looked chic and cool.

'It'll probably storm later,' Blake remarked, glancing up at the sky. 'I hope that hat doesn't ruin.'

'The lady in the hat shop warned me it would go like a limp rag if I ever got it wet. Do you honestly think it will rain?'

'Sure to by the end of the day.'

'We can stay under cover, sipping champagne.'

'I came here to have a bet, Juliana, not sip champagne.'

'I thought you came here today to be with me! Truly, Blake, everyone from work is dying to meet you. Now you tell me you're going to be slipping away to spend all afternoon fighting your way through to the bookmakers or standing in long totalisator queues. You do realise the promotional marquees are in the middle of the course proper, don't you?'

'Good God, why didn't they get one of the decent ones down the end of the straight?'

'Don't be such a snob. There's nothing wrong with our being in the centre. Firstly, you'll get a much better view of the races. Special tiered seats are being set up near the finishing-post. You couldn't be in a better spot. And the company has hired a couple of hostesses whose job it is to go round putting everyone's bets on for them. What more could you ask for?'

'You…and me…naked…on a desert island?'

Heat zoomed into her cheeks. 'Don't say such things out loud,' she hissed, aware of the people all around her.

Blake's chuckle was cynical as he leant close. 'You can't fool me any more with that prim and proper act. I know the real you, Juliana. I only hope none of the other gentlemen here today knows the real you as well…'

Her eyes jerked up to his. 'You…you still don't trust me, do you?'

'I put trust in the same category as love, my sweet. It's very nice in theory but awfully suspect in practice.'

Any further chit-chat was terminated by their arrival at the toll gates. Blake withdrew his wallet and paid the entrance fees, after which he took her elbow and urged her inside.

'Don't get your knickers in a knot, Juliana,' he pronounced brusquely on seeing her distress. 'I don't believe in worrying about things one can't change, which includes the past. We've started our marriage anew this past week with a clean slate and a damned sight more interesting sex-life. Let's leave it at that, shall we?

'Of course,' he added darkly as they walked together past the beds of roses and down towards where they could cross into the centre of the track, 'I would cast a dim view if any man here today showed any more than a work-like interest in you. A very dim view indeed…'

No man dared.

Blake, in full millionaire mode, was a formidable husband and companion. It would have taken a brave male to try to muscle in on the woman on *his* arm, especially when that woman was his wife! Juliana still gained the impression that Blake sized up every one of her colleagues, from the nineteen-year-old mailboy to the thirty-three-year-old field sales manager to the national sales manager, who was pushing fifty and very happily married.

Juliana had to work hard to hide her frustration with

Blake. What did she have to do to persuade him that she hadn't been playing around while he was away?

Nothing, she finally realised. He would believe what he wanted to believe. To change her behaviour for fear of feeding his ill-founded suspicions was not only non-productive but extremely stressful. She felt tense enough as it was, having Blake give everyone the once-over with that penetrating gaze of his.

The women, she noticed, stared at him openly and swooned behind his back. And why not? He was like a young Robert Redford with his classically featured face, blond hair and blue eyes, not to mention his tall, athletic body, encased very attractively that day in an elegantly casual tan suit and open-necked blue shirt. All this, plus the fact that he was as wealthy as any Onassis, made her handsome husband pack a pretty powerful punch.

'I think it's the wrong spouse doing the worrying,' she muttered under her breath on one occasion.

Blake shot her a dry look over his shoulder then returned to give his bet to the simpering hostess.

They all traipsed out to see the race in question—the third of the day. Juliana's choice stumbled out of the barrier and was never sighted. Blake's was beaten by a short half-head.

'If I'd been putting on my own bets,' he grumbled, 'I'd have had the winner.'

'Sure,' she said ruefully. 'You'd also have had every other horse in the race, even the donkey I bet on.'

'True,' he grinned.

They were still sitting on the seats near the winning-post, everyone else having gone back inside their respective marquees.

Juliana glanced up at the sky. Black clouds were sweeping in from the west, a sure sign of the storm Blake had predicted earlier.

She sighed. 'I suppose we'd better get back under cover. It's looking mighty ominous overhead. Good grief!' she suddenly exclaimed. 'Do you see who I see over there?'

She nodded over to where Owen Hawthorne was standing near the rails on the other side of the track, arm in arm with none other than Virginia Blakenthorp. It was the first time Juliana had seen either of them since her marriage, which was not surprising, she supposed, since Blake didn't socialise with his old crowd any more.

'If you mean our respective exes,' he said in a bored tone, 'then yes…I see them.'

'Do you think they might be going out with each other now?'

'I certainly should hope so. They're engaged.'

Juliana sucked in a startled breath. 'Owen's *engaged* to Virginia?'

Blake settled narrowed eyes upon her. 'Yes. Why? Does that bother you?'

'Well, I…I…no, not really. I'm sure they're admirably suited. But if you knew that, why didn't you tell me?'

He shrugged. 'I didn't think you'd be interested.'

'I'm not *interested*. I'm just…just…'

'Jealous?' Blake suggested blandly.

Juliana glared her exasperation. 'It's not a matter of jealousy, but of guilt.'

'*Guilt?*'

'Yes, guilt. I felt guilty getting married so quickly after I broke my engagement to Owen. He loved me, you know, despite his shortcomings. I wasn't totally insensitive to his feelings. Virginia I wasn't so concerned with. Girls like her rarely stir me to sympathy. But I didn't like either of them to think I only married you for your money.'

'But you *did* marry me for my money, darling. I knew that from the start. It was my ace card in securing your services as a wife. Of course, it has taken some time for my investment to bear fruit...'

He leant over and kissed her with almost insulting tenderness. Juliana gasped when his lips finally lifted from hers, her eyes pained as she looked up at him. But her pain soon changed to a justifiable anger.

'There are many wealthy men in this world,' she snapped, 'whom I wouldn't touch with a barge-pole, let alone marry. If it were just your money I wanted, Blake, then why do I still work, why do I always insist on buying my own clothes and paying my way?'

His shrug was indifferent. 'Very well, so I used the wrong word. You married me for my position and power. Why deny it? I've never minded, Juliana. You know that. I've always admired your honest ambition. I especially admired your refusal to pretend love, quite unlike that lying bitch over there.'

The venom in Blake's voice gave rise to the unnerving suspicion that he might really have been in love with Virginia. Maybe he still was. His assertion that night that he'd broken his engagement because Virginia wanted to become a lady of leisure after their marriage suddenly didn't ring true.

'What really happened with Virginia, Blake? Did you find out she had another lover?'

'No,' he returned coldly. 'I found out her family was stony-broke, yet the day before she'd been telling me what a killing her daddy had made on the Stock Exchange that year. I suddenly realised she wouldn't look at me twice without my money. Hell, during those months of near-bankruptcy most of my so-called friends deserted me in droves. I thought Virginia was different from the usual society girl because she worked. But she was only working because she *needed* to work, not because she wanted to. I was nothing to her but a meal-ticket, a means for her to embrace the type of empty, lunch-flitting, charity-committee exis- tence females of her ilk thrive on!'

He lanced Juliana with a savage scowl. 'Now, if you're finished with the third degree about *my* life, why don't I hear some truths about yours? Have you been seeing Owen Hawthorne while I've been away?'

'No!'

'Who, then?'

'No one!'

'Don't lie to me, Juliana.'

'I am *not* lying to you.'

'You'd better not be. I thought I could let bygones be bygones but I've suddenly realised I'm not that noble. There are some things in life that a man just cannot tolerate being deceived about, and his wife's extra-curricular activities is one of them. If I ever find out you *have* lied to me in this, Juliana, you might discover a Blake you've never seen before.'

He stood up abruptly. 'Come on, let's go back inside before this storm breaks right over our heads.'

Stunned by Blake's clearly jealous warning, Juliana said very little for the rest of the afternoon. Was his jealousy inspired by male ego and possessiveness? she kept wondering. Or something far deeper and more vulnerable?

She dared not hope Blake was falling in love with her, but somehow she couldn't help hoping. It was what she wanted more than anything else in the world. Why, if Blake loved her, she could endure anything. Anything at all!

Not, however, his sister Barbara, who was waiting for them when they arrived home that afternoon.

CHAPTER NINE

THERE was no warning of Barbara's presence inside as Blake parked his car and cut the engine. No strange car taking up one of the two empty spaces in the four car garage, or parked in the street outside. The first they knew of their unexpected visitor was when they came into the kitchen.

'There's someone to see you, Mr Preston,' Susanne announced in her starchy Mrs Dawson voice. 'Your sister. She's in the study.'

Juliana grimaced, turning away to place her hat and bag on the breakfast bar. Susanne saw the reaction and almost smiled, but managed to hold herself together. Clearly, she didn't like Barbara any more than Juliana did.

'She seemed upset,' the housekeeper added.

Blake frowned. 'I see… Maybe I'll go in and talk to her alone, Juliana,' he said, glancing at her over his shoulder.

'Be my guest,' she returned drily.

He shot her an exasperated look. 'Women!' he grumped. And marched off.

'What's up, do you know?' Juliana asked as soon as Blake was out of earshot.

Susanne shrugged. 'Mr Preston's sister wouldn't confide in me. Maybe she's left her husband. Or

136

maybe he's thrown her out.' She turned away and continued her preparations for the evening meal. 'I presume I should cook enough for one more for tonight's dinner?'

Juliana groaned silently. Having Barbara over for the odd meal was bad enough. But to have her stay didn't bear thinking about.

'I suppose so,' she sighed. 'I sure hope that's all you'll have to do for her.'

The housekeeper's eyes jerked up. 'I hope so too! If there's one woman I can't stand it's...' Suddenly she bit her bottom lip and busied herself back on the vegetables. 'Sorry, Juliana. I shouldn't have said that. It's none of my business. Mr Preston can have here whomever he likes. My job is just to do the housework, not voice opinions.'

Juliana patted the other woman on the shoulder. 'It's all right, Susanne, I understand your feelings entirely. The woman's a right pain in the butt. But, as you say, she is Blake's sister and we must make her as welcome as we can. Of course, if you decide to short-sheet the bed and add the odd funnelweb spider to her night-time glass of water then I'll turn a blind eye.'

Both women burst into laughter, and were still giggling when Blake strode back into the room, looking like thunder.

'Might I request a pot of black coffee?' he said sharply. 'That crazy female in there has been downing my Johnny Walker like water, along with some damned tranquilliser or something. I can't get any sense out of her. Bring the coffee in when it's ready, would you, Juliana? Maybe you, being a woman, might be able to get to the bottom of the problem. All Barbara's done since I walked in is cry! And before you tell me you and she don't get along—as if I didn't know that already—then just do it for me, OK?'

'Of course, Blake,' Juliana agreed. 'I'll do what I can.'

'Thank you.' And, whirling, he was gone as abruptly as he'd come.

Susanne shook her head then started making the coffee. 'Men aren't too good at just listening, are they?'

Juliana frowned. 'Blake used to be when he was younger…'

'Was he? Oh, well, I didn't know him them.'

'He was very nice. Very kind and considerate.'

'*Was* he?' There was no doubting the surprise in the housekeeper's voice.

Juliana's smile was rather sad. 'He's still like that underneath,' she said. 'It's just that life's been hard on him, what with his mother's suicide, his father's premature death and then his having to work so hard to save the family company from bankruptcy. He had to become tough to survive, I guess. When men have to be like that at work all day, they don't always know how to switch off when they come home.'

'You're probably right. My Fred was a bus driver. He used to tell me that by the time he came home after driving in the traffic all day his nerves were shot to pieces.'

'That's probably why he played golf,' Juliana suggested. 'It's supposed to be a very relaxing game. Your husband would have especially appreciated all that walking in wide open spaces.'

'Yes...' Susanne seemed thoughtful while she put the finishing touches on the coffee-tray. 'Yes, I suppose that could have been so.' She brightened as she handed Juliana the tray. 'I always thought he just wanted to get away from me. But I can see now that he might have *needed* that relaxation. As it was, he still had a heart attack before he should have...'

Now her face started to fall, tears pricking at her eyes. Juliana was happy to leave her to her memories, hopeful that she might have given the poor woman a different slant on what had clearly been an unhappy marriage. Maybe that was why Susanne had never had children. Or maybe the not having children had created the unhappy marriage. Who knew which came first, the chicken or the egg?

Juliana hesitated at the study door, taking a deep breath to prepare her for the fray. With both hands full, she had to kick the door instead of knocking on it. Blake swept it open, smiling in rueful relief at her.

'Thank the lord,' he whispered.

Juliana peered over his shoulder to where Barbara was slumped in one of the deep armchairs, her face buried in her hands. By the shaking of her body she was still weeping, though quietly. Despite her strong dislike for Blake's sister, Juliana was moved to some sympathy. Not much. But some.

'Why don't you make yourself scarce?' she suggested to her husband. 'I'll call out if I need you.'

'You have no idea how grateful I am that you're doing this. You're a grand girl.'

'Don't thank me till later. I might just murder Barbara if she turns on me the way she used to.'

'I think you've finally turned the tables on *her*, Juliana.'

'We'll see, Blake. We'll see...'

Juliana allowed her husband to escape while she moved into the room with as much enthusiasm as a man going to the gallows. Barbara, she knew from experience, was not given to accepting gestures of kindness with a good grace. Blake's sister saw kindness as weakness. Juliana scooped in a breath and braced herself.

'Some coffee, Barbara?' she offered as she put the tray down on the sleekly lined grey desk.

Barbara muttered something unintelligible.

Juliana poured the coffee anyway, dropped in two cubes of sugar, stirred it thoroughly then presented it under Barbara's nose as a *fait accompli*. She waved it away with dismissive impatience.

'Blake said you were to have coffee, Barbara. So damned well take this and drink it!'

And so much for my sympathy, Juliana berated herself.

Barbara grudgingly mopped up her tears with what looked like a man's handkerchief, took the cup and saucer and started to drink, hiccuping after every mouthful.

Despite the ravages of the tears she was looking pretty good, her diet-slim body encased in a black silk dress that must have cost a king's ransom, es-pecially with the matching coat that was draped over the back of the chair. Her hair, Juliana noted, was a more flattering shade of blonde than the last time she'd seen her, and her skin was clearly the skin of a woman who'd always had the best of facials. Barbara, at twenty-eight, was no raving beauty. But she was a classy-looking woman. No doubt about that.

'Feel like telling me what's wrong?' Juliana suggested once Blake's sister had finished the first cup and had started on the second.

'No,' Barbara pouted.

It was reminiscent of many pouts Juliana had been on the receiving-end of before. A bitter resentment welled up inside her. What in God's name was she doing, taking pity on this woman, trying to help her?

'Fair enough,' she said brusquely, standing up from where she'd been balancing on the arm-rest of a nearby chair and heading for the door. No way was she going to beg or cajole Blake's spoilt brat of a sister into womanly confidences. No way was she even going to stay around and watch her sulking.

'Where…where are you going?' Barbara wailed.

Juliana stopped, gritted her teeth, then turned slowly around. 'Upstairs to my room. It's been a long day and I'd like to change.'

'But Blake said…I know he asked you to…to…'

'To what? Listen to your problems? Give you advice? Let's be honest, Barbara—you don't want my advice. You can't stand me any more than I can stand you. This was a hopeless idea of Blake's from the start. Tell *him* your problems. I can't deal with them, or you.'

'Please don't go,' she cried out with such desperation that Juliana hesitated. 'Blake won't understand and I…I don't know what to do. Henry's cut off all my credit cards. He…he says he doesn't care where I go or what I do as long as he doesn't have to pay for it.'

'And why is he acting like this? Don't go telling me he doesn't love you, Barbara. The man loves you to distraction.'

'Because he's a jealous old fool!' Barbara burst out. 'He thinks I'm having affairs behind his back.'

'And are you?'

Barbara looked uncomfortable for once in her life. 'Not really affairs…'

'But there have been other men.'

'Well, of course there've been other men! Do you honestly think I could go my whole life only sleeping with that old coot?'

Juliana sighed. 'So you *did* only marry Henry for his money.'

'Don't you come the high horse with me, Juliana. You're not so lily-white yourself. If ever there was a girl who's always had her eye on the main chance then it's you!' She wiped her nose again and gave Juliana one of those supercilious, scoffing looks she specialised in. 'You weren't exactly in love with Blake when you married him, were you? Good God, you were engaged to another man a couple of weeks beforehand! So don't you start looking down your nose at my marriage, madam. You married my brother for his money and don't think everyone doesn't know it!'

Juliana sucked in a hurt breath for a second till she decided not to let this woman do what she had always done: make her feel rotten. *She* knew she hadn't married Blake for his money, and that was all that mattered. Having re-gathered her composure, she eyed Blake's sister with a mixture of contempt and pity. The woman really was a pathetic creature.

'Don't presume to judge my marriage, Barbara,' she said with as much forbearance as she could muster. 'Or the reasons behind it. Blake and I are a very special case.'

'Oh, I don't doubt that! You and he were always as thick as thieves, even when you were kids. And so secretive! All those afternoons you used to spend in his room,' she sneered. 'I mean, girls like you start young, don't they?'

Now Juliana had heard enough. There was a limit to everything. 'Get out,' she said quite calmly.

'W-what?'

'You heard me. Get out. Right now.' Striding over, she swept the coat up from the back of the chair and threw it at the open-mouthed woman.

Barbara got unsteadily to her feet. 'You have no r-right to do this. Blake…Blake said I could stay till I s-sorted myself out.'

'He will retract that once I've told him what you just said. Now *move*!'

'I will not!' she resisted stubbornly. 'I have a right to stay here if I want to. This is my *home*.'

'You left this home when you married,' Juliana pointed out icily. '*I* am mistress of this house now.'

Barbara's upper lip curled in open contempt. 'Too true, you little slut. That's all you are. All you'll ever be to my brother. His mistress! Oh, you might have a marriage certificate, but he never wanted you as his wife! All you are is a legitimised whore! Blake will never want any woman other than sexually. Darling Mummy screwed him up good and proper. And what she didn't screw up, darling Daddy did!'

Her laughter was quite lewd. 'Speaking of screwing, I'll bet you never guessed who was one of the many *ladies* Daddy was having on the side, did you? Oh, I see it's dawning on you. Yes, your own darling mother. Our own sweetly caring cook, Lily! Don't look so shocked, Juliana, dear. You couldn't have been ignorant of your mother's appetite for sex. Like mother, like daughter, eh, what? *You* certainly must be good at it for Blake to marry you. He always told me he'd only ever marry for money. That's why he dumped poor old Virginia as soon as he found out she was flat chat. Yet he married you!'

She smiled an ugly smile as she slipped into her coat. 'I guess some habits die hard. Maybe he decided to install a nice regular bedmate for him to have between trips overseas. Yes, that must be it. He has his little black book full of international good-time girls to cater for him while he's away and good old reliable Juliana to fix him up at home, the way she always did.'

Juliana grimaced as she gulped down the rising nausea in her throat. Her head began to whirl.

It wasn't true. Mum couldn't have been sleeping with Matthew Preston. She would have known it if she were!

But, even as she denied it to herself, Juliana remembered the cigar smoke she used to smell when she came home from school. Matthew Preston had smoked cigars.

As for Barbara's accusation about Blake and other women overseas…

Juliana swallowed again, then lifted her chin proudly. 'I don't believe a word you've just said, Barbara. You're a jealous, vindictive bitch. You've always been a jealous, vindictive bitch. In your hate for me you don't even care if you ruin your own brother's happiness. For we *are* happy. I know that won't go down too well with you, since you've made such a mess of your own life. Not that I give a damn about that! Blake always told me people got their comeuppance. I didn't believe him before. Now I do. You've made your bed, Barbara. Go home and lie in it. Meanwhile, I'm quite happy to lie in mine, with Blake by my side. He cares about me. Whether you believe that or not is immaterial. *I* do. And he does not sleep around!'

Barbara laughed. 'Really! Well, why don't you check out the top drawer on the left-hand bedside chest in his room? That's where he keeps his little black book. You'll find all the women in it plus their phone numbers. I dare you to have a look tonight before you curl up in your cosy little bed. Maybe you won't be so smug then. Maybe you'll realise exactly what you are to Blake. Why, you're no more to him than your mother was to my f—'

Juliana slapped Barbara's face so hard that the sound reverberated in the room. Or was that Barbara's scream?

She would have slapped her again if Blake hadn't raced into the room.

'What in God's name is going on in here?' he demanded to know.

'Barbara is just leaving,' Juliana said with stunning outward calm. 'Aren't you?'

Barbara was staring at her, frightened perhaps by the look in her sister-in-law's eyes.

'And she won't be coming back,' Juliana finished.

Blake looked first at his pale-faced wife, then at his defiant sister. For a long moment the air tingled with electric tension. Which way would his loyalty go?

Finally, he turned to Barbara with a hardening expression. 'I don't know what you've just said to Juliana, but if it's what I think it is I'm going to strangle you with my bare hands.'

For the first time, Barbara looked worried, then she became aggressively defensive. 'What *I* said to *her*? You should have heard what *she* said to *me*! Called me a bitch, told me I had made my bed and now I had to lie in it. She's cruel and horrible, Blake. I don't know why you married her. You didn't *have* to marry her to get what you wanted, you know. She would have been as easy as her...'

She gasped as she realised she'd really put her foot in her mouth.

'You have five seconds to get out of here,' Blake said in a low, steady voice that was infinitely terrifying. 'Out! Don't walk. Run! As fast as you can or I won't be responsible for what happens to you.'

Panic-stricken now, Barbara glanced from one to the other, then, with a sob, ran from the room. They heard her high heels clack hurriedly across the marble foyer, heard the front door bang.

'Juliana,' Blake said thickly, and gathered her into his arms.

She went, collapsing, unable to think of anything but what he'd just confirmed with his action. Her mother *had* been his father's lover, had perhaps contributed to his mother's suicide. It was all so appalling, so…shattering.

'I…I never knew,' she sobbed. 'I never knew…'

'Hush, my darling. Hush. It's all in the past and quite inconsequential now. There's nothing to feel too terrible about.'

Juliana struggled out of his arms, tears streaming down her face. 'Nothing too terrible? Good God, how can you say that? My own mother was responsible for your mother's death!'

'No…' Blake shook his head. 'She never knew about Father and Lily. I swear to you. They hid it very well. I only found out quite by accident when I came home unexpectedly from university one night and saw Dad slipping down the back stairs from your flat. He only had trousers on. It didn't take much to put two and two together. I knew Dad had been having affairs for years.'

Juliana stared at him. 'You're talking about the night of my graduation, aren't you?'

Blake sighed. 'Yes.'

'Oh, God...' She pressed her fingers against her throbbing temples. 'How you must have despised him. And my mother!'

'I never despised Lily, Juliana. She was the nicest woman I ever knew, but she was also lonely and vulnerable. My father was a handsome, charming, sophisticated man. She didn't stand a chance against him. As for my father...I didn't despise him either. I knew what he was, knew he had this weakness for warm, beautiful, giving women like your mother. Sure, I was disillusioned for a while. What son doesn't want his father to be a paragon of perfection? And the young do judge harshly. But eventually I understood why he craved escape from my mother's relentless jealousy and possessiveness. Women like that make men want to run, and run and run. They kill all that's good in a relationship. They make loving anyone a living hell!'

'Which is why you've never loved anyone,' Juliana said, and looked away. 'Nor wanted them to love you.'

'I certainly don't want that kind of love. But I do want *you*, Juliana. I have ever since you were thirteen.'

Her eyes snapped back, rounding with shock.

His own expression was self-mocking. 'Remember that day by the pool when you felt my muscles?'

She nodded, her mouth dry.

'I wanted to grab you then, kiss you, force you. I was a virgin myself, would you believe it, but it was your virginity on the line that day, Juliana. It took every ounce of my control to dive into that pool and swim away from you.'

'I...I had no idea...'

'Do you think I didn't realise that? You were still a child, despite your rapidly growing body. But I was nineteen, and a nineteen-year-old boy's desires are very strong. Still, I soon found a remedy,' he finished almost bitterly.

Juliana was silent for a few seconds.

'I...I was very jealous of all those girls,' she said softly.

Blake smiled. 'Were you? I'm glad.'

'Glad?'

'Glad that you suffered as much as I was suffering.'

'You weren't suffering, Blake Preston! You were having the time of your life!'

'Was I? Oh, Juliana, if only you knew...I used to watch and wait for you every time I came home from university just to catch a glimpse of you, to marvel at the way nature was turning you into such a beauty. I kept thinking to myself, Soon...soon she'll be sixteen, soon she'll be at the age of consent...'

Juliana was startled. 'You...you planned to seduce me when I turned sixteen?'

'Do you want me to deny it?'

'Well...no, I suppose not. Not if it's true.' Yet she did feel somewhat dismayed at the thought.

'Good lord, Juliana, I was a spoilt, sex-crazed rich

kid who thought he could have any girl he wanted. Believe me when I say I had never been knocked back. Yet the only girl I really wanted was you, probably because you were forbidden; a challenge. Why do you think I came home early from university that night? I couldn't wait another day to see you. I had no idea that was the night of your graduation ball. I thought, it being a Wednesday, you'd be home. Then there was my father, coming down from a rendezvous with your mother.'

His laugh was derisive. 'Seeing him changed everything. Oh, I still wanted you. I might even have seduced you that night if you'd let me. But you didn't, Juliana. You told me off and made me see reality, which was that we could never be happy together while my father was having an affair with your mother. It was an impossible situation. As much as I tried telling myself that I could still have you if I wanted you, I couldn't bear to see the look in Lily's eyes when and if she found out both she and her daughter had been ill-used by Preston men. I also thought it was only a matter of time before *you* found out about them. But you never did.'

'No, I never did,' she murmured, still astounded by all that Blake had told her. She had no idea she'd been the object of such a long sexual obsession. He'd certainly hidden it very well. There again, she'd hidden her own love for just as long, even from herself.

'Barbara only knew because I told her one night in a drunken binge shortly after Dad's death.'

'I'm surprised she didn't tell me sooner,' Juliana said with a catch in her voice.

'I warned her not to.' Blake gathered her still shaken self back into his arms, laying her head on his shoulder. 'I never dreamt she would come out with it at this late stage. I'm sorry, Juliana. I won't let her hurt you again. I promise.'

'She's always hated me.'

'No, she's always *envied* you. Your beauty; your honesty; your love of life.'

'I don't love life very much tonight.'

'You will. I'm going to make you forget Barbara, and the past. I'm going to make you forget everything, Juliana, but here and now.' And, tipping up her chin, he kissed her with such passion that she was well on the way to forgetting before they left the room.

CHAPTER TEN

JULIANA woke the next morning, once again in Blake's bed. His side was empty, the bedside clock said seven-fifteen and his shower was running.

Friday, she thought. And groaned. Friday was not her favourite day at work. The sales teams came in for their weekly meeting and she never seemed to get anything done. To tell the truth, she didn't feel like going to work at all that day. She felt tired and troubled after the happenings of the night before.

Blake had not been able to dispel all her distress over what she'd found out about her mother and his father, no matter how hard he'd tried. In fact, the more passionate he became, the more perturbed she felt underneath, about a whole lot of things, the main one being what exactly did she mean to Blake? Was Barbara right? Was she no better than a legitimised mistress?

Juliana breathed in sharply. Oh, my God, the book... The little black book. That was one thing she *had* forgotten about.

She stared at the top left-hand-side drawer, then at the bathroom door. The shower was still running strongly. Dared she look?

And what if the book was there, with a whole lot of women's names and phone numbers in it? What would that prove? It did not mean Blake was still using either the book, or the women. He might simply not have thrown the rotten darned thing away after they were married.

Her stomach twisted. The urge to know if it was there, a reality, and not another one of Barbara's malicious inventions, was compelling.

I won't look inside, Juliana vowed. I just want to know if it exists.

Her hand trembled as it reached for the knob on the drawer, but there was no turning back now. The decision had been made.

She yanked it open.

Three neat piles of various coloured handkerchiefs greeted her, behind which lay a battered copy of *The Power of One*. Peeping out from under the novel was the corner of—not a little black book—but a little dark blue one.

Juliana frowned. Was this it?

There was only one way to find out.

Holding her breath, she eased the small leather-bound note book out from under its hiding spot. As she started to flick through it, her heart began to thud. Her fingers slowed. Her eyes widened.

Each successive page revealed a stunning array of women's names and numbers, listed under the city they lived in. Jennifer in London; Simone in Paris; Carla in Italy; Maria in Greece; Ellie in Bangkok; Jasmine in Hong Kong; Midori in Tokyo; Cindy in New York.

And that was only a sample.

The list was staggering. There were even some interstate numbers. Girls in Sydney and Brisbane and Canberra and Adelaide and Perth.

The sudden snapping off of the shower sent Juliana into a panic. Shoving the book back, she banged the drawer shut and dived back under the sheets. With some difficulty she resisted the silly urge to pretend she was still asleep when Blake came back into the room, a towel slung low around his hips.

'You still in bed?' He smiled wryly and walked across the room to fling open his wardrobe, well aware, Juliana thought despairingly, of how incredibly sexy he looked like that. His daily twenty laps in the pool, plus all his other sporting activities kept his broad-shouldered, slim-hipped frame in top condition. The skiing in winter, the tennis in summer, not to mention the odd hit of squash and the occasional game of golf, all kept the fat away and those gold-skinned muscles well-toned and rippling.

'You're going to be late for work if you don't get up,' he remarked as he dropped the towel and casually drew on brief black underpants.

'I...I think I'll take a sickie.'

This brought a sharp glance over his shoulder. 'That's not like you. Aren't you feeling well this morning? Your period's not due today, is it?'

'You know damned well it isn't,' she snapped before she could stop herself.

Blake frowned at her for a moment, then with a casual shrug turned back and kept on dressing.

Juliana watched him with a gradual sickening in her

stomach. He was so beautiful, yet perhaps so frighteningly amoral. His dark suspicions over *her* having an affair probably reflected the fact that he was having them himself, right, left and centre. Men were renowned for their double set of standards where sex was concerned. And it wasn't as though Blake's father had set him a good example…

Juliana cringed inside again to think of what had been going on under her nose all those years. Not that she blamed her mother—Blake was right about that. A woman of her nature and susceptibility to men wouldn't have stood a chance against a man like Matthew Preston. Any woman would have found him hard to resist. Lily would have been putty in his hands.

Just as I am putty in Blake's hands, Juliana thought with a growing sense of despair. He hasn't fallen in love with me. He only *wants* me. I've been fooling myself where that's concerned. Oh, maybe he almost meant it when he said there would never be another woman for him. The women in those books probably weren't *women* to him. They were merely bodies. There were too many of them to be anything else.

Weren't?

Who said they were in the past tense? Juliana mocked herself. They could be well and truly present, *and* future.

Still, the lingering hope that Blake no longer used that little book and would not have any need to use it in future revived her naturally optimistic nature. She could cope with Blake's not loving her if he didn't cheat on her. And really, she had no evidence of any actual cheating. The book's existence proved nothing. Barbara's knowledge of it actually proved that Blake had had that book for years!

'Do you want me to ring your office for you?' he offered as he tucked a white shirt into his pin-striped navy trousers.

Suddenly the prospect of moping around the house all day, worrying about everything, was too awful to contemplate. What could she achieve by it, except get herself into more of a mental and emotional muddle?

'No, thanks,' she told him. 'No need. I've decided to go in after all. I'll just have to be a little late.'

'I'll say. You usually take ages getting ready. Well, I'm off downstairs for breakfast. See you tonight.' He came over and pecked her on the forehead. 'Don't forget, we've got that dinner-party at Jack's tonight.'

Juliana pulled a face. 'I had forgotten. Oh, well... It won't be too bad, I suppose. Jack's good fun, and I do want to thank him personally for those tickets to *Phantom*.'

Blake patted her cheek. 'That's my girl.'

Juliana's heart sank as she watched her husband stride confidently from the room, putting on his suit jacket on the way. He was already in his business mode, his bed and its occupant quite forgotten.

There would be no inner turmoil while *he* sat at his desk that day, no more worries over his wife's loyalty. He had her now in the palm of his hand. And how he knew it! She would be ready and waiting for him when he came home tonight, both for the dinner-party and any other party he might want afterwards.

Juliana swallowed at this thought. Blake had certainly turned her heightened sexuality to his advantage. He seemed to be enjoying the power he now had over her in bed to have her do whatever he desired, to reduce her to a wildly willing partner who didn't know the words 'no' or 'stop' or 'don't'. Not that she could blame him, she supposed. What man didn't want a woman to be his sexual slave? And what woman didn't want her man to be as skilled and imaginative as Blake was? The situation was a double-edged sword all right.

With a sigh Juliana climbed from the bed, gathered her clothes up from where they were scattered over the floor and made her way slowly back to her room. She wished she could be really happy about the way things were going in her marriage; wished she could dismiss all thought of that infernal notebook. But she knew its existence would be a constant thorn in her side. She also knew that the next time Blake went away on business she would be sorely tempted to see if he had left it behind or taken it with him.

He left it behind, and she was ecstatic.

The occasion was the last week in November. And, while Blake was only away three short days in Hong Kong, the days leading up to his trip had been the wrong time of the month for Juliana, and she figured if Blake was ever going to be suspect it might be after he'd been deprived of sex for a while.

Juliana hadn't dragged up the courage to actually look in the drawer till the very evening Blake was due back. She felt so elated at finding that book still in its hidey-hole that she impulsively decided to go and meet him at the airport, despite there being barely enough time for her to make it by the time Blake's plane touched down shortly after nine o'clock.

Some impulses, she realised after she saw Stewart Margin's reaction to her last-minute appearance, were not such a good idea. Blake's secretary was sitting in the waiting lounge next to Gate Three, his nose buried in a newspaper, when she stepped from the moving walkway and hurried over.

'Hello, Stewart,' she said, quite happily at that stage.

His eyes snapped up, his face showing instant alarm. 'Mrs Preston!' He shut the newspaper noisily and scrambled to his feet. 'What…what are *you* doing here?'

'Just thought I'd come along and meet my husband.'

'Does—er—Mr Preston know you're meeting him?'

'No. Why? Is he late again?'

'No. His plane's already landed. It's just that…well—um—' He shrugged uncomfortably, looking as though he wished he were anywhere else but here.

Juliana started wishing the same. She shouldn't have come. It had been a stupid thing to do. Naïve and stupid.

Her earlier elation died. How could she have believed Blake would be pleased she was here, waiting for him like an adoring little wife? Their relationship might have changed, but not *that* much. Just because they now slept together in his bed every night, all night, it did not mean he would want her fawning all over him in public.

Stewart's muttering something under his breath added another dimension to Juliana's dismay. Dear heaven, surely Blake wouldn't start thinking things, because she was here with Stewart, would he?

Though not having openly continued with his crazy accusation about her having had an affair the last time he'd been away, Blake *had* become more possessive—even watchful—over her. When Jack had mildly flirted with her the night of his and Gloria's dinner-party, Blake had glared at his host with a withering coldness.

On one other occasion he'd questioned her rather sharply when she'd been very late home from work. Half-flattered, half-frustrated, Juliana had impatiently explained that she'd left the office on time, but had been caught in a traffic jam. Blake's considered and very chilly silence for several minutes afterwards had given her the disquieting feeling that he hadn't believed her.

A premonition of impending doom swept through her.

She might have turned and fled if passengers hadn't started filing from the flight tunnel into the lounge where she and Stewart were standing. Blake was the third person along, his blue eyes narrowing when he saw them both together.

Juliana gulped, plastered a bright smile on her face

and determined not to let her inner disquiet show. After all, she *was* innocent.

'What are you doing here, Juliana?' were Blake's first words. His tone was measured. Not exactly accusing, but definitely not happy.

'I couldn't wait to see you,' she said, truthfully enough. And, stepping forward, she held him by the shoulders while she kissed him on the cheek. His body felt stiff beneath her hands, his skin coldly unwelcome.

She drew back, her smile strained now.

'How nice,' was his flat reply. 'How did you get here? You always said you'd never drive at night in the city.'

'I caught a taxi.'

'You should have asked Stewart to drive you. After all, you did know he would be meeting me, didn't you?'

Juliana could feel her discomfort developing into a fully fledged fluster. 'Well, yes, I did, but I—er—it was a last-minute decision to come…'

'Oh?' His smile was blackly sardonic. 'Was it quicker to come here than go home?'

Stewart, Juliana knew, lived in the northern suburbs of Melbourne, a long way from their bayside home.

An angry exasperation cooled her embarrassing blush. She straightened her shoulders and gave Blake a reproachful look. 'No,' was all she said, determined not to be verbally bullied like this. Hopefully Blake's nasty innuendoes were going over poor Stewart's head, though from the look of the young man's obvious agitation she didn't think so.

Truly, Blake was being unforgivably horrible. Yet there she'd been, less than half an hour ago, dying for him to go home. Now she felt absolutely wretched.

Blake at last acknowledged his secretary's presence. 'Hello, Stewart. Everything all right here while I was away?'

'A few small problems, Mr Preston. Nothing I couldn't handle.'

'Where are we parked?'

'The usual spot.'

'Fine. Let's go, then. Sorry, Juliana, but Stewart and I will be talking shop during the drive home. I hope you don't mind sitting in the back on your own, but, let's face it, neither of us had any idea you'd be here, did we, Stewart?'

'We certainly didn't,' the secretary agreed quite forcefully.

'I don't mind,' she said, as civilly as her fury would allow. Never again, she vowed. Never again!

It began to drizzle on the way home, the temperature dropping as well. No one, other than Melbournians, would have dreamt summer was only two days away. Dressed only in lightweight forest-green casual trousers and a cream silk blouse, Juliana hugged herself in the back seat of the company Ford, wishing Stewart would turn on the heater. He didn't, and she stubbornly refused to ask.

She glared, first at the back of Blake's head, then out at the rain-spattered pavements, her nerves stretched to breaking-point by the time Stewart dropped them off at the house. She wasn't sure which of them was going to snap first, but it was obvious, by the tension between them as they went inside, that a fight was brewing.

In a way, Juliana would have appreciated the chance to clear the air, but Blake, it seemed, was content to let silence be his weapon. After delivering his luggage to Mrs Dawson for her to do his washing, he strode into the living-room to pour himself his usual night-cap. Juliana trailed after him, strung up and irritated. She wandered around the room while Blake downed a very stiff drink, then poured himself another. Not a word had passed between them. Suddenly, it was too much for her and she whirled on him.

'Don't you ever do that to me again!' she burst out.

'Do what?' he returned blandly.

'You know what, Blake. Don't play the innocent with me.'

His laughter was bitter. 'I thought that was my line.'

'See? You're doing it again. Making nasty innuen-does.'

'Is that what I'm doing?' He quaffed back half the second whisky then topped up the glass.

'You know that's what you're doing. And it's so unfair. I have never been unfaithful to you. Not the last time you were away, nor this time!'

'Is that so?'

'Yes, that's so!'

'In that case you won't mind coming upstairs with me now, will you?' He turned and stared at her over the rim of his glass while he drank. His gaze was hard and cold, yet appallingly sexual. Juliana felt her skin begin to crawl with a ghastly excitement. 'I feel like making love to my wife.'

He placed the empty glass on to the coffee-table with a clunk, then began to walk towards the door. Checking mid-stride halfway across the room, he turned to eye her still standing there. 'Aren't you coming, darling?' he asked in a softly mocking tone. 'A faithful wife who is so anxious for her husband to come home that she meets him breathlessly at the airport must surely be in need of a little loving.'

He held out his hand to her.

She stared at it for a long moment, then slowly lifted her eyes to his.

'Yes, Blake,' she said, her heart breaking. 'I am. But that's not what you're offering, is it? What *you're* offering I can get in *any* man's bedroom.'

She could see that she had stunned him with her counter-attack. Stunned and infuriated him.

'I don't doubt it. You've become quite the little sensualist lately, haven't you?'

'And that bothers you?'

For a second, his nostrils flared, his eyes glittering angrily. But he quickly gathered himself. 'Why should it? Do you think I was *happy* with our previous sex-life? Good God!'

Juliana looked away from his scathing contempt. '*I* was,' she said brokenly.

He scoffed his disbelief.

'At the time,' she added, her gaze returning to his.

'And what happened to change all that, if you don't mind my asking for the umpteenth time?'

She simply stared at him, unable to think of a reason other than the truth. And she couldn't tell him that.

He started walking slowly towards her. 'Cat got your tongue, Juliana? Shall I fill in the blanks for you?'

He stopped right in front of her, his face mocking. 'I know exactly what happened,' he said in a low, dark voice. 'You met some bastard, some wicked, clever bastard who took no notice of your ice-princess routine, who took no notice of your prudish little ways, who simply *took*!'

His hands were busy on her blouse as he spoke, unflicking the buttons, parting the material so that he could easily unsnap the front fastening of her bra. His eyes darkened as they swept over the rosy tips, already hard with arousal.

'You found out you liked it that way, didn't you? Nothing too gentle or sweet for this new Juliana...' And his hands started putting his words into actions.

She bit her bottom lip to stop any sound from escaping, her eyes pained when he bent to replace his hands with an even less gentle mouth. The appalling thought that Susanne could come into the room at any moment only seemed to add to her excitement. And her shame.

The shame finally escalated when his hands went to the waistband of her trousers.

'No...' she said shakily, and staggered backwards, fumbling as she did some of the buttons back up. 'No!'

she cried. 'You're wrong. About me. About everything! It…it wasn't like that. I'm not like that. Oh, I
can't stand this any more. I can't stand it, I tell you.
I have to get out of here, away from you. I…I have
to…'

She left him, standing there with his jaw dropped
open. She didn't stop to pick up her bag, just swept
her car keys from where they hung on a peg on the
kitchen wall and raced for the garage. Susanne, luckily, was nowhere in sight. No doubt she was busy
washing in the laundry or watching television in the
family room.

Pressing the remote-control panel that opened the
garage door and the front gate, Juliana leapt into her
car and fired the engine. Blake must have thought
she'd run upstairs, for he hadn't followed her into the
garage. It wasn't till she was roaring up the street that
her rear-view mirror caught him racing out on to the
wet pavement, waving his arms at her to stop.

But she did not stop, and after a couple of intersec-
tions she knew he wouldn't be able to find her. She
swept the small sedan up several side-streets and
screeched to a halt in a dark lane, only then realising
she was shaking like a leaf.

Slumping across the steering-wheel, she started to
cry. And once she started she could not stop.

Finally, she was all cried out, but the weeping, she
found, had not solved anything. It simply left her
drained of every ounce of strength, both physically
and emotionally. There was no energy left, no fight,

no will. She really could not go on. She also could not go home. Not yet. No…certainly not yet…

Like an automaton, she started up the car and drove slowly, aimlessly. Somehow she found herself going towards the city on the road she usually took to go to work, the water on her left, houses on her right. Swinging round a curve she spotted St Kilda pier in the distance stretching out into the grey waters of the bay.

Juliana remembered how, as a teenager, she'd often spent hours walking along that pier, idly watching the horizon or the student artists who used to sit there, painting the boats. It had been a type of refuge for her whenever she'd been troubled in some way. Usually, by the time she left the pier, things had seemed more in perspective. Less catastrophic. The water, it seemed, had had a soothing, calming effect.

Despite the late hour, she pulled over and parked in one of the parking bays across from the pier, making her way over via the arched walkway that spanned the busy road. Down the steps she went and along on to the pier proper.

Practically deserted, the place was, yet she didn't find it creepy. There was one man—a drunk by the look of him—leaning on one of the posts, and further along a lone fisherman was trying his luck. The rain had temporarily stopped and a faint moon was shining through the clouds. The water looked pretty black, but still peaceful.

Juliana walked over to a private spot and leant against the railing to peer blankly out to sea. The water lapped softly around the posts underneath her pier. Moored boats rocked gently in front of her. Gradually, a peace stole over her tormented soul. Yes, she'd been right to stop here.

She was standing there, reviving her spirits and the will to go on with her marriage, when something hit her on the back of the head.

CHAPTER ELEVEN

'SHE'S coming round…'

Juliana moaned again when some person—a doctor, presumably—pulled up successive eyelids and shone a bright light into each eye. She lifted an uncoordinated hand to push the pencil-thin torch away.

'Hi, there, Mrs Preston. I'm Dr Trumbole. How are you feeling?'

'My…my head aches,' she managed to get out, her voice sounding slurred.

'I'm sure it does. But don't worry. You've got a nasty bump on the back of your head and a mild concussion, but you'll live.' He smiled down at her. 'I'll get the nurse to give you something for the headache.'

'How long does my wife have to stay in hospital?' Blake asked from where he was standing at the foot of the bed, looking almost as bad as Juliana was feeling.

'We'll keep her in for another day, just as a precautionary measure.'

'So she might be able to go home tomorrow?'

'I don't see why not, provided she can go home to nothing but strict bed-rest for several days. No work of any kind. She shouldn't even walk around much. I trust that won't be a problem?'

'She won't lift a finger.'

'Good. I must go and start my rounds. The nurse will be back shortly with some tablets for you, Mrs Preston. Now don't worry if you feel sleepy soon after taking them. They'll contain a sedative as well. Goodbye, Mr Preston.'

'Goodbye, and…thank you, Doctor. You've been most kind.'

The doctor patted Blake's shoulder. 'Someone had to reassure you that your wife was not going to die.'

Once they were alone Blake came forward to sit on the side of the bed, picking up her hand between his. His sigh was weary. 'God, Juliana, don't ever do anything like that again. You had me so darned worried. When you didn't come home all night I rang the police. They told me you answered the description of an unconscious lady found on St Kilda pier. Apparently some old bum contacted them about you but he'd done a flit by the time they and the ambulance arrived. Since you had no ID on you, they had no idea who you were.'

As she stared at his grim expression, a horrible thought came to mind, making her stomach churn. 'Blake, I wasn't…I mean…whoever attacked me…he didn't…didn't…'

'No, no. He didn't touch you other than to hit you. From what the police have gathered he just took your keys and stole your car. Must have followed you from where you'd parked it. They've already located the car, stripped and burnt out in a park somewhere.'

Tears pricked at her eyes. 'My poor little car…'

'I'll buy you another car.'

A type of resentment welled up at his offer. Did he think he could solve every problem that easily? Just whip out his chequebook? Well, it would take more than money to erase the memory of last night. Much more than money...

'No, Blake. I'll buy my own car.'

He dropped her hand and stood up, exasperation on his face. 'For pity's sake, Juliana, would it hurt you to let me buy you a damned car? There's a limit to independence, you know, especially for a man's wife!'

She just looked at him, not having the energy to argue. Eventually, he let out a disgruntled sigh and sat back down. But he didn't pick up her hand again.

'All right, all right, I'm being irrational,' he admitted. 'But I feel so rotten about last night. I acted like a pig out at the airport. Then, when we got home, I treated you abominably. There was no excuse for what I did. I hope you will accept my apology, Juliana. I assure you nothing like that will ever happen again.'

He'd barely finished his stiffly formal and not really appeasing words when the ward sister bustled in with a glass of water and two huge white capsules.

'Here we are, Mrs Preston. If these don't shift your headache, nothing can. Only problem is getting them down. Drink plenty of water with them. Here...let me help you sit up.'

Juliana gulped the bombs down, lying back afterwards with a ragged groan. Her head was killing her.

'Poor dear,' the sister soothed, and straightened the bedclothes. 'You'll feel better soon. Did the doctor tell you you'd probably drift off to sleep?'

She nodded.

'Nice nurse, that,' Blake remarked after she left.

'Mmm.'

'I'll go once you get sleepy.'

'All right.'

A heavy silence descended. Juliana was in too much pain to make idle chit-chat, let alone tackle the problems that still beset their personal relationship. Blake's apology did not alter the fact that, underneath, he believed she was an adulteress. Maybe he thought he would now magnanimously push this belief to the back of his mind, but Juliana knew it would lurk there, poisoning what could have been so good between them.

How could she happily go to his bed knowing he thought she'd done all those intimate things with some other man—or men? And what of Blake, being prepared to sleep with a wife he thought was a two-timing tramp? What did that make her, if not what Barbara had accused her of being? Blake's legal whore…

Juliana's heart sank to an all-time low. She might have wept if her aching eyes and whirling head hadn't started feeling so heavy. A yawn captured her mouth. She closed her eyes.

Though almost asleep, she flinched slightly when she felt Blake's lips on her forehead.

She thought she heard a sigh. Was it hers, or his? She didn't hear him leave the room at all. By then, the sedative had done its work.

Juliana did go home the next day, despite still feeling exhausted. Though maybe it was more an emotional exhaustion than a physical one. Depression had taken its hold and she could not seem to throw it off.

Susanne, perhaps sensing that all was not well with her, fussed like an old mother hen. Nothing was too much trouble. A television and video were set up in Juliana's bedroom. Piles of books were collected from the local library. Magazines appeared in droves, donated by Susanne's sister.

Juliana was only allowed out of bed to shower or to go to the bathroom. Her own local doctor visited daily to check on her progress. Vitamins were prescribed along with tablets that looked suspiciously like tranquillisers. Juliana flushed them down the toilet. Flowers arrived in abundance from people she worked with, with a couple of the girls dropping by regularly for visits after work, bringing good cheer, chocolates, fruit and more magazines.

But, despite everything, Juliana remained depressed.

Blake, of course, was the reason. Juliana would have liked to talk to him about their relationship. Really talked in a deep and meaningful way. But he was so unapproachable in his manner and attitude that it was impossible.

Though superficially kind and considerate, he began treating her more like a distant invalid relative than a wife. She felt he did what he did through duty, not true caring, their meetings awkward and strained.

He would stop by briefly in the morning for a few moments' stiff conversation before breakfast, telephone her once during the day with a couple of brisk questions about how she was feeling, then condescend to eat his meal with her in her room at night, though he silently watched the news on the television while they ate. He also suddenly seemed to have to retire to his study every evening after dinner to work or make phone calls. There was certainly no question of his ever coming into her bed at night, not even just to hold her or be with her.

Juliana began to fear that Blake was using the situation to regress to their earlier separate-bedrooms, separate-lives status. And, while she didn't want to be used like some whore, the intimacy of sex might have broken down the emotional barriers Blake seemed to be re-erecting. But making love never came up in their meagre conversations, though admittedly the doctor might have told Blake that was out for a while. She was lucky if she got a peck goodnight, let alone a hug or a proper kiss.

It depressed Juliana further to think that if Blake couldn't actually sleep with her he didn't want to touch her at all. Was that marriage?

Well, they had never had a real marriage, she decided unhappily, and it had taken this crisis to show up the weaknesses in their relationship. Yet she had once deluded herself into thinking that their marriage was strong. How crazy could one get?

But of course that had been before she'd realised she loved Blake, before she'd started wanting so much more than her husband had been prepared to give. Well, she *had* got more, in a physical sense, but Juliana was gradually coming to the conclusion that, even if they resumed their sex-life, their marriage was still doomed to failure. It was like a time-bomb ticking away, waiting to self-destruct. Her problem now was, did she want to wait for the time-bomb to explode, or take her future into her own hands and walk away with her self-respect and pride intact?

When Saturday came and Blake still went into the office, Juliana almost despaired.

'I can't take much more of this,' she muttered to herself, and, throwing hack the covers, she drew on her old pink dressing-gown and slowly made her way downstairs.

Susanne was busily polishing the foyer floor when she looked up and saw Juliana. 'You're not supposed to be coming down here,' she scolded. 'The doctor said maybe tomorrow you could sit by the pool in the sunshine. Tomorrow is not today. And you don't even have slippers on! Oh, truly, Juliana, do you want to catch your death of cold?'

'You sound just like my mother used to,' Juliana said, a lump forming in her throat. 'She...she was the cook here, did you know that?'

The housekeeper looked up at her with real surprise. 'No...no, I didn't know that.'

Juliana traced her hand over the elegantly carved knob at the end of the balustrade, a knot in her stomach. 'I'm not really cut out to be the lady of the house, I suppose. I should have known it wouldn't work...'

'Juliana, what are you talking about? You're one of the nicest ladies I've ever worked for. Why, you're a *real* lady, not like some of those stuck-up madams who think money has given them class. All I can say is, your mother must have been a real lady too, because you're a credit to her. Don't ever let me hear you putting yourself down again, do you hear me?'

Juliana blinked her shock at the other woman's giving her a right dressing-down. But maybe that was what she needed to jolt her out of this crippling depression.

'And another thing,' the housekeeper raved on, her face flushed with emotion. 'I think that after Christmas you and Mr Preston should plan a little holiday away together. If my Fred and I had spent more time alone together we would have been a lot happier. Your Mr Preston works too hard. And so do you. There comes a time, you know, when if a couple don't have a baby it gets too late. They drift apart and everything becomes just awful.'

She stepped forward and touched Juliana compassionately on the sleeve. 'Now I know how much you love that handsome husband of yours. My heart almost breaks with the way you look at him sometimes, but there's no use thinking *you* can change his cold little ways. Mr Preston is one of those men who doesn't want to appear weak in front of a woman. But put his own flesh and blood in his arms, and he'll melt to mush. I'll bet my lotto money on it!'

Juliana stared at the other woman.

A baby...Blake had asked her to have a baby. But she hadn't been prepared to take the risk.

But loving someone was always a risk, and she prided herself on not being a coward.

Tears of gratitude filled her eyes as she looked at this stern-faced but kindly woman whom, till recently, Juliana had held at arm's length. 'You could be right. Yes, you could be right. I'll discuss a second honeymoon with Blake when he comes home. Thank you, Susanne. I feel much better now.'

But she didn't really get the chance to discuss a second honeymoon with Blake. He came into her bedroom late that afternoon with a big cardboard box in his arms, 'Hello, there,' he greeted. 'You're looking much better.'

She put her book down with a ready smile, remembering her new resolve not to give up on this marriage till she had fired every bullet she had. 'I went downstairs for a while. What have you got there?' she asked with real curiosity in her voice. Blake was the only person who hadn't brought presents to her sick-bed, maybe because everyone else had inundated her with them. Of course, it was typical of Blake not to give presents.

'A little get-well gift,' he told her.

As he carried the box across the room, whimpering sounds emanated from the holes in the sides.

'Oh, Blake! It's a puppy, isn't it?' She clapped delightedly. 'Show me, show me!'

'Patience!' he commanded, and placed the box on the bedcovers next to her, opening the lid flaps to reveal the most adorable bundle of black canine fur she'd ever seen.

'Oh, Blake!' She swept the puppy up into her arms, whereupon it immediately started madly licking her face as if to show its gratitude at finally escaping that awful prison of darkness.

'What breed is it?' she asked.

'Labrador.'

'You're cute as a button, aren't you, darling? That's what I'm going to call him—Buttons.'

'I thought he might keep you company while I'm away.'

Juliana's eyes jerked up. Blake was looking down at the puppy with no readable expression on his face. He looked, as always, incredibly handsome in a dark grey business suit. But his handsomeness no longer mattered to Juliana. It was his heart she coveted.

'You're not going away again before Christmas, are you?' she asked with a catch in her voice.

'Have to, I'm afraid. There have been some problems with a shipment of video games. When the container ship arrived last week we only had half the stock. The best and quickest way I can sort this out is to go over there personally.'

'Over where?'

'Tokyo.'

'I…I see…'

'I don't want to go, Juliana. I have to.'

'Of course you do!' She forced a bright smile to her lips. 'And you're right, Buttons will keep me company, won't you, sweetheart?'

Buttons reacted enthusiastically to her attention with some more manic licking.

'When do you have to leave?' she asked, keeping her eyes down.

'Tonight.'

'*Tonight*!' she gasped, her eyes snapping up.

'Yes. My flight leaves in a little over an hour. If I go immediately, there's still a chance I can get the rest of the stock flown over and into the stores before Christmas.'

'Are…are you packed?'

'Yes. I called Mrs Dawson from the office this afternoon.'

'She didn't say anything.'

'I asked her not to.'

'And when will you be back?'

'No later than next Thursday.'

'That long…'

'I should be finished in Tokyo within a few days but I'm going to drop off at Hong Kong on the way back.'

Juliana's stomach tightened. What had been the woman's name in Hong Kong? Jasmine, wasn't it? Jasmine… God, but that was a depressingly sensual and feminine name. No doubt Jasmine had everything else to match as well.

'So, what's the attraction in Hong Kong?' she asked a touch sharply.

'I have some business to do there as well.' He bent down to kiss her lightly on the cheek. 'I'll be as quick as I can.'

Juliana bit her tongue to hold her silence. She had no evidence that Blake was dropping off in Hong Kong to see some woman. He hadn't taken the address book last time he went overseas. Why should he this time?

Because you haven't been living as husband and wife for quite some time, came a darkly cynical voice. Not since a week before the *last* time he went overseas. Maybe he *needs* to see this woman.

'Blake!'

He was striding from the room when his name burst from her lips. Checking, he turned to frown at her obviously emotional outburst. 'Yes?' he asked. Almost warily, she thought. Or was it wearily?

She had wanted to tell him how much she would miss him, but suddenly the words would not come. 'Th-thank you for the puppy.'

His smile was definitely wry. 'My pleasure. *Au revoir*. Look after yourself, and don't go walking along deserted piers in the middle of the night.'

Within moments of his leaving, the terrible temptation to race into his room and see if that little blue book was still there gripped her in its tenacious hold and refused to let go. Juliana didn't know which would be worse—not looking and so keeping her optimistic hopes alive, or risking seeing that empty spot in the drawer.

In the end she could not stand the not knowing.

Clutching the puppy in her arms, she made her way shakily into Blake's room and opened the drawer. All the breath rushed from her body. It was there! Dear heaven, it was there!

She sank down on to the bed and buried her face into the pup's furry side, her whole body trembling with emotion. But gradually the strange feeling that something wasn't quite right started wiping the relief from her heart, replacing it with an increasing unease. Lifting puzzled eyes, she stared once again into that drawer.

And then it struck her. The book wasn't where it had been before, peeping out from under the novel. The novel was still there but the address book was sitting on top of it in full view. Someone had recently taken it out then put it back in a different spot.

Why?

There were a host of innocent explanations, but somehow Juliana wasn't comforted by any of them. Finally, she put the pup on the bed, picked the notebook up and started flicking through it again, not knowing what that would prove, but doing it anyway.

She saw the torn-out page straight away, and knew, before a closer inspection confirmed it, that it was the page which had included Jasmine from Hong Kong. Pale but oddly composed now that she knew the awful truth, she replaced the book, picked up Buttons and returned to her room.

She sat on her bed, staring dry-eyed into space.

Five days, she had to think about all this. Five days in which to make up her mind whether she could live with, and continue to love, a man who was unfaithful. Five days to find a way to survive this utter, utter hell.

CHAPTER TWELVE

JULIANA lay back on the deckchair by the pool, doing her best to keep calm. Blake would not be home for a few hours yet. If she started becoming agitated now, she would be a mess by the time he arrived.

But it was hard to stay calm on the day one was going to ask for a divorce.

She had decided not to tackle Blake about Jasmine, or any of the other women in that book. Really, they were only a symptom of the true disease that was destroying their marriage, which was that Blake no longer trusted or respected her. She could have coped without his love. She could not cope with his lack of respect.

Buttons' sudden barking had her twisting round to see what was upsetting the little devil. Already that week he had chewed up two shoes, one fluffy slipper, the leg of a chair and anything else anyone left lying around. Susanne had forbidden him to come inside till he'd learnt to behave himself.

Juliana squinted over to where the barking was coming from. But the sun shining in her eyes made it difficult for her to see into the shadows of the wide patio. She could just make out someone sliding the glass doors back and scooping up the frantic animal, someone tall and…

The light glinting on his blond hair as he broke out of the shadow sent a panicky rush of air into Juliana's lungs.

'Blake!' She scrambled to her feet, hastily drawing a see-through floral wrap over her brief red bikini. 'What are you doing home this early?'

He came forward, idly stroking the puppy while he frowned at her fluster. 'I caught an earlier flight. Is there a problem with that? Are you going out?' His narrowed gaze flicked over her scantily clad form. 'You don't look as if you're going out.'

'No, I'm not going out, but I…I…' She was floundering, for how could she say that she wanted to be more formally dressed to face him with her news?

'You what, Juliana? Have I come home at an inopportune time? Is that it?'

His sarcasm was the last straw. Her eyes carried total exasperation as they raked over him. She shook her head in a type of weary frustration. 'Yes, Blake,' she agreed grimly. 'You came home at an inopportune time. I had a plan, you see, a timetable in my mind. I was going to be so calm and reasonable about everything. Mature and, yes…as kind as I could be. Because I thought the way you were was probably not your fault. But I can see now that I would have been wasting my time. So I'll just say it out straight. I want a divorce, Blake. I can't take it any more.'

He said nothing for several seconds, his face stiffly unreadable, his hand frozen mid-air above the dog's head. Finally, he lowered the pup gently on to the cement then straightened to glare at her. 'You can't take *what* any more?'

Juliana sighed. 'Not here, Blake. Not here…' And she turned to walk back towards the house.

His hand shot out to grab her arm, twisting her back to face him. 'Who is it?' he demanded to know. 'Tell me!'

She shook her head again in utter defeat. 'Please, Blake, I don't want a scene. I just want a divorce. You promised me we would call it quits after the first year if our marriage didn't work out. Well, the year's almost up and I'm not happy with you. That's the kindest way I can put it.'

His eyes widened with a look of dawning horror, his hand dropping from her arm. 'My God, you've fallen in love, haven't you?'

Her lips parted in surprise before she realised he meant fallen in love with someone else. But by the time she recovered her composure, the damage had been done. A guilty blush had already joined her goldfish gasp.

'It's not bloody Stewart, is it?' he ground out. 'Or Hawthorne again? For pity's sake, don't tell me it's Hawthorne!'

Juliana's eyes mirrored her deep sadness. 'It's no one, Blake. You've got it all wrong, as usual.'

'No, I haven't,' he pronounced with ironic insight. 'I've got it right, at last. You had an affair with someone while I was away those three weeks, and now you've fallen in love with him.'

Juliana stared up at him in total disbelief. 'Do you

honestly think I would have been making love with you the way I have been if I was in love with someone else?'

'You *haven't* been making love to me lately! As for those other times…you wouldn't be the first woman to hide her guilt behind a burst of passionate love-making. You probably hadn't fallen in love with the bastard back then. It was probably only another grotty little affair. For God's sake, why don't you admit it? You've already asked me for the divorce. The least I deserve is the bloody truth!'

'All right, Blake. You want the truth? You can have it. Yes, I have fallen in love with someone. And yes, he is a bastard! You're so right about that. But you're wrong about the timing. I already knew before our sex-life improved that I loved him. There was no doubt in my mind at all. It was a certainty. And the reason it was a certainty was because my secret love was none other than my own husband. You, Blake! I'd fallen in love with *you*!'

All the blood had begun to drain from his face during her speech, only to have colour jerk back at the end.

'Me!' he exclaimed, clearly stunned.

'Yes, you.' Her laughter was only just this side of hysterical. 'Funny, isn't it? Most men would adore to have their wives love them as I realised I loved you, have *always* loved you.'

'You've…*always* loved me?' he rasped.

She shrugged with the sort of indifference despair brought. 'I didn't realise it till I thought you might have died in a plane crash. It's amazing how almost losing a person makes you aware of what their value is to you. I…I…' She swallowed and tried to gather what inner resources she had left, looking up at two very shocked blue eyes with a growing bitterness. 'Yes, Blake, I've always loved you. Maybe from the very first moment we met.' Now her laughter was mocking. 'Blake Preston…my hero…my prince. Only my prince doesn't *want* my love. He never has. Love and he parted company a long time ago.'

'Juliana…darling…'

'Oh, don't "darling" me, you unfeeling, unfaithful rat!' she exploded, anger a much safer emotion than maudlin sentiment.

'*Unfaithful*!'

If she'd thought he was startled before, he was totally flabbergasted now. 'Since when have I ever been unfaithful?' he demanded, black clouds quickly gathering behind those momentarily wide eyes.

'Since you went to see your precious Jasmine in Hong Kong for starters!' she countered, and knew immediately by his face that she had hit the mark.

'Did you think I didn't know about your book of names?' she scoffed. 'Well, I did! Barbara was only too happy to tell me about them. She even told me where to find them. And I looked! Oh, yes, I looked more than once. It's amazing what a woman in love will do when she's desperate. And you almost got away with it this last time. If I hadn't noticed the rotten thing had been moved, if I hadn't picked it up and saw the page missing, I wouldn't have…have…'

Her voice trailed away when she found herself staring down at a small velvet box resting in Blake's outstretched hand. He also had the most peculiar look on his face, as though he was trying not to cry.

'Jasmine and I were once lovers,' he said shakily. 'A million years ago. All those women were my lovers...a million years ago. That book hasn't left my drawer for so long that I'd almost forgotten it was there till I had cause to look up a number again, the number of a certain woman who is married now but who is also a top jeweller. I needed Jasmine's number, Juliana, because I wanted to buy you this.'

And he flicked open the box to reveal an incredibly delicate but beautiful diamond ring. 'I never bought you an engagement-ring the first time round. I was going to court you properly this time, *make* you fall in love with me, because...you see...I had discovered how much I loved *you* the night you ran away. When I saw you lying unconscious in that hospital bed I knew that if you died, if I ever lost you, I would simply stop wanting to live...'

He dragged in a deep breath, letting it out with a shudder. But then his mouth curved back into a wry smile. 'Of course I had trouble admitting any of these radical feelings. How could I possibly have done the one thing I'd vowed never to do? Especially with my beautifully cool, independently ambitious wife, who didn't love me back, and who I mistakenly thought was having an affair, or affairs! I fought my feelings all that next week but, once I accepted that they wouldn't go away, that they were *real*, I decided to do something about them. Since you were still with me, I rationalised that this other man—or men—meant nothing to you. It was only sex. Yet *our* sex was better than ever! So I decided then and there that I would make you fall in love with me if it was the last thing I did. And now…now you tell me you loved me all along!'

Tears flooded Juliana's eyes. 'Oh, Blake…is it true? You really love me?'

'Do I really love her…?' He shook his head and for a split-second she saw a flash of pain that told her he'd been through as much hell as she had. Which he must have, she conceded, thinking all that time that she was being unfaithful to him, grappling with his jealousy, but still deciding that if he could win her back he would try to forget her infidelities and go forward.

He took the ring from its bed, tossed the box away then picked up her left hand. Both their hands were trembling. He slipped the diamond on her ring finger till it rested against the plain gold band.

'With this ring,' he said, 'I thee wed. With my body, I thee worship…'

And, sweeping her hard against him, he kissed her as though he would never let her go.

And he never did.

Diana Hamilton is a true romantic and fell in love with her husband at first sight. They still live in the fairytale Tudor house where they raised their three children. Now the idyll is shared with eight rescued cats and a puppy. But despite an often chaotic lifestyle, ever since she learned to read and write Diana has had her nose in a book—either reading or writing one—and plans to go on doing just that for a very long time to come.

Look out for THE CHRISTMAS CHILD
by Diana Hamilton
in Modern Romance™, December 2000

SAVAGE OBSESSION
by
DIANA HAMILTON

CHAPTER ONE

SHE should never have married him. She'd been such a fool to even consider the possibility that it could work. Such a damned fool!

Beth's small fists beat uselessly against the broad window-ledge and a sudden hot spurt of tears blurred the view of South Park's magnificent gardens. Clamping her teeth together, she turned from the window and back into the body of her bedroom. No time to weep, no time to begin the battle to overcome the shock that left her coldly aching inside, no time to try to come to terms with what she had seen, what she had heard.

So maybe tonight's dinner party was a blessing in disguise, she informed herself drily. Acting the part of the woman Charles Savage had married—the perfect hostess to his business colleagues, people who could be useful to him—would help her to ride the pain.

But she knew that small, frigid consolation was nothing but a chimera when she met the mute misery in her reflected green eyes. How could she begin to come to terms with the knowledge that Zanna Hall, the woman who had been the obsessive love of Charles's life, was here again? Obviously at his invitation, and, what was worse, so much worse, complete with their illegitimate two-year-old son, the fruit of their passionate, ill-fated affair!

5

For a moment the shocking intensity of the pain she had kept under control since her miscarriage three months ago threatened to pull her slender frame apart, but she conquered it, denied it, before it reached the intolerable level that would leave her useless, fit for nothing.

Compressing the sweet curve of her mouth, she lifted a comb, frowning at the slight tremor of her hand, and dragged it through her straight dark hair, setting the elegant bob to rights. She would do what she always did at this time when they were entertaining. Stick rigidly to routine, that way she might be safe, come through the advancing ordeal with her dignity intact.

Dignity, or at least the show of it, was all she had. She certainly had no pride or self-respect to hold on to. She never had had, not where Charles was concerned. Couldn't have done, or she never would have agreed to marry him.

Deliberately closing her eyes to that degrading piece of self-knowledge, she walked briskly out of the room and made her way to the kitchens. Check with Mrs Penny on progress in the kitchen. Their guests would begin to arrive at any moment now. Rooms were ready. Business discussions would go on through most of the weekend. Two wives tagging along this time, needing to be entertained tomorrow while the men were incommunicado. Gentle tours of South Park's gardens always went well, especially so in this glorious June weather. Tea on the terrace, idle female chit-chat, maybe a drive down to the village in the morning to look at the Norman church, the picturesque remains of the abbey.

And never a hint of what she was going through, what she was feeling.

Entering the enormous kitchen, Beth was greeted by the scent of freshly chopped herbs and Mrs Penny, who had been cook-cum-housekeeper at South Park—apart from one brief and fateful absence three years ago—since Charles's parents had lived here, said grumpily,

'As if there isn't enough to do!' She was doing something unnecessarily vigorous with a fish kettle and her small shrewd blue eyes were snapping as she glanced sideways up at Beth. 'You do know, ducky, as how that madam is back? Walked in as large as life demanding tea to be sent to the study, milk and biscuits for the nipper. Dead spit he is, too. Shameless, I call it.'

Rigidly, Beth turned to inspect the freshly prepared vegetables put ready on the butcher's block. So Mrs Penny had picked up the unmistakable likeness between father and son. It was, after all, quite unmissable.

Trying to will the stiffness out of her neck and shoulders, she fastened her eyes on the various pans. No point in advertising her misery and humiliation. Fresh peas, courgettes, tiny potatoes and baby broad beans, all picked from South Park's walled vegetable garden early this morning, but her interest was feigned, doing nothing at all to block out Mrs Penny's relentless tirade.

'And when I went to collect the tray, not ten minutes ago, she was still there and telling me, if you please, how she'd come to stay. "I'd like you to prepare a room for me, Mrs Penny," she said—all bossy, like, ''and one for Harry, of course.'' That's the nipper. Nice little lad, he looked, and it's not his fault, is it? Can't hold that against him, poor brat. And I told her straight, I did. ''I'm afraid as how I'm much too busy, Miss Hall. It is still Miss Hall, isn't it?'' And she never contradicted, said oh, no, she'd gone and married Tom or Dick—or Harry's dad!' As if to emphasise her extreme busyness, she stamped to the sink and turned the tap on a head of lettuce. Shouting above the gush of water, she declared, 'I can't think what that man of yours is about, giving her houseroom, that I can't! She's been nothing but trouble, that I do know!'

Beth knew perfectly well why Charles was giving Zanna houseroom, but it was something she couldn't bear to think of right now so she replied repressively, with unconscious and ironical truth, 'I'm sure Mr Savage has his reasons.'

And Mrs Penny snorted irrepressively,

'Don't you ''Mr Savage'' me, ducky! Charlie-boy it's always been, since I first came to work for his folks when he was ten years old. And Charlie-boy it always will be!'

Beth shuddered. She wished she had Mrs Penny's confidence, her sense of belonging—come what may. At one time, blessed with the power of love, with the blind hope of youth, she had possessed all that. Possessed the determination to force her darling Charles into loving her, truly loving her, sure that, given time, he would forget that wild, turbulent, ill-fated passion that had been his obsessive love for Zanna Hall.

Fool.

Forcing a smile, she said as lightly as she could, 'If everything's under control, I'll go and wait for the first of our guests. It's late enough to forget about tea. Charles will offer drinks. I'll go and root him out.'

But she didn't. Of course she didn't. She had been on her way to do just that, guessing he'd be in his study because, half an hour before, as she'd been putting the final touches to the dinner table, she'd heard his car.

Nowadays, he no longer bothered to announce his arrival. Their marriage had degenerated into a distant thing, both coolly polite on the surface because anything else would have been unthinkable, but withdrawing from each other, the tide of their relationship inexorably ebbing.

Approaching the study, she'd painted the tiny, impersonal smile on her face, almost habitual now because she'd promised herself that she would never allow him to see just how much pain and distress his physical and mental movement away from her gave. For him to even guess at the passionate love she still bore him would be unproductive, would probably dismay and disgust him into retreating still further from the rocky shores of their marriage. She'd grown into the habit of biding her time, waiting, hoping, being all that he needed her to be and no more. Never anything more. Not now.

The study door had been ajar, just a little, and her hand had been upraised to push against the smooth wood when that husky, horribly remembered voice had stopped her in her tracks. She would never forget Zanna's siren tones. Not even if she lived to be a hun-

dred. And at first it hadn't made sense; nightmares
rarely did, did they? Because Zanna had broken away
three years ago, or nearly, leaving Charles devastated,
living in brooding isolation at South Park, a meaty subject for gossiping village tongues. So she couldn't have
returned, could she? She couldn't be saying,

'I had to come to you again, darling. That ill-
begotten marriage is finished now. Over. And I won't
pretend I'm not glad—I can't be that much of a hyp-
ocrite. Besides, our son needs to get to know his father,
you won't deny that. As a single parent I've given
Harry all the love in the world, but he still needs his
father.'

Instinctively, Beth's hand had eased the door open,
just a little, the reflection of puzzled disbelief in her
deep green eyes changing to shock as they took in the
picture that would be printed on her retinas for all time.

Zanna, as flamboyantly lovely as ever, her red-gold
hair curling bewitchingly around her heart-stopping
features, Charles, hovering above her as she lounged
back in one of the leather-covered armchairs, the stern,
hard features softened to an expression that Beth hadn't
seen for months. Was never likely to see again outside
of tormenting dreams. And the child.

Around two years old. Playing on the floor with a
paperweight in his chubby little hands, banging the
smooth glass temporary toy gleefully down on the
thick carpet, oblivious to the vibrations that were making the air above his innocent head hum. Oblivious of
his true parentage, for now. Of the remarkable family
resemblance, the raven hue of that silky hair, the deep,
deep grey of the black-fringed eyes, the cast of the

features that would, in time, be an almost mirror-image of the man whose eyes were now fastened on him with all too naked longing.

Slipping away, unseen and unheard, she had made it to her bathroom in time to part with her lunch and had then forced herself to confront the unbelievable, the shock and pain of knowing that Zanna was back, complete with the son Charles had longed for.

Following the break-up of his tempestuous relationship with Zanna, Charles had married her, Beth, not exactly on the rebound but with a cool calculation that had almost taken her breath away.

He had wanted a wife, a child to inherit—several children, in point of fact. And she, Beth, was suitable, had proved herself capable, in Mrs Penny's absence, of running South Park like clockwork and, as an added bonus, acting as his hostess when he entertained business contacts, stepping into the shoes Zanna had vacated.

His proposal had hit her like a bomb, and she had been suffering from shell-shock when she'd accepted, must have been to have ignored the well-meaning advice of her parents and Allie, her best friend and business partner. But still sufficiently in control of her wits to keep him in ignorance of the way she felt about him.

A man of his urbane sophistication, possessing the drive and ambition that had wrested the family-owned communications business out of the undistinguished dust of failure and planted it firmly back on its feet, would have thought her a fool of the first water if she'd leapt into his arms and confessed that she'd loved him from afar ever since she'd been a starry-eyed teenager! That most of the village girls had yearned over the darkly brooding good looks of Charles Savage of South Park, the unattainable, the impossibly sexy Charles. That those other girls had grown out of the state of infatuation, had found real, attainable men-friends, but that she, Beth Garner, had done no such thing, had loved him always, could see no end to that love.

The arrival of the first of the weekend guests had Beth thrusting her misery to the back of her mind, and, as if by telepathy, Charles was there, by her side, no hint in his steely gunfighter's eyes of the emotion he must have felt when he met his son for the very first time.

Or had it been for the first time? she wondered tormentedly as he smiled at her over the head of one of the visiting wives, the slight curve of his mouth doing nothing to bring warmth to those narrow, steely grey eyes, but doing everything to bring that bitter-sweet stabbing pain to the pit of her stomach.

This overriding sexual awareness of him was something she was going to have to school out of existence, she recognised with a hopeless anguish that was down to the fact that she had been trying to accomplish just that ever since he had made it plain that he was no longer interested in the physical side of their marriage.

She saw him suddenly frown, those smokily unreadable eyes probing hers, and she said quickly, far too brightly, 'Why don't I show you to your room, Mavis? I just know Charles is about to offer Donald a drink, and—'

'I rather think they'd both appreciate the chance to freshen up,' Charles cut in smoothly, lifting the two pieces of expensive luggage and ushering his guests towards the stairs, tossing back over his shoulder, 'The others should be here at any moment, they're arriving together. Wait, would you, darling?'

No, thanks, Beth thought sickly as his tall, leanly supple body disappeared round the bend in the staircase. He probably wanted to break the news of the arrival of the principle guests—his former lover and their son—in private. It wouldn't be the type of information he would want to impart in front of a houseful of business associates!

Well, that was his problem. She mounted the stairs quickly, intent on gaining the privacy of her own room. As far as Charles was aware, she didn't know Zanna and Harry were here. And, stupidly, she had the craziest feeling that until he actually spoke of their presence she didn't really have to face up to it.

It was something too awful to be faced, she thought jaggedly as she neared the head of the stairs, trying to ignore the knowledge that Charles must have contacted Zanna, told her that his ill-considered marriage to little Beth Garner had irretrievably broken down. Was over. Finished. The conversation she had overheard had made that much clear.

Had he pleaded with his former lover? Confessed he hadn't been able to get her out of his system?

Unwanted questions prodded at her mind, like a tongue probing an aching tooth, increasing the pain, her head awash with unwelcome conjectures as she took the corridor that led away from the guest wing and down to her own room.

And what had been Zanna's reaction? Easy. No problem in working that one out. She'd probably regretted the break-up as much as he had, her pride keeping her away until it had been too late to do anything about it because by the time she had discovered she was expecting his child he had married his temporary housekeeper!

And having disappeared from the scene she'd kept well away from it. No real problem there, either. The pampered only child of wealthy parents, she and her baby would have been well taken care of. She had probably spent the last two and a half years with them at their villa in the south of France where her parents had repaired to spend their early retirement.

But she was back on the scene now, with a vengeance, and no, Charles couldn't have known of Harry's existence until he'd contacted her, explaining that as far as he was concerned his marriage was over. Nothing on earth would have kept his son from him, had he known. And nothing on earth would keep him from him now. Just as nothing would keep him apart from the only woman he had ever loved.

She was shaking all over as she reached her room and, childlike, she bunched her hands into fists and knuckled them to her mouth, biting down on the whitened skin, welcoming the distraction of physical pain. Somehow, somehow, she had to keep a hold on herself, ride out the storm until Sunday afternoon when the weekend guests would leave. And just behind her Charles reminded coldly,

'I asked you to remain downstairs.'

He hadn't set foot inside this room since her miscarriage three months ago, had kept severely to the room they had once shared, the master bedroom, and his intrusion here, now, under these circumstances, was a violation of her space, her privacy, and the only way to combat an incipient breakdown was to keep her head, her dignity, to somehow fight fire with fire.

So she shrugged, just a little, maintaining a veneer of cool collectedness at enormous cost to her mental equilibrium.

'I'm quite sure you're perfectly able to greet your guests and settle them in.' Her voice, in her own ears, sounded strangely brittle. 'It's time I showered and changed.'

She forced herself to turn and face him then, her head rigidly high, her tongue feeling dry, too large for her mouth, as she dragged the words out, 'If I'm to make myself presentable, dispense drinks and small talk to your guests, and help Mrs Penny with the final touches to dinner—she can't make a successful mayonnaise no matter how hard she tries, bless her—then I don't have time to hang around waiting for latecomers. We don't want anything to upset the routine and ruin the weekend, do we?'

It was the longest speech she'd made to him in ages, and there was a warning there, if he cared to look for it. She would go to pieces when he told her he wanted a divorce, that he wanted to marry Zanna, the only woman he was capable of loving, to marry her and claim his son. And she would rather not have that hap-

pen until the weekend was over, their guests safely out
of the house.

Just for a moment she thought she saw a flash of
anger deep in the unrevealing smoke-grey eyes, but
then it was gone, or perhaps it had never been, she
decided as his habitually bland expression gazed
straight back at her.

Her eyes dropped, the contact was too painful, and
when she found herself hungrily watching his long,
very beautifully sculpted mouth she dragged in a raspingly painful breath and turned away, walking over
towards the generous hanging cupboard, making a
show of sorting through the garments for something to
wear.

The best way to rid herself of his presence was to
begin to undress, ready for her shower, she informed
herself cynically. He hadn't wanted to look at her, to
touch her, in months. She hadn't known why, not until
now.

Almost defiantly, she kicked off her shoes, lifting
her hands to the buttons of her light cotton blouse, but
her desperate ploy didn't work because he said tonelessly, 'Zanna Hall is here,' and Beth froze, her back
to him, her heart pounding because this was crunch
time. He was going to tell her something she didn't
think she was strong enough to hear, and he went on
levelly, his deep rough-velvet voice under strict control, 'With her son. Harry is two years old. They will
be staying for a few days.'

'Oh, really.' If she sounded uninterested she
couldn't help it. To pretend indifference was the only
way she would be able to handle this.

In retrospect, she was thankful that he had never told her he loved her, said those words she would have given anything in the world to hear, the words that would have opened the dam of her own deep love for him, had her confessing the abiding strength of her passion. Had she been fool enough, unguarded enough, to do so then this weekend would have been even more humiliating, more degrading—if that were possible.

'Aren't you going to ask why?'

He had moved. She could tell by his voice that he was standing much closer now and she shivered, biting out, 'No,' tightly, very quickly, because she already knew why Zanna was here, with Charles's son; she didn't need him to spell it out.

Blindly, she dragged the first garment to come to hand out of the cupboard, still with her back to him because she couldn't bear to see the final rejection in his magnificent eyes when he told her that he no longer wanted her as his wife.

He swore then, softly, almost inaudibly, and, clutching the dress close to her chest like a piece of armour, she heard him say, the first intimation of strain in his voice, 'For some reason best known to herself, Mrs Penny refused to make a room ready for Zanna and young Harry.' Attuned to every last thing about him, she heard the softening of his tone as he mentioned the child. His child. The son he had wanted. The son she had been unable to give him. And he was going to ask her to do it, to make time to settle them in, make them comfortable. It was unbelievable! And she was proved right when he went on, a rare and raw emotion colouring his voice, 'I wonder if you'd mind—?'

'I've already said I'm pushed for time.' She was ready for him; she'd learned that particular trick ever since she'd made herself face the fact of his growing distaste for her. A useful defence mechanism. 'You invited them here, apparently. You find them somewhere to sleep—I don't care where. It's up to you.' And walked rapidly, rigidly, like a jerky puppet, across the bedroom floor towards the door of her bathroom, still clutching the dress in front of her.

Her voice had emerged coolly, and she didn't know how it could have done because there was a scream building up inside her and her heart was pattering hysterically beneath her breast, and she slammed the bathroom door behind her, ramming the bolt home, leaning against the smooth dark wood.

Not that Charles would have attempted to follow her, of course. He had lost what interest he'd ever had in her when she had miscarried their child. Nowadays they treated each other like strangers—only this evening had he broken the habit of distance that had been deepening ever since that dreadful night three months ago. And no prizes for guessing why, she thought on a flare of anger, dragging her clothes off with shaking hands.

'Are you all right?'

The last thing she had expected was this rare show of compassion, a softening of the austerely crafted, remote features. But then, she thought, side-stepping him, her hands tightening on the coffee-tray, he was probably sorry for her. His pity was the last thing she wanted.

'I'm fine. Shouldn't I be?' she challenged, then regretted the impulse because she didn't want to give him the opportunity to tell her exactly why she should be feeling so very far from 'all right'. Dinner had been an ordeal she would rather forget, with Zanna's vibrant beauty, her easy wit, making her the centre of attention. And heaven only knew what had been going on inside the Clarkes' heads! Donald Clarke had been Charles's company accountant for years, right through the time of his tempestuous affair with Zanna. She had lived here at South Park in those days, on and off, had acted as his hostess at many a weekend such as this. Donald and Mavis would be dying to retreat to the privacy of their room to chew over the scandal of Zanna's return. And they could hardly have forgotten the wild obsession of Charles's love-affair with the woman who, even then, had left a string of broken hearts in her wake, or forgotten his brooding desolation when she had finally walked out on him, too.

'I thought you might have had one of your headaches,' Charles said, a thread of tension running through the expressed concern. 'You have that pallid look about you.'

As he took the tray from her and waited for her to precede him through the kitchen door she muttered, 'Thanks!' meaning his unflattering description, and nothing to do with the way he'd appeared to help her with the unwieldy tray. True, since the road accident that had resulted in the loss of their child, she had suffered from violent headaches, a legacy not only from the concussion, but from grief. But did he really have to draw her attention to the fact that beside the glowingly vibrant beauty of his former lover, the mother of his child, she looked like a sadly anaemic mouse?

'If you'd like to call it a day, I'll make your excuses,' he offered as they walked through the vast hall together, and she glanced up at him quickly, suspicion narrowing her glittering green eyes. But instead of the suspected sarcasm, a desire to be rid of her, see her tucked up in bed and safely out of the way, she saw only compassion. And she looked away quickly, hot tears in her eyes. She had known she was losing him long before now, had tried to deny it, to hang on to hope, but his action in bringing Zanna here, and their son, meant that all hope was gone.

And he was standing too close, the tautly muscled length of him, his breadth of shoulder, the sexy narrowness of hips moulded by the fine dark suiting making the muscles around her heart clench with pain, and when she caught her breath on a strangled sob he put the tray down on one of the tables set against the panelled wall and cupped her face in his hands, the narrowed eyes dark with sympathy, his mouth tight as he told her, 'I'm so sorry, Beth. The last thing I ever intended to do was cause you pain.'

And at that moment she believed him. His obsession with Zanna had been legendary, and it still lived. He probably didn't want it to, but it did. There was nothing he could do about it, and the existence of their child made her impossible to resist.

Beth made a huge effort to control herself, fighting

the almost irresistible impulse to lay her head against his chest and weep for the love she had lost without ever having it. If he knew just how much she was breaking up inside he would pity her even more. And that she simply could not stand. So she said thinly, jerking her head away as if his touch, instead of making her yearning for him unbearable, in fact disgusted her,

'I'll believe you—thousands wouldn't!' And he could make what he liked of that, anything, just as long as he never learned the truth—that she loved him so much she would die for him if she had to. 'I think I will go to bed.' She swung on her heels, not looking at him. 'I'd be grateful if you would make my apologies.'

Needless to say, she didn't sleep, didn't even try to. She stared the ruins of her marriage in the face as the light faded from the sky at the end of the glorious June day, alternatively loving and hating him.

The love had begun as an infatuation. She'd been fifteen and yearning over the sexy Charles Savage had been quite the fashion for the village girls. Recently down from Oxford with a first-class degree, he'd driven fast cars and brought a new girlfriend home every weekend, or so it had seemed. His mother had been dead for many years at that time, his father losing his grip on reality. His younger brother, James, had been around then, too. But he'd refused to have anything to do with the ailing family business, leaving it to Charles to knuckle down and retrieve the fortunes of the family at South Park.

Staring from her lonely window at the purple dusk,

Beth wondered what had happened to James. The last she'd heard, through Charles, had been the news of the death of James's wife, Lisa. Somewhere abroad. She should have made it her business to find out more, to write to him, expressing her sympathy. She had never met Lisa; she and James had not even attended hers and Charles's wedding two years ago. There had been a rift between the brothers, that much she had known, although Charles had always refused to talk about the younger man. And, at the time, she excused herself—she had been suffering badly from the miscarriage of her child. Nevertheless, she should have made some effort to express her sympathy…

She sighed. She didn't know why now, of all times, she should be thinking of James. Except that, remembering earlier times, when she'd first fallen in love with the unattainable Charles Savage, she could recall one incident with utmost clarity.

It would have been around five years ago. She and her bosom friend, Alison, had just started up in business on their own, but they'd made time to go to the May Day hop in the village hall. Charles and James had put in an appearance, as they usually did, and of course, by that time, Beth's contemporaries had got over their collective infatuation for the heir to South Park, were going steady with more prosaic, yet attainable local boys.

But not Beth, of course. What had begun as a fashionable schoolgirl crush had, annoyingly, grown into love. Not that she'd confided in anyone, of course. Not even Allie. It was a secret she'd kept to herself—as if it were a pernicious vice—only James, it seemed, guessing the truth.

That was the first time she'd seen Zanna. She'd swept into the village hall on Charles's arm, looking like a rare hot-house orchid in a field of common daisies, and James had followed, a pale carbon of his devastating brother, his features sulky. And later, sweeping her round the floor in a duty dance, James had told her,

'You never did stand much of a chance; Charles was always attracted by the rarer species. But this time he's cast his net and captured the incomparable Zanna Hall, so you, my dear little sparrow, won't get a look-in.'

At the time, she'd been too mortified by the way he'd guessed the truth about her to say a word. Besides, from the way Charles looked at the newest lady in his life, he was clearly besotted. And she wondered now if James had resented his brother's easy conquest of the most delectable females around, and if that lay behind the rift. In any case, shortly after that, James had married. He'd been working abroad at the time, as a civil engineer, and as far as she knew he'd never brought Lisa to South Park.

She wondered, fleetingly, if he had been surprised when his brother had married the insignificant Beth Garner and knew he wouldn't be surprised at all to learn how the marriage had broken up. His long-ago words at the May Day dance had been prophetic.

She woke feeling grim. She had fallen asleep on the wide window-ledge and she stumbled to her feet, her movements ungainly. Feeling her way around the furniture, she located the light switch and banished the darkness.

If only she could banish the darkness within, she thought despairingly, looking at her smooth, lonely bed and knowing she would never get to sleep until something had been sorted out.

One way or another.

Contrary to her earlier, shock-numbed instincts, she knew she couldn't get through the night, the rest of the interminable weekend, without talking this through with Charles.

It would take courage to go to the room he had thrown her out of after her illness. But she could manage it. She had to.

He had taken her to the master bedroom when she'd first entered South Park as his bride; it was there she had known those nights of ecstasy, the immature hope that one day, sooner or later, he would grow to love her as she loved him. There that their child had been conceived.

But, returning from hospital, she had found that her things had been moved to the room she now occupied, and he'd explained that he thought it best if they slept apart until she was fully recovered. Not that he'd been unkind about it, she thought with a tiny shudder. He'd never been unkind, ever; he'd been a considerate, warm, appreciative—if demanding—husband. Even after the accident and her miscarriage, when any affection he'd felt for her had died along with the child they had lost, he had still treated her with respect and politeness.

Which made his cruelty in bringing Zanna and their son here all the more devastating.

Yet he wasn't a cruel man. Self-assured, fairly ruthless in his business dealings, frustratingly enigmatic at times and sometimes impossible, he was all of these things. But never deliberately cruel.

Clinging to that knowledge, she tightened the belt of her silky robe and left her room, her soft mouth set with grim determination. She wasn't going to stand meekly by and watch her life and her marriage fall apart without trying to do something about it.

That Charles would choose to stay with her, having never loved her, particularly since, following the accident and the miscarriage, she had been told she might never conceive again, when he could have the woman who had once dominated his life, and the child they had created together, was a pretty forlorn hope, but she was an optimist, wasn't she? She had to be, to have agreed to marry him in the first place!

But even that failed her as she reached the corner where the corridor turned to lead to the master bedroom suite. With the influx of house guests, all the rooms were occupied, so where else would Zanna sleep, except in his bed?

Walking into that sumptuous room and finding them tangled together in the huge bed was something she simply couldn't face, and the determination that had brought her this far drained out of her, leaving her limp and shaking, leaning against the wall for support, her heartbeats frantic.

But finding them together would settle the thing once and for all, wouldn't it? she told herself tiredly.

She couldn't go through the remainder of the weekend not knowing what was going on, not knowing for sure. She was out of shock now, and had to know.

Pulling away from the wall, she walked doggedly on down the dimly lit corridor then gasped with anguish as she saw the glimmer of a night-light from the partly open door of the nursery.

Charles and Zanna had put their child in the room she had so lovingly created for her baby! She didn't know how much more she could endure! Yet, driven by a need she couldn't put a name to, she silently approached the open door, moving like a sleep-walker.

And through the gap she saw them. The sleeping child, the parents looking down on him. Charles, his dark hair rumpled, his towelling robe revealing long, tautly muscled, hair-roughened legs, his arm around Zanna's naked shoulders—naked except for the narrow shoestring straps which supported her clinging satin nightdress—and he was saying softly,

'Don't worry about it. Everything's going to work out. There isn't a man alive who wouldn't welcome that child into his family. And I'm no exception.'

CHAPTER TWO

'SO WHAT'S happened?' Allie wanted to know, her round face very serious. And Beth turned from the stance she had taken up at the sash window, looking down on the deserted Sunday-afternoon high street of the market town and replied evenly,

'Nothing's happened. I feel like getting back to work. Lots of married women do it.' That was her story, and she was sticking to it. Best friend or not, she couldn't confide in Allie; she would, and quite truthfully, say 'I told you so!'

'If you say so,' the other girl said slowly, stringing the words out, then jumped up from the sofa, her smile brisk now. 'I'll make a drink, then we can see what's on the books. Tea or coffee?'

'Oh… Tea, please.' Beth tugged herself together— she'd been miles away, wondering how she was going to come to terms with life without Charles, and caught the quick upward jerk of her friend's brows and warned herself to be more careful.

Watching Allie walk through to the kitchen of the small flat above the agency office, Beth pulled in a deep breath, exhaling it slowly. So far she'd done well. The struggle back to self-respect had begun and she deserved to feel proud of herself.

As soon as the last of the weekend guests had departed earlier that afternoon she had made up her mind to drive over to see Allie. She hadn't driven since the accident. Charles had been behind the wheel on that terrible day when a drunken youth had overtaken on a blind bend and had caused the accident that had cost her the life of her unborn child.

There hadn't been a thing Charles could have done to avoid it, and the fact that he had emerged with minor cuts and abrasions, while she had landed in hospital with a severe concussion, several broken ribs and a dangerous miscarriage, had been the luck of the draw.

So today nerving herself to take her car out had been the second positive step back on the road to the recovery of her self-respect.

And the first had come when Charles had turned to her after they'd speeded the last of the departing house guests on their way, telling her quietly but with a firmness that brooked no argument, 'Come to the study, Beth. Zanna and I have something to tell you.' He turned back towards the house, sunlight glinting on his raven-dark hair, highlighting the harsh, angular planes of his face, and if there was any expression in those narrowed smoky-grey eyes she couldn't read it.

But this time she was arguing, fighting her corner, and she had tossed back at him levelly, 'Sorry. I've an appointment. Whatever you have to tell me will have to wait.' Wait until she had sorted out the next few weeks of her life, could present her husband with a *fait accompli*. She knew damn well what he and Zanna had to tell her and she needed to get her say in first. There were winners and losers in every game but she was determined to make sure that, as far as appearances went, she didn't come out of this hateful mess in second place.

Ignoring the sudden angry line of his mouth, she had stridden away, her feet crunching on the gravel as she made for the garages. From deep inside the house she had caught the sound of childish, gurgling laughter and she'd had to fight hard to control the insane impulse to hurl herself into Charles's arms and beg him not to leave her.

Aware of those brooding grey eyes on her back, she had forced herself on, her head high, telling herself that, despite her other shortcomings, Zanna was a good mother. Throughout the last dreadful two days she had observed the care the other woman lavished on the child and Beth had to rub that fact in, that and every other known piece of information, rub it in until it hurt, because that was the only way she could prevent herself from begging Charles to stay with her.

And the deeper the pain the more likely she was to regain the pride she had thrown away when she had agreed to be his wife, she had assured herself, steeling every nerve and muscle to open the door of the Metro Charles had provided her with shortly after their marriage, the car she hadn't had the guts to drive since the accident.

'Are you saying you want to come back into partnership?' Allie asked now, returning with two mugs of tea, and Beth shook her head, making herself smile as she took one of them and sank down on the sofa.

'Not necessarily.' The Helpline Agency, which they'd started together, was run from here, not ten miles away from South Park, and Beth didn't want to be this close.

Working locally, she wouldn't be able to avoid seeing Charles and Zanna and their son from time to time. Besides, her parents still lived in the village although her father had retired from medical practice a year ago, and they would expect her to visit them regularly, and every time she did she would have to drive right past the impressive gates of the South Park estate.

'Well, I can't see the lord of the manor allowing his wife to scrub floors, clean offices, cook for private dinner parties or dance attendance on a senile old lady,' Allie grinned, flicking through a much thumbed leather-bound book. 'Though you're not qualified for nursing duties, of course. And I can't see—'

'Anything in the secretarial line? That I am qualified for,' Beth put in, hoping she didn't sound too desperate. She needed to earn her living, be independent, and a part-time post, which was what the agency specialised in, would tide her over until she could find something permanent, as far away from here as was possible to get.

'Sorry.' Allie wrinkled her nose. 'Plenty last week, but nothing this. There's only one, and that's not suitable.'

'Pity.' Beth took a sip of scalding tea, trying to hide her deep disappointment. Nothing was ever easy, and walking straight into a job as she had hoped was, apparently, not on. She would have to get right away and look for permanent work. Not so simple. She could take the car, of course, since it had been a birthday gift, but she wouldn't, on principle, touch a penny of the generous allowance Charles paid into her private account. Finding affordable accommodation while she looked for work could be a headache.

And because Allie was astute, highly adept at picking up vibrations, Beth decided she had to show an interest, and she managed idly, 'So what's so unsuitable about the only position you appear to be unable to fill?' and had to force herself to keep her cool when Allie dismissed,

'It's in France. An English writer living in Boulogne—he moved there years ago, apparently, buying and renovating a small farmhouse a few kilometres inland.' Allie bit unrepentently into her third chocolate biscuit and said through a mouthful of crumbs, 'It sounds a peach of a job. His permanent English secretary did a runner with a German hunk she met at Le Touquet and left him stranded. He wants a temp to take over while he hunts for another permanent lady—someone on the wrong side of fifty, and prim with it, so he says!' She tapped the open book in front of her reflectively. 'Betty Mayhew—you remember her, of course—is dead keen. And if he's still unsuited by the time she finishes her stint with Comtech, she can have a stab at it.'

'Betty was always good at getting what she wanted,' Beth reminded Allie smoothly, recalling the vibrantly attractive blonde who seemed to sail through life, and men-friends, with insouciant ease. She had been one of the first secretaries she and Allie had signed up all that time ago, and if she'd set her sights on a spell in north-west France then, for once, she was going to be disappointed.

Bitchy! she scolded herself tartly, then added decisively, 'Pity to miss out with a new client. I'll go. And
don't think I've lost all my skills,' she admonished,
deliberately misinterpreting her friend's pole-axed
stare. 'I've done a fair bit of work for Charles, off and
on; I've kept up to date, believe me.'

'Oh, I do,' Allie came right back. 'I do. But will
Charles mind having an absentee wife? And don't
think he can come up with something flash and buy a
helicopter to ferry you home at five on the dot each
evening,' she grinned. 'Part of the trouble my client is
having is because he often finds he works best at night
and has been known to wake his secretary in the small
hours to take masses of dictation!'

Beth shrugged, avoiding Allie's eyes, telling her,
'That won't be a problem. Charles has to spend a great
deal of time away from home himself,' and that was
the truth. Since the accident he'd been away more often
than not. 'He won't mind at all if I'm away for a few
weeks.' And that was true, too. He and Zanna would
be very happy if she were to make herself scarce. They
wouldn't want her to hang around, making scenes,
once they'd explained what was going on. And she
didn't want that either. She would beat a dignified retreat. It was, after all, the only thing she could do.

She stood up gracefully, her natural poise coming to
her aid. Allie could make what she liked of the situation and one day she, Beth, would tell her friend the
truth behind it all. But not yet. She wasn't strong
enough to face the sympathy, the 'I told you so's. And
she was more than thankful that her parents were away,

taking the world cruise they'd promised themselves
when her father had retired.

'Give me a ring tomorrow, would you?' she asked.
'After you've fixed everything.'

'I can do better than that,' Allie said, her brown eyes
serious. 'If you can promise me that Charles Savage
of South Park doesn't live up to his name and come
to beat me up for sending his wife abroad.'

'That's about the last thing he'd do.' Beth made herself smile, aching inside because she knew the reverse
was true. Charles would probably send Allie champagne and flowers for months for so opportunely helping him to rid himself of a wife he no longer wanted,
the wife he had never pretended to love.

'If you say so!' But Allie was already reaching for
the phone, punching numbers and, five minutes later,
after intense conversation, she replaced the receiver
and told Beth, 'He's weak with relief, or so he tells
me. He has work piling up to the ceiling and you can't
get there soon enough.' She scribbled rapidly on a card
and handed it over to Beth. 'His address and phone
number. If you get lost, you're to ring and he'll come
to your rescue. And the same applies if you want meeting at Boulogne. Shall you fly, or cross by ferry?'

'Take the car on the ferry.' Beth tucked the pasteboard into her handbag and rose to go. If she was going
to be completely independent then she might as well
start now, and, although her heart was beating like a
drum as she turned the Metro through South Park's
gateposts, her soft mouth was set in lines of sheer determination, her green eyes cool.

Charles had made no secret of his reason for marrying her. He had wanted an heir, a family to enjoy all he had achieved. That he had distanced himself from her, emotionally and physically, after she had lost their child and the prognosis for her ever conceiving again had been unhopeful, had come as no surprise. What did surprise her, in retrospect, was her stupidity in agreeing to marry him in the first place. She had been besotted, she thought grimly, young enough and gullible enough to believe that she could teach him to love her.

But then, she excused as she garaged the car and locked it behind her, she hadn't known that Zanna would come back, bringing their love-child along with her. How could she have known? She would have run a mile if she had been able to look into the future because, although she had been prepared to fight for Charles Savage's love, she didn't stand the ghost of a chance when Zanna was around. She never had done, and never would, and her strength lay in recognising that miserable and unalterable fact of life.

Her head was high as she walked through the hall and up the stairs. The whole house felt empty, very silent. Maybe Harry was still having his afternoon sleep and Charles and Zanna were taking advantage of it. She tried to tell herself she didn't care, but knew she did. The pain was almost too much to bear.

But she had to hold on. Had to pretend she was leaving of her own free will. Entering her room, she began to pack methodically, forcing herself to stay calm because if she let go, only for an instant, she would fall to pieces. And when she was ready to leave she would find Charles, say her piece and go, and that would be that. But it didn't work out like that, things never did, because Charles walked in through her door, making her jump out of her skin, and she spun round on her heels, her hand to her throat, her face running with fire.

And he said tautly, his austerely attractive features hard, 'Do you have a few free moments to spare for Zanna and me, yet?'

Beth shuddered suddenly, her whole body going cold. Ignoring the initial sarcasm coming from him, she saw his smoky eyes narrow as they fell on the open suitcase, and she got in quickly, 'I don't particularly want to hear whatever it is you and Zanna feel you want to say. It can't be important.' She turned her back on him, not willing for him to read the misery on her face.

She had to walk away from him before he got the chance to throw her out of his life; it was the only way she could salvage her pride, regain her self-respect. She wouldn't let herself crawl, or weep. Not in front of him, especially not when his old and only love was somewhere near—with the son the two of them had created together.

She heard the sudden angry hiss of indrawn breath a mere milli-second before his hard hands clamped down on her shoulders, dragging her round to face him, and her chin tilted up rebelliously as he grated blackly, 'What the hell's got into you?'

She could have told him, but wouldn't give him the satisfaction, or the opportunity to put his love, his need for Zanna and his son, into words. She could bear anything but that.

'Please let me go.' The heat from those strong fingers seared her skin through the thin fabric of her blouse, threatening to rob her of all her hard-won poise, and when his grip merely tightened she ground out quickly, hoping his anger at her refusal to listen to what he and his precious Zanna had to tell her would prevent him from guessing just how much his touch affected her, 'If you'll stop mauling me, I'll say what's on my mind.'

At the acid inflexion of her tone his hands dropped to his sides, his mouth going hard. It had worked like a charm, and if he thought his very touch disgusted her then that was a bonus. And she said tightly, before her will-power deserted her completely, 'I don't need to tell you how our marriage has been disintegrating these past few months.' She didn't specify dates, although she could have done, to the day. She couldn't bear to remind him, or herself, of the tragedy that had marked his loss of interest in her. 'I think it's best if we have a trial separation.'

She turned from him then, forcing herself to make her movements smooth and sure, taking a pile of lingerie from her dresser and adding it to the contents of her suitcase. Her heart was beating with a heavy, sickly rhythm, but he couldn't know that, and, although she couldn't see him, she was fully aware of the tense watchful look in those narrowed gunfighter's eyes, the tension that would be holding that powerfully crafted body rigid.

'Is that what you want?' There was a tightness in that deep husky voice that, had she not known better, she could have imagined to be pain. But she did know better, she reminded herself scornfully. He might not love her, and he assuredly wasn't planning on being faithful, but he wasn't an uncaring man and might be concerned about her future welfare.

Beth nodded, unable to speak for the moment because this was goodbye, wasn't it? Goodbye to the man she had always loved, to the future they might have had together had things worked out differently. Swallowing the painful lump in her throat, she bent to snap her case shut, the wings of her short, sleekly styled hair falling forwards to hide her face as she struggled to find her voice.

And then she managed, 'It is. I've got a job to go to, so you have no need to worry, and I suggest we get in touch in a month or two, to finalise things.' By then the whole locale would know she had gone, that Zanna had replaced her, returned to where she belonged. And by that time, although she knew she would never get over the pain, she would have created her own life away from him, gained in self-respect. And something bitter, deep inside her, made her add, 'And don't slam the door as you leave. It might wake Harry.'

'We might as well call it a day.' William Templeton dragged his fingers through his wiry light-brown hair, his craggy face drawn with fatigue. 'And thank you, Beth. We've done some good work—I can feel it in my bones.' His radiant smile suddenly flashed, transforming his plain, craggy features and Beth smiled back, she couldn't help herself; he was that kind of man.

She could even forgive him for knocking her up at four this morning, his fertile mind bursting with ideas for the mid section of his current book which had proved, up until then, a sticking point.

'Coffee?' Beth closed her shorthand notebook and laid it down beside the ancient electric typewriter on the cluttered desk, but William shook his head.

'I'm going to crash out for a couple of hours, and I suggest you do the same. If you're still asleep at noon I'll make lunch and wake you. OK?'

She nodded absently as he bumbled out of the book-filled study, physical tiredness and the relief of achievement making him look older than his forty years, making his chunky body in the worn old cords and battered sweater sag. And, momentarily, her green eyes softened.

During the ten days she'd been at the old farmhouse she had grown to like and respect the author. Despite his enormous commercial success he gave no signs of self-importance and although he worked her hard he was fair, paying excellent wages, insisting that she took plenty of time off to make up for his erratic working methods.

But although she had worked at full stretch for the last five hours, taking down his rapid-fire dictation, she was in no mood to go back to bed. She wouldn't sleep, she would simply lie there, prey to the thoughts she was still struggling to keep at bay.

Ten days wasn't nearly enough time to recover from the trauma of losing Charles, she told herself as she took herself off upstairs to shower in the slope-ceilinged bathroom beneath the eaves. She doubted if she would ever recover but hoped that, with time, she would come to terms with it, would be able to get on with her life without having to guard her thoughts and emotions so completely.

Coming to France had been the best thing she could have done, she assured herself as, dressed now in a full emerald-green cotton skirt and a navy sleeveless top, she made and drank some coffee in the heavily beamed farmhouse kitchen.

William, bless him, kept her hard at work, leaving her little time to fret. On her arrival he had greeted her as if she were a saviour and her self-esteem had been further enhanced when he'd praised her lavishly for the way she had tackled the piles of dog-eared hand-written manuscript that had accumulated since he had been without a secretary.

But Mariette Voisin, who came in most days to tackle the housework, would be arriving at any moment and, although the elderly French woman spoke only garbled English, she was incorrigibly curious and subjected Beth to a barrage of almost unintelligible questions at every opportunity, so she rinsed out the earthenware coffee-cup she had been using and slipped out into the morning sunshine.

The converted farmhouse lay in a leafy hollow along a tangle of narrow lanes between Boulogne and Le Wast and when Beth had eventually managed to find it, that first day, she had known it would be the perfect place to hide.

Hide from whom? she scorned, kicking out at one of the pebbles that littered the dusty lane. No need to hide when no one would come looking. Charles would be only too thankful that she had voluntarily removed herself from his life.

Frowning, she pushed the intrusive thoughts of him out of her mind, deliberately trying to relax. Crouched over her shorthand notebook for five long hours made her body crave air and exercise and here, in these lovely sun-drenched lanes with the thick forest trees never far away, was the perfect place to take it. And suddenly, as often seemed to happen in this enchanted land, she rounded a bend and came across a hidden hump-backed stone bridge which spanned a dancing stream, and leant there, catching her breath, grateful for the shade of the overhanging trees.

Then, as the sound of an engine disarranged the sleepy pattern of birdsong and bees, she flattened herself against the parapet, leaving as much passing space as possible on the narrow track, then turned as the vehicle stopped behind her, probably a tourist, bemused by the seemingly aimless wandering of the lanes.

But the polite half-smile died on her soft lips and her heart flipped, stopped, then raced on. And Charles said from the open car window, 'Get in.'

She couldn't move. She literally couldn't move a muscle. She didn't know what he was doing here, how he had found her, why he had bothered. She opened her mouth, but no words came, and she just knew she must look like a dying fish, and that made hot colour run from the slash of her V neckline to the roots of her hair; then she heard him mutter a violent expletive as he slid out of the car to tower over her.

'Don't give me that blank stare, woman. We have met before.' His teeth closed with a snap, his eyes raking her pale face. 'I'm the man you married, re-member? Promising to love, honour and obey. So get in the car.'

His strong hands were clenched at his sides, bunched against the black denim of his jeans. He looked as if he would like to shake her until her head dropped off, and she pushed the word 'no' past her dry lips and saw his mouth go tight, the skin growing taut across the hard cheekbones and aggressive jaw.

'I'm blocking the road and I'm not moving another inch without you.' And that should have given her fair warning of his intention to manhandle her into the pas-senger-seat, but she was still in shock while he walked round the front.

When he slid in beside her she managed huskily, 'I'm here on a job and I'm already late back,' which was a downright lie but one he seemed to swallow because he said, his deep voice silky smooth now with an underlying menace she had never heard from him before,

'So direct me. I'll take you there.'

And there was no way she was going to be able to get out of that. She could refuse point-blank and he would simply drive away with her. Anywhere, the mood he was in. She had never seen him this angry before.

Something inside her shivered and contracted as she glanced up at his stony profile, and she gave directions in a thin, sharp voice and wondered if he knew just what kind of hell he was putting her through.

She had just set her foot on the long, tough road back to some sort of acceptance of her ruined marriage and he had to appear to plunge her back to square one. And she was shaking inside as she said into the prickly silence, 'How did you know where I was?'

'Allie, who else?'

Of course. Who else? Beth and her best friend from schooldays had kept in close touch even after she'd married and left the Helpline Agency. She would have been the first person Charles would have asked.

'But why bother?' she asked dully, slowly, unconsciously, shaking her head.

He shot her a hard sideways look, a look that boded ill for her peace of mind, and his voice was grim as he told her, 'Did you think for one moment I'd simply let you walk away?'

CHAPTER THREE

BETH sagged in her seat, her eyes closing. Now why hadn't she thought of that? Of course he wouldn't allow her to simply walk away, to take that sort of initiative.

Charles Savage's middle name had to be determination. A tough character, he always had to be in control. He hated loose ends. He would have to know exactly what his estranged wife was doing, and where she was doing it. Besides, he would want a quick divorce, wouldn't he? He would need to keep tabs on her, know exactly where she was.

'Very cosy.' The biting edge of sarcasm as he braked the car made her eyes wing open. They were in the cobbled yard at the front of the old stone farmhouse, the tubs of geraniums around the walls making bright splashes of colour.

'Yes, isn't it?' She was giving as good as she got. He might have brought her down, but she wasn't out for the count—not as far as he was going to be allowed to see. 'I love it. I'm quite at home here already.'

Home. The very word cut through her like a blade. Home was where he was, and she would never be there again. Never was such a desolate word but she resolutely blinked back tears and shot him a bright, glittering look, ignoring the curl of anger on his mouth.

'Come along in, if you have something to say. You

43

can't have come all this way just for a change of scenery.'

She let herself out of the car and swept over the yard ahead of him, willing herself to stay calm. So far she had avoided the agony of hearing him tell her he wanted a divorce, wanted to be free to marry Zanna and take her and their son to live with him.

She had run, but not far enough or fast enough, and he had caught up with her like Nemesis. And she was going to have to listen now, and not betray a thing.

If he knew how long she had loved him, how passionately, he would feel sorry for her. And that she could not, would not stand. The humiliation would be the final, deadly straw. Far better, for both of them, if he continued to believe that theirs had been a loveless marriage, on both sides, and that she had decided that that type of sterile relationship was no longer enough.

It was silent in the square, stone-flagged hall and he stood in the open doorway behind her, blocking out the sun, and his voice was ice as he remarked, 'Just the two of you, is it? You and the celebrated author? Quite an idyllic set-up.'

'As you say.' Her voice was brittle, hard. It had to be, because to deny what he was obviously thinking would be to reveal a tiny chink in her armour. No need to tell him that she slept in the annexe, as had her predecessor, had her own small private sitting-room with a tiny bathroom above, built into the roof, and only came into the main house to work, to take her meals. No need to let him know that, loving him, no other man really existed for her.

'Come through to the sitting-room,' she invited, her

level tone belying the sickening race of her heartbeats. 'William's still in bed, but I'm sure he won't mind, in the circumstances.'

She went to move away, towards the door next to the study, but her wrist was caught in a grip of steel and his mouth was a bitter line as he snapped, hauling her against the hard, lean length of his body, 'Had a hard night, did he?'

'We both did!' Being so close, feeling his vital body warmth, the hard thrust of perfectly honed muscle and bone beneath the casual jeans and sweatshirt, was bitter-sweet torment and her taunt was in direct response, a defence mechanism she had no control over, and she put defiance into her eyes, to hide the anguish, meeting his, seeing the involuntary jerk of a muscle at the side of his jaw, feeling a tiny stab of triumph because he, after all, could be jealous.

But the triumph was hollow, short-lived. She was still his wife and, as such, his property. He had wedded and bedded her, and her body, for three short months, had carried his child. And then he had never made love to her again because, knowing the odds on her ever conceiving again were impossibly long, there had been no point. Yet, even so, he still regarded her as his possession; his masculine ego would snarl at the the thought of her going to bed with any other man.

Her throat clogged with misery, she tried to drag herself away, but his grip merely tightened and his voice was thick as he stated, 'Beth, we have to talk. Don't you see that?' And for an insane moment she almost believed he cared, that there was still something left of their marriage, that something could be salvaged from the ruins. Slowly, she looked up at him from between her long dark lashes, felt a betraying tremor run through his body, and heard William say from the head of the stairs,

'Is everything all right, Beth?' His voice was roughly aggressive because it wasn't every day he came across a total stranger manhandling his secretary.

So the moment was over, and she must have imagined that jealousy, and had to put it down to wishful thinking because Charles, when he answered for her, sounded almost bored, completely urbane, totally in control.

'Perfectly all right, Templeton. I was passing and decided to drop in on my wife.'

'Oh. I see.' He sounded wary, coming down the stairs slowly, and Beth sighed.

When she had first arrived she had told her employer that she was separated from her husband. A broken marriage was nothing unusual these days. And he had accepted that, and if he had jumped to the conclusion that the separation was of long duration, and amicable, she hadn't put him right.

She had been feeling too raw to go into any details. And now he probably imagined that he would come down each morning to find an irate husband on his doorstep.

That kind of complication she could do without! And if she wanted to keep her job she would have to convince him otherwise.

'Beth, would you ask Mariette to bring coffee to the study—you'll join us, Savage?' William faced the younger, much taller man, his expression faintly belligerent. He had obviously showered recently and changed into lightweight fawn trousers and a crisp white shirt, looking far more alert after his sleep, younger, tougher.

'Thank you.' Charles dipped his dark head, the tone of his voice almost contemptuous, his mouth grim, and Beth slipped away, the palms of her hands slicked with perspiration.

The two men were acting like adversaries, circling each other, ready to fight to the death for their territorial rights. She couldn't understand it. She might still be married to Charles but that state of affairs wouldn't last long because he wanted to be rid of her. And although William might be annoyed because his working routine was being disrupted by an unwelcome visitor, he must know that it was a one-off, wouldn't happen again.

She would have to make that very clear as soon as Charles left. She needed this job and had every intention of keeping it, intending, once she had proved herself capable and reliable, to ask if he would employ her on a permanent footing.

Mariette wasn't in the kitchen so Beth made the coffee herself, glad of the respite. Seeing Charles again, so soon, had been a shock and she needed time to brace herself to act as if she didn't really care when he asked her for a divorce.

But she couldn't make the simple task last all morning and when she carried the tray into the study she was no nearer gaining total control over her emotions than she had been when Charles had appeared out of the blue, bundling her into his car.

And the atmosphere inside the small, book-lined room did nothing to help her equilibrium. William was behind his desk, his eyes glowering, and Charles was pacing the floor, like a caged tiger trying to break out.

'How long are you staying in the area?' William questioned abruptly.

Charles, his narrowed eyes watching every move Beth made as she poured coffee, answered silkily, 'As long as I need to,' his steely grey eyes hardening as she handed him his cup. 'Making yourself indispensable to yet another man?'

Although fiery colour washed her face Beth's body went icy cold. That had been a direct reference to the fact that, for six months before he had come out with his astonishing proposal of marriage, she had worked as a temporary housekeeper-cum-social-hostess at South Park.

Beth remembered, as if it were yesterday, the morning when Charles had walked into the Helpline Agency. Mrs Penny, he'd explained, had fallen and broken her hip and it would be months before she would be fit for work again. And everyone knew that, not long before, Zanna had walked out of his life, leaving him bereft. Her heart had ached for him, because she had known what it was like to love hopelessly. But at least Charles had known a spell of intense happiness with the woman everyone knew he was obsessed by.

'I need a miracle—a Jill of all trades,' he'd confessed, his austere features softening in a smile which looked rarely used these days. 'Someone to act as temporary housekeeper, occasional secretary and sometime hostess when I entertain business colleagues for working weekends. It would be for some months, certainly until Mrs Penny is fit to return. But by then I should have got something sorted out regarding the other duties.'

To this day, Beth didn't know just what madness had prompted her to offer. Heaven knew, she and Allie had been busy enough with administering the rapidly expanding agency, and her secret love for Charles Savage, that hopeless thing that had refused to die the death or go away, would merely be fanned into a raging conflagration if she were foolish enough to spend so much time with him.

But Charles had had no such qualms, of course. Why on earth should he? He'd been openly relieved, and even the brooding severity of those gunfighter's eyes— and everyone around had noticed just how much more brooding they had become since Zanna Hall had left him—had lightened to silvery pleasure as he'd told her,

'That would be ideal. Living in the village, you'd be able to go home each evening, and as I shall be working in the City for most of the week you'll have plenty of time to organise the weekend arrangements when I decide to entertain. And there is daily help with the cleaning and so on, so you won't find stepping into Mrs Penny's shoes as well too arduous.'

But, as it had happened, he had spent far less time away than he had led her to expect, and her stupid, hopeless love for him had been fanned, just as she had privately predicted...

And William was perceptive enough to pick up her distress now because when she judged her hand was steady enough to carry his coffee to him his kindly eyes looked directly into hers with compassion—and just the hint of a question. Then he turned to Charles, whose silence seemed to contain a threat.

'Where are you staying?'

'In Boulogne.' He named one of the most prestigious hotels, his voice curt, and put his half-finished coffee down on the tray. 'But I haven't come here to exchange pleasantries. I'd like a word with Beth. In private.' He stalked to the door, as if he could no longer endure the confinement. And he cut through the beginning of the older man's expostulations with a grim, 'I realise she's your secretary, Templeton, but first and foremost she is my wife.'

In the tense, waiting silence, Beth heard the drumbeat of her own blood as she resisted the urge to scream. She felt like a bone being tugged between two snarling dogs, and didn't know why.

'Beth?' William's voice sounded indecisive. 'Is that what you want?'

She nodded mutely. Charles, in this mood, would get exactly what he wanted and wouldn't care about the methods he used. And as he was here they might as well get the unhappy discussion about their future out of the way. And when that was settled she could make her peace with her employer, reassure him that he wasn't about to be caught up in the middle of a nasty ongoing matrimonial drama. Once Charles had her agreement to a rapid divorce, he most certainly wouldn't want to set eyes on her again, much less waste his precious time in seeking her out and causing disruption at her place of work.

Charles was standing at the door, waiting, the dark

line of his brow impatient, and Beth walked reluctantly towards him, her stomach lurching, her feet like lead. Hearing him put his request for a divorce into words was going to be one of the worst things that had ever happened to her.

But she would survive it, she told herself firmly as, her head held high, she walked through the door, refusing to meet his eyes.

'Here!'

She had walked out into the sun-drenched morning, making for the stone bench against one of the courtyard walls, instinctively knowing that she would need to be sitting down while she listened to what he had to say to her. Already her legs were shaking. But she turned at his barked command, saw he was holding the car door open for her, and sucked in a ragged breath.

'Don't treat me like a dog!' she snapped, forcing anger through her bloodstream. Better anger than helpless misery, far better. 'I don't come to heel at your command.'

'So I'm beginning to notice. Nevertheless, get in.'

'Whatever you have to say to me can be said here.' She stood her ground, digging her heels in. 'There's no one around, it's quite private.'

'I have no intention of staying on Templeton's property,' he told her grimly. 'So do you come willingly, or do I have to make you?'

Beth compressed her lips to trap a shuddering sigh. The warning in his ruthless gaze was unmistakable. Better to get into the car under her own steam than have him put her there. If he touched her again her body would betray her, demonstrate how much she still

wanted, needed and loved him. And she couldn't think
why he had taken such an instant dislike to the harm-
less William. He should be shaking the other man's
hand, slapping him on the back because he had, after
all, provided his unwanted wife with a job, a wage and
living accommodation!

She shuddered violently as he slammed the car door
behind her as soon as she'd settled in the passenger-
seat, biting down on her lower lip as he stalked round
to take his place. She had known he was capable of
anger; she'd had enough confidential conversations
with the wives of his employees and business colleagues who'd accompanied their husbands on those
working weekends at South Park to learn that though
he was always fair-minded, willing to listen to the
other person's point of view, his icy anger when someone failed to live up to his exacting standards was
something to be avoided at all costs.

But she, herself, had never experienced it until now.
It made her feel small and vulnerable, threatened, as if
she didn't know him at all, as if he had become a
dangerous, menacing stranger.

While they were leaving the courtyard and heading
for open country at what Beth considered to be a dangerous speed, she forced herself to stare grimly ahead,
to display no emotion at all. She wasn't even going to
ask where the hell he thought he was taking her. She
couldn't trust her voice.

And he was silent, too, handling the fast car with
steely concentration. Beth wasn't surprised. Since the
accident the lines of communication between them had
broken down.

Previously, they'd always been able to talk, about everything under the sun. And that was just one of the things that had further cemented her love for him when she had first gone to work for him at South Park.

Eventually, he braked the car at the foot of a forest track, the tyres spinning, scattering small stones, and Beth let herself out of the car, closing the door and leaning against it with weak relief.

The tension, the unspoken rage coming from him had been more than she could bear and she dragged in a deep breath of the slightly cooler air, scented by the forest trees, spiced by the faint tang of the ocean, and rubbed the beads of perspiration from her short upper lip with the back of a clenched hand.

And he was standing in front of her, a dark, silent presence whose soft-footed approach made her heart leap and twist inside her.

But there was something different now, as if the concentration needed to handle the fast car with safety had exorcised that coiling anger. And her unguarded eyes winged up to his, then dropped, veiled by heavy lids and the thick dark sweep of her lashes as she recognised the softening of his eyes, his features.

Compassion? Pity? She didn't need it. He had always treated her with kindliness and respect, even after she had lost the child he had set his heart on. He would be feeling sorry for her, knowing he was about to tell her exactly why Zanna had returned after all this time.

He wasn't a deliberately cruel man; he wouldn't want to cause her pain. But there was nothing he could do about it because Zanna, for him, had been an obsession. Still was. Always would be. Everyone had known that, which was why the people who really cared about her, her parents and Allie, had warned her against accepting his marriage proposal.

She should have listened to them. She'd been too sure of her ability to make him forget the other woman, learn to love her. She had been so sure he would, especially when she gave him the child he had told her he wanted.

'Come, we'll walk.' His deep voice was thick with what had to be regret for what he was about to do to her. But she didn't want his pity. She wanted his love but had never had it. And never would now.

'Come,' he repeated, and held out one hand. But she pointedly ignored it, stepping aside, giving him a wide berth as she began to walk up the lonely forest track. And he followed, overtaking her easily, anger back in every rapid stride as he thrust onwards, taking a narrower, rarely used track, and she tagged after him because there was nothing else to do and he would only drag her along, the mood he was in, if she gave in to her instincts and sat down on the loamy floor of the forest and put back her head and howled.

And just when she thought she was fated to follow him through this lonely place for all time he flung over his shoulder, 'When you walked out on me you should have said you couldn't bear to touch me. I just might not have bothered finding you!'

'I don't know why you did!' she hurled right back, her breath coming rapidly, due more to the knowledge that they were at last beginning the final confrontation than the pace he had set.

As long as he never discovered just how much she

longed for his touch and how often, during the past three months, she had cried herself to sleep, aching for the physical intimacy they had once shared and which he, for obvious reasons, shunned, she would be able to hang on to the new beginnings of her self-respect.

'I would have thought you'd be far too busy back at South Park with Zanna—and young Harry!'

They had reached a clearing, the tall trees like a cathedral vault overhead, golden sunlight filtering through, making the silent shadows dimmer. And he stopped, and turned, facing her, and, for a moment, an image of pain flickered over his face. And then nothing. His features could have been carved from marble as he told her, 'I understand your jealousy. But don't let it warp your very existence. I promise you, Beth, there will be others for you.'

She didn't know how she stopped herself from slapping him, stopped herself from yelling out all her disgust and rage. But she managed it, remembering in time that, believing as he did that their marriage had been without love on both sides, he would naturally assume that she would find someone else.

And now was the time to get everything straight, and she steeled herself for that, wondering if he could hear the heavy, panicky beat of her heart in this dim green silence.

Taking a hold on herself, she told him calmly, 'I know why Zanna came back with Harry. I overheard you talking together the day they arrived.'

There, it was out. He had no need now to break the 'news'. And she heard him drag in his breath and then expel it slowly, the tight span of his shoulders relaxing beneath the soft dark fabric of his sweatshirt.

'So at least you understand about that.' His fine eyes darkened with something she couldn't put a name to and, almost too late, she saw the trap she had walked into.

She had told him she'd overheard that conversation, and she knew he would be remembering, too, the things that had been said. How he'd already told the woman he loved that the ill-begotten marriage he'd entered into with the unsuitable Beth Garner was over. And how, because of that, Zanna had returned, bringing their son. She'd done her best as a single parent, but Harry needed his father, too.

Fleetingly, Beth wondered why Zanna had walked out on Charles in the first place. Their deep, obsessive love for each other had been the talk of the neighbourhood gossips for months.

Then, quickly, she pushed those thoughts out of her head, painfully aware of Charles's intent gaze. One way or another she had to extricate herself, step back from the trap she had almost walked straight into.

Somehow, Charles had to be made to believe a lie, believe that she had walked out on him, not because Zanna had returned and Charles wanted a divorce, but because she, Beth, had decided she'd had enough.

Walking out on him before he could ask her to go was the only way to salvage her pride. She had nothing else left.

'Of course I understand,' she told him crisply, resisting the impulse to hug her arms around her slender body because, despite the warmth of the day, she was

cold inside, aching with it. 'But it isn't really important. It was nothing to do with my reasons for wanting
a separation.'

'Which were?' He had moved closer to her and the
very forest trees seemed to hold their breath. Beth
couldn't speak, her heart beating crazily, making her
head spin.

She couldn't lie to him, not about a thing like that,
she agonised, looking up at him, the bones of his face
tight with tension. She simply couldn't do it. How
could she deny her love for him? The love that had
been growing, maturing and strengthening since she
was fifteen years old?

'Your reasons, Beth?' he pressed darkly, his eyes
narrowing as they swept her anguished features.

She flung out breathlessly, retreating, 'The same as
yours, I imagine. We both know what these last few
months have been like. The marriage simply didn't
work out.'

And he could translate that any way he wished, she
thought distractedly, trying to stifle a betraying sob.
And the most likely interpretation he would put on her
evasive answer would be to believe that she, like himself, had grown tired of the sterile relationship, had
long since reached the stage when even physical interest was totally dead. The way she had refused to take
his hand back there, avoiding his touch, would reinforce that opinion.

'I don't believe this.' He looked as if she had
slapped him, and she didn't understand—her brain was
too confused and tired to work anything out. And why
didn't he simply take what she had handed him on a

plate, cut and run—right back home to the eagerly
waiting Zanna? Why drag this awful confrontation out?

She couldn't stand much more of this. Her emotions
had been dragging her down ever since she had eaves-
dropped on that conversation, trying to avoid the inevitable, running away when he'd told her that he and
Zanna had something to say to her.

Weakly, she closed her eyes, doing nothing to prevent the hot salty tears that trickled down her cheeks.
All she wanted was for him to leave her alone, allow
her some dignity. He had got exactly what he wanted,
hadn't he? Did he have to have his pound of flesh,
too?

'Beth. Don't.' His voice was raw and before she
knew what was happening his arms were around her,
dragging her close into his body, and for one insane
moment she allowed herself to melt, to cling to him,
blocking her mind to the way things were.

'Tell me what's wrong,' he whispered darkly, one
strong hand cradling her head into the solid angle of
his shoulder, and the blood began to beat thickly
through her veins, drugging her, and only when his
other hand began a slow caressing movement along the
length of her spine did she realise what she was doing.

She was allowing him to take the initiative, all over
again, as he always had in their relationship. Not content with tossing her aside as soon as the woman he
really loved appeared back on the scene, he wanted a
run-down on her battered feelings.

Well, she wasn't going to pander to his male ego.
Wrenching her head away from its dangerous resting
place, she bunched her hands into small fists and

pushed against his shoulders, at the end of her tether, grinding out, 'Leave me alone, can't you?'

Her efforts to push him away were worse than futile; they seemed to be heightening his desire to subdue her, she thought frantically, noting the rapid rise and fall of his deep chest, the savage glitter of his narrowed eyes as he tightened his hold on her squirming body and bit out, 'Why the hell should I? You're still my wife, damn it!'

And then the world went very still, very silent, only the chaotic drumbeats of her heart sounding wildly in her ears, only her own sobbing, burning breath, the quick, rasping hiss that escaped his clamped lips before his mouth possessed hers in a brutal kiss that was like nothing that had ever gone before, his big body subduing her panicky attempts to escape, carrying them both down to the soft forest floor, down and down to a hot dark warmth from which there was no way out. A burning, feverish heat, all sense and reason gone because, although he no longer wanted her in his life, she was still, legally, his possession, and he was stamping his brand, this one last time, just to prove his domination.

And this was going to be rape.

CHAPTER FOUR

BUT it wasn't rape. Of course it wasn't.

As far as Charles was concerned, Beth's responsive body was all fire and fury, matching his own. It had been so long since he had touched her, wanted her, that when she felt his hard body covering hers all logical thought flew out of her head, her arms reaching up to twine around him, gathering him closer.

And, as if her eager response triggered a more caring approach, the tenderness that had always been an intrinsic part of his passion in the early days of their marriage, his kiss gentled, his mouth tasting hers now, exploring a world within a world, searching, finding the gateway to her soul.

Because her soul, her heart, her mind and body would always belong to him, no matter what happened, Beth thought, and closed her mind off as his sure fingers undid the buttons of her top and slid the soft fabric from her gleaming satiny shoulders, and surrendered herself to him and the moment—the future, the past no longer important.

Groaning softly, he buried his face in her breasts and her throat arched back, her hands avidly stroking the magnificent breadth of his back beneath his sweatshirt, the strong arch of his ribcage.

It wasn't a journey of discovery; she was simply coming home. She knew and worshipped every inch of his hard male body, and when he lifted his head and looked at her from narrowed, glittering eyes, she could only whisper his name.

'Kiss me,' he commanded roughly, his skin pulled tight across his angular cheekbones, and she lifted eager hands to his head, her fingers twisting in the dark softness of his hair as she pulled him down, her lush lips parted, receptive.

And when she thought she would die from the sweet, melting torment of his mouth he rolled away from her, his eyes holding hers with scorching intensity as his hands went to the buckle of the leather belt that spanned his narrow waist. And her whole body was shaken with fine tremors of need.

For far, far too long she had ached for the love he had denied her and their mating on the soft forest floor was explosive, a wild, tumultuous release that left her satiated, her delicate body bruised by passion, curling immediately into the sheltering warmth of his as she fell asleep with the utter suddenness of a child.

Waking slowly, Beth felt flutters of cool air beating against her naked skin and she made a tiny mewing sound of distress then opened her eyes, focusing on the tall, dusk-shadowed man. He was fully dressed now, zipping up his jeans, and, at her small sound of protest, he was on his knees in front of her, his hands rubbing her arms and shoulders, his voice rough at the edges as he told her,

'You're cold. I'll help you dress.'

And he did, his fingers deft and sure, making up for her clumsiness. Her brain was in shock at what had happened, the lovemaking he had forced upon her to begin with but which she, craven idiot that she was, had then actively encouraged.

She felt so ashamed of herself that she wanted to die.

She had slept in his arms for hours, his body half covering her, keeping her warm, and now she was stiff and cold, back to reality, the fantasy and magic all gone.

Because there had been no magic at all, she reminded herself as she forced her feet into her sandals, merely stupidity on her part and the natural masculine desire to brand a possession—even if he no longer actually wanted it.

Ineffectively trying to smooth the crumpled folds of her skirt, she whimpered her self-disgust, and Charles said thickly, his face remote, 'Have my sweatshirt.' He was already beginning to strip it off and although the extra warmth would have been welcome it would be his warmth. She shook her head impatiently.

'No, thanks,' she said, and set off quickly down the track. 'I have to get back.' Back to the security of the old farmhouse, her own little room. She would think about how to explain her long absence to William some other time. Just now the degrading way she had behaved left no room for anything else in her head.

One minute she'd been telling her husband that she understood why he'd taken his former mistress back into his life, saying that, in any case, she had been thinking about a separation for some time, implying that he could have the divorce he so obviously wanted if he were to legitimise his son. And the next... Well, the next minute she had been locked in his arms, writhing around on the forest floor, practically begging him to make love to her!

'Beth.' He caught her arm, just above her elbow, swinging her round to face him. It was already late afternoon and the heavy canopy of leaves cut out the light and his face was shadowed, remote. 'We have to talk.'

'Not now!' She dragged her arm away and watched his hands fall to his sides, his mouth clamping in a grim line. She swung away again, her slender shoulders rigid with temper.

How could he expect her to discuss the divorce he wanted, sordid things like settlements or whatever, when he had so recently filled her body with the explosion of his passion? How could he bring that hateful subject up? Couldn't he see how she was almost disintegrating with self-disgust, her anger the only thing keeping her together?

And she snapped through her teeth, 'Just drive me home. I never want to see you again!'

'If that's what you want,' he ground out tightly, overtaking her with long, furious strides, stalking ahead and flinging over his shoulder, 'But Templeton's house is not your home. Never forget it!'

Dog in the manger, Beth thought angrily, her burning eyes boring into his back as he swung through the trees on the track ahead. He no longer wanted her as his wife, yet he couldn't bear the thought of her being with another man.

Not that her relationship with William was in any way sexual. She was here to do a job, and after taking off for the best part of the day, when what she and

Charles had had to say to each other would have only needed ten minutes at most, she might not have a job to go back to, she thought sniffily.

Charles reached the car well ahead of her and was waiting, holding the door open, and she got in, not able to look at him because he had reduced her to the status of a plaything, had decided to indulge in one last sexual romp before he tossed her out of his life forever.

And she, poor fool, had urged him on! She disgusted herself, she really did!

He drove back to the farmhouse in silence—the air in the cabin of the car was thick with it—and as she fumbled to release her seatbelt he glanced at his watch, his brows drawn together in a heavy bar of impatience.

'Nothing's been resolved. Not a damn thing.' His fingers beat an irritated tattoo on the wheel and she slid out of the car quickly as he threatened, 'But I'll be back. Make no mistake about that.'

Her fingers quivering on the door, Beth retorted sharply, 'Don't bother. Make all the arrangements for the divorce through my solicitor,' and banged it shut, wincing as a moment later she heard the powerful engine roar to life, scattering the handful of foraging hens when the car shot out of the courtyard on an angry, full-throated snarl.

She was shivering with reaction as she crept round the side of the house, making for the kitchen. She couldn't face her employer until she'd pulled herself together. Trying to come up with a reason to excuse her hours-long absence wasn't going to be easy. She certainly couldn't tell him the truth, tell him that she'd spent the afternoon making love with her estranged husband, sleeping naked in his arms!

Mariette was in the kitchen, podding broad beans ready for the evening meal, her small black eyes gleaming with curiosity, and Beth could almost see the wheels in her brain turning as she tried to find the English words for the endless questions that were obviously right there on the end of her tongue.

Giving the housekeeper a wan smile, Beth scurried through to the annexe to the privacy and safety of her own room. It would be a long time before she got over the trauma of what had happened this afternoon, the disgust she felt for her own behaviour. She simply wasn't up to facing anyone until she could face herself.

But she would have to face William, she reminded herself sharply as she emerged from the shower and dressed in a fresh skirt and cotton-knit sweater. When his secretary disappeared for hours on end he was entitled to an explanation.

She found him in the airy sitting-room of the main house, the room they took their meals in, and he had his back to her, standing by the window with the pages of manuscript she'd typed previously in his hands. And he turned sharply as she entered and, amazingly, there was nothing on his bluntly good-looking face but relief.

'Are you all right? When you didn't come back I thought that brute had done something to you. I was beginning to panic.'

'I'm sorry.' Thick hot colour slid over Beth's face as vivid pictures of exactly what 'that brute' had done to her flooded her mind. But she couldn't put that into words, could she? And she began to gabble, 'Our—our discussion took longer than I'd bargained for. I'll make up the time, of course.'

'Don't even think of it,' William dismissed gruffly. 'Just as long as you're all right.' He moved over to the table Mariette had already set, poured wine and handed her a glass. 'Sit down and drink this. You look as if you need it.' And as she gratefully sank down on to the sofa he sat beside her, his big-knuckled hands hanging between his knees, questioning, 'Was it to do with a divorce? When you came here you told me you were separated. My advice is, give him what he wants. He'll take it, anyway—he looks that type.'

Beth nodded, too choked to speak, twisting the stem of the wine glass around in her fingers, and William patted her shoulder awkwardly, his voice gruff as he added, 'There aren't any children, are there?' and she shook her head.

No, there were no children. Just Harry. Just Charles's son. But not hers, of course. Never hers. She had lost her child, along with all her foolish dreams of happiness, three long months ago.

Her eyes filled with sudden unstoppable tears and William said quickly, 'I'm sorry. None of my business. But if the brute's made you unhappy my advice is cut and run. Forget him and don't look back. It never pays. And don't forget, if you ever want to talk it out, need a shoulder to lean on, I'm here.' He had gone very pink, changing the subject rapidly. 'I'm going to be up to my eyeballs in research tomorrow, so why don't you take the morning off, go into Boulogne, have lunch and bring back some fish for supper?'

'Are you sure you won't need me?' He was doing his best to be kind, manufacturing an errand as an excuse for her outing, despite the hours she'd wasted today.

He was a dear, and not to know that she would much prefer to work flat out. Hard work was the only thing that would take her mind off her misery. But she couldn't throw his kindness back in his face, especially when he beamed, 'I've told you. I've got to get a few facts straight before I can go any further, and I prefer to do my own research. And I'm partial to fish, straight from the boats. See if you can get a couple of good sole.'

'Yes, of course.'

She did her best to look pleased, more than grateful that he hadn't bawled her out for disappearing for hours, staying away with the stranger who had invaded the privacy of his home, a stranger he obviously disliked as intensely as Charles disliked him. And, just for one weak moment, she was tempted to confide in her kindly employer.

It would be a relief to talk about the pain and misery she'd endured, the insecurity of knowing that her husband no longer pretended to want her in any meaningful way, the dreadful shock she'd sustained when Zanna had come back on the scene. She'd never talked about it to anyone, never hinted—even to her parents—that anything was wrong.

Sighing, she pushed the weak moment aside. Who was she to burden others with her misery? William was only her employer, after all. If she told him the whole truth she might only manage to embarrass him. No one

wanted to be burdened with another's troubles. And
she had their future working relationship to think of.

Beth parked her car on the quai Gambetta and made
for the fish stalls, the pale lemon skirts of her light
cotton dress swinging around her long, slender legs,
the wind from the sea tossing her glossy dark hair,
setting it flying around her face.

There was a spring in her step this morning, a half-
excited, half-fearful hope in her heart, a hope she had
tried to kill—and, having failed, was determined to act
on.

She bought the fish William wanted, two large sole
fresh from the boats, and hurried back to the car, oblivious to the bustle of locals and the British tourists who
were buying the famous Boulogne mussels and oysters
to take home on the ferry. At any other time she would
have lingered, enjoying the sounds, sights and smells,
used the holiday William had given her to explore the
ancient town which Henry VIII of England had once
captured and where Napoleon had spent three years
preparing to invade in his turn.

But, even though she half feared she was going on
a fool's errand, she had to see Charles. In answer to
William's question he had given the name of his hotel
and, before she steeled herself to face the irretrievable
breakdown of her marriage to the only man she had
ever loved, ever could love, she had to see him one
last time.

Trying to steady her racing heartbeats, to warn herself that nothing might come of this one last meeting,
she found a space on a multi-storey car park, rum-

maged in her handbag for her small hand-mirror and
checked her reflection. Her huge green eyes were over-
bright, feverish, too big for her small, pointed face.
And her full, wide mouth still looked swollen from the
passionate imprint of Charles's sensual onslaught. And
there were lines of strain, too, deepening the hollows
beneath her cheekbones, painting dark smudges beneath her eyes.

Pushing the mirror back into her bag, she snapped
it shut decisively and left the car. Bewailing the havoc
that was the result of a sleepless night wasn't going to
achieve a thing.

She had lain awake, tormented by memories. For
months, ever since the accident, he hadn't come near
her, hadn't so much as touched her hand, carefully
avoiding any physical contact, spending more and
more time away from home.

Yet yesterday afternoon he had acted as if he was
starving for her; his hoarse cry of male exultation as
he had driven her to the wild heights of ecstatic fulfilment and then exploded catacyclismically inside the
throbbing sheath of her body had surely been more
than the climax of pleasure gained from having a final
sexual fling with a wife he no longer cared about.

Could he have made love to her with such tumultuous passion, shown such tenderness, if she no longer
meant anything to him? It was a question she couldn't
answer, but was determined to ask.

If there was any hope, no matter how slight, for their
marriage, then she was going to put up a fight to keep
him, she vowed staunchly as she walked back down

the hill from the old town, through the maze of little streets with their tempting shops and restaurants.

Praying he hadn't already left for home—last evening he'd clearly been pushed for time, as she'd noted when witnessing his impatient glance at his watch—she hurried on, her high heels tapping on the cobbles. If there was the remotest chance of saving their marriage then, clearly, he must recognise Harry as his son, see him regularly, make provision for his future.

Despite the loss of her own child, Beth was sure she could come to terms with such a state of affairs—if only she could be sure that his obsession with the boy's mother was a thing of the past!

'Well, well—look who's here!' The husky drawl was unmistakable and Beth's feet froze to the spot while cold apprehension crawled all over her body. She didn't believe this was happening, she simply didn't believe it!

She turned her head slowly towards the pavement tables outside the restaurant she'd been so blithely passing and her heart wrenched painfully inside her as she met Zanna's scornfully derisive eyes.

Her mouth dry as dust, she could only stand and stare, transfixed, as Zanna's lush scarlet lips parted in a parody of a smile.

'Charles said you were taking a working holiday—a euphemism, if ever I heard one.' She put her coffee-cup back on its saucer and leaned back in her chair, her red-gold hair curling on to the delicately tanned shoulders the low-cut white sundress she was wearing left bare. And her voice was brittle now. 'But we all know why you took to your heels, don't we? Your prim little mind couldn't face the fact of Harry's existence—you couldn't even bear to discuss the ramifications, could you? Not that your pigheaded cowardice makes a scrap of difference; what's happened has happened and even if your delicate sensibilities are offended you can't alter a thing.'

'I have no intention of trying.' Beth had found her voice now but it emerged sounding rusty, as if she hadn't used it in a long, long time.

Charles had sought her out for one purpose only—to discuss the divorce. And even then he hadn't been able to be parted from the woman he had loved for years, the woman who had only recently come back into his life. She wondered hysterically what the other woman would say if she told her how those discussions had never taken place and exactly how they'd been side-tracked!

But she held her tongue, biting back the bitter words because, although they would show Charles in a bad light, they would also reveal her own total vulnerability to him—the way she had behaved like a sex-starved wanton while he, as she had originally and logically believed, had only been putting his mark of possession on her for one last time—his sexual arousal down to the fact that he had disapproved of his titular wife living under the same roof as her employer.

And at that moment she hated everyone—Charles, Zanna, but most of all herself—and she clipped out emotionally, 'You can have what you want. It won't be long until your bastard can legitimately take the name of Savage!'

The moment the scathing words were out, she could

have bitten her tongue off. None of this mess was the child's fault, and from what she had seen of him during that dreadful weekend he was utterly charming, a well adjusted, confident little boy who resembled Charles so strongly that every time she had looked at him her heart had contracted, breaking up a little more.

'I'm sorry,' she murmured huskily, appalled at herself, but Zanna obviously took no offence, the thickness of her skin unbelievable as she shrugged.

'You're quite right, of course. That's what I plan and that's what is going to happen.' And then, amazingly, she patted the vacant seat beside her. 'Sit down. Charles shouldn't be long. He took Harry to watch the ferry docking and we arranged to meet here.' She inspected the face of her tiny jewelled watch. 'He should be here any moment; we're flying south this afternoon.'

South to the sun, to the exotic playgrounds of France, where the two of them could enjoy a romantic idyll, making up for the wasted years when they had been apart, their tiny son completing their bonding. She might have known that he wouldn't install his mistress and son at South Park until after the divorce, when he could take her there as his wife.

'No. Thanks,' Beth muttered, feeling ill. Did Zanna really expect her to sit and wait for the husband who so patently wanted her out of his life? Did she really expect the three of them to sit together, drinking coffee, making polite and meaningless conversation? That sort of thing might happen in the sophisticated circles Zanna moved in, but to Beth the whole idea was incredible.

'As you like.' The other woman gave a careless shrug. 'Run and hide from the facts again—it doesn't bother me. I always knew you weren't woman enough to hold him.' She gave a vicious little smile. 'Charles is strong meat. I never did think you could cope with a man that sexually dangerous, that overpowering.'

Wordlessly, Beth stumbled away, tears of humiliation blinding her. Like every young girl around, just emerging into womanhood, she had been irresistibly drawn to the dark potency of Charles Savage's intimidating masculinity. But, unlike the others, she hadn't grown out of it, found a man more easily tamed.

She, blind fool that she was, had believed she could handle the forceful and dangerous masculinity she sensed in him, could tame that dark presence with the strength of her love. And despite all that had happened, everything she knew, she had clung to that hopeless belief right up until half an hour ago. Fool!

At last, subsiding breathlessly into her car, she hauled herself together. Zanna knew, and had always known, that only a woman as powerfully seductive, as wilful as she was, could carve a place for herself in Charles's heart—carve it and keep it.

And now she, Beth, knew it too. And, at last, finally and with no looking back, accepted it. She would show the world that she was capable of living without him, could handle her life and her future—no matter how empty it seemed.

The rest of her life began right here and, no matter how tough the exercise, she would never look back.

Her hand quite steady, her features set, she reached for the ignition...

CHAPTER FIVE

THE August heat was stifling, thunder brewing ominously. Beth pushed her overlong fringe out of her eyes and tried to concentrate on transcribing her shorthand. She would have to make the effort to drive into Boulogne to get her hair restyled; the normally sleek and elegant cut was growing out of hand.

But what did it matter? she thought tiredly, closing her eyes, her shoulders slumping. Her brave intention to get on with her life, never looking back over her shoulder, had suffered a fatal set-back. How could she avoid staring back into the past when, two days ago, she had discovered she was pregnant?

Two days of remembering that afternoon, over six weeks ago, when her child had been conceived. Two whole days of alternating between the incredulous joy of knowing that her body harboured a brand-new life, a precious life, created with the man she loved, that the fear that the accident had impaired her ability to conceive had been unfounded, and the consequent despair that came of knowing that it was all too late.

Charles already had a child, a son he had welcomed and acknowledged, the woman he had never stopped loving with a passion that amounted to obsession ready and willing to take her place as his second wife.

Which left her, Beth, where?

In an extremely difficult situation.

Her parents would be returning from that world cruise by the middle of next month, and, although they would be saddened by the news of her impending divorce, they would be understanding and supportive. But she could hardly stay at her parents' home, waiting for the birth of her child, while, a scant quarter of a mile away, Charles, his new wife and their son were settling in at South Park. It would put them all in an impossible situation. A situation she couldn't face.

'Are you all right?'

Beth recognised the rough concern in William's voice and opened her eyes, straightening up over her work, feeling guilty.

'I'm fine. Just hot.' She gave him a tight smile. Lately, she had kept her smiles to a sparing minimum, tried to make their relationship more formal. Charles had seen what she had not—that William was more interested in her as a woman than as a secretary.

But then, she excused herself wearily, her love for Charles had been so staunch for so many years that it had blinkered her to the rest of the male sex.

'We're in for a storm.' He came to stand behind her, putting his hands lightly on her shoulders, and she felt her whole body tighten with rejection.

He was a highly intelligent man, a considerate and kindly employer, and he would make some woman an excellent husband. But she wasn't that woman. Her feminine intuition had picked up enough vibes to warn her that he thought she might be. He was an honourable man, not the type to want an affair. And, recently, her eyes had been opened, had seen what Charles had so quickly assimilated. It was all there, if one had the wits to look for it—the way his face lit up when she walked into a room, the way his eyes lingered on her lips, the way he touched her when there was no need to do so. As now.

She shifted abruptly, uneasily, in her seat, and his hands fell away immediately, but he told her quickly, 'Leave that. There's no rush to get it off. My publishers don't set deadlines.'

He moved to the other side of the room, and even though her back was to him she could hear him fiddling with the papers on his desk and her eyes stayed glued to the pages of shorthand waiting to be transcribed into neatly typed manuscript form.

His current book was finished, apart from the few pages to be typed, and when that was done her job here would be over and she would be free to go, and, although she had found security here, of a kind, she couldn't wait. She had her future life to sort out, not to mention that of her unborn child, and she needed to be alone, completely unpressured, before she could decide how best she could support herself and her baby.

'It's far too hot to work,' he mumbled from the other side of the room and then, more briskly, 'Besides, it's almost time for dinner. Mariette left cold beef and salad. Why don't you go and freshen up?'

And as she got to her feet, about to cry off dinner, plead a headache as an excuse for a really early night, he forestalled her. 'Your temporary job here is coming to an end. I'd like to discuss that with you over dinner.'

'Of course.' She covered the typewriter and walked to the door, her clothes sticking to her in the sultry heat. He was, first and foremost, her employer. If he wanted to discuss the termination of her job then she had no right to refuse him.

A generous employer, too, she reflected as, ten minutes later, she stood gratefully beneath a cool shower in her own tiny bathroom. She had saved most of the excellent salary he'd paid her, and she knew how to live frugally—which she would do when she was back in England and looking for work which would enable her to provide for both herself and her baby.

It wouldn't be easy, she thought as she patted herself dry and pulled a loose-fitting light cotton dress over her scanty underwear, fastening the buttons that went all the way down the front. Although it was designed to be belted, she opted to leave the filmy garment loose. It was too close and sultry to be constricted by anything remotely tight.

William probably wanted her to stay on until the end of the week, for although the remainder of the typing would only take another few hours there was always the chance that, having read through it, he might decide to make a few minor alterations. And that would suit her fine, she thought as she walked back into the main house, astonished to find that William had already set the table and brought the cold food from the fridge.

Not a huge or daunting task, she knew, and her soft mouth curved in an amused smile. But William was old-fashioned, and he liked to make himself appear incompetent where anything smacking of domesticity was concerned. Mariette was paid to put his meals in front of him and, on the rare occasion when she left early, that task fell to Beth.

'You look beautifully cool.' The appreciation in his voice as he looked at her from the other side of the room made Beth curse herself for her unguarded smile. Over the past few weeks, when her eyes had been opened at last to his growing awareness of her as a woman, she had been careful to keep everything formal, on a very businesslike footing indeed.

Not that she was apprehensive about it; she wasn't. He wouldn't make a move, say anything out of place, without encouragement. She was quite sure he wasn't that type of man. And encouragement she most definitely wasn't going to give. So she said tonelessly, 'Appearances can be deceptive. I just wish the storm would break to clear the air. I'm practically melting.'

'I've got just the cure for that!' William rubbed his hands, looking pleased with himself. 'Champagne on ice. Just the ticket, wouldn't you say?'

Without waiting for a reply, he filled two flutes, the liquid foaming, spilling on to the carpet, then handed one to Beth, and stood awkwardly, licking the drops from his fingers.

She sat down on the sofa, setting the glass aside. She didn't want the drink; alcohol would turn the niggling ache at the back of her eyes into a full-blown headache. Besides, she was only here with him now to discuss the termination of her part-time employment. So she asked him, 'When are you expecting me to leave? Would the end of the week suit you?'

The remainder of the typing would take a mere hour or so, and that would give her four whole days to make any alterations he might require, pack her gear, and decide how to tackle her future. Four days to get herself ready to leave the relative safety of this peaceful backwater cocoon.

'That's what I wanted to talk to you about.' He sat beside her, a little too close for her liking. He looked ill at ease, running a forefinger round the inside of his shirt collar. 'When my previous secretary ran out on me I immediately got in touch with an agency which specialises in placing people in full-time employment. And now, it seems, they've come up with someone who fits the requirements I laid down at the time. Fiftyish, a dedicated spinster, very efficient, no family ties to speak of, willing to live and work in France and able to start in the autumn when I'm due to begin my next book.'

'Great.' Beth was pleased for him. He was one of the nicest men she had ever met and deserved to have things run smoothly for him. He led a peaceful, uncomplicated life, rarely socialising, his head full of plots and words, leaving little room for anything else.

'Well—'

He didn't seem over the moon about the prospect, Beth noted. His thick brows were drawn together in a frown and his forehead was wet with sweat. Though that, of course, wasn't surprising, she thought wryly. The air inside the little room was like a hot wet blanket.

Outside, thunder cracked violently, making her flinch, lightning illuminating the room for one electrified second, and William mopped his brow with his shirt-sleeve.

'That sounded close. Not frightened, are you?'

'No.' The only thing that frightened her, scared her

silly, was the prospect of carrying the burden of her love for Charles through the remainder of her life. Resolutely, she pushed that bitter little reflection out of her head, shrugging. 'Should we eat? It's getting late.'

Not that she was hungry; she wasn't. But she craved solitude, the time needed to work out her future, and as far as she was concerned the discussion was over.

William had found himself an admirable full-time replacement and, although he hadn't said so, she was taking it for granted that she would be free to go at the end of the week.

But he said heavily, 'I'm not happy about your going. I'm sure the woman the agency came up with is admirable, but I'd rather you stayed. Permanently. Would you?'

He was perched on the edge of the seat, his eyes pleading directly into hers, his hands knotted together between his knees, looking as if he was waiting for a decision which would affect the rest of his life.

Beth sighed. A few weeks ago she would have jumped at his offer. The work was stimulating, her surroundings idyllic, the pay more than she felt she deserved and the man himself a poppet. But that had been before she had seen the way he looked at her, before she had realised that he was seeing her as more than a secretary. Before she had discovered she was pregnant.

'Would you?' he repeated thickly. 'And I do mean permanently—' The rest of his words were drowned under another crack of thunder, lashing above them and retreating to rattle among the hills, and the rain came down in torrents, flailing against the walls and windows, and William's face was knotted with frustration as he raised his voice to shout above the fury of the storm,

'I'm asking you to marry me, Beth. As soon as your divorce comes through we'll—'

'You can forget that, Templeton.' The steely, incisive voice made Beth's heart stand still and the room went quiet, and cold. It was as if Charles carried his own atmosphere around with him; even the tumult of the storm seemed to have abated, obliterated beneath the greater, icier violence of his tightly controlled rage.

He was standing in the open doorway, his black, rain-wet hair slicked to his skull, water darkening the fabric of his blue denim shirt, plastering it to the lean hard masculine frame. And he said, his narrowed gunfighter's eyes pinning William to his seat,

'I did knock, but got no reply. You were both, obviously, heavily otherwise occupied.' The steel-grey eyes slid to Beth, making an assessment of the filmy garment she wore, the long level look an insult in itself, and her own eyes dropped as she felt the hectic onslaught of painful colour flood her face.

He could put what interpretation he liked on the scene he had walked in on, and they wouldn't have heard him knock, would they? In the rage of the storm they wouldn't have heard a bomb if it had exploded on the doorstep! But her mind was out of control, her thoughts too chaotic to put into words. She was still in shock, booted there by his unexpected and unwelcome arrival. And it was the bemused William who found his tongue first.

'What do you want?' It wasn't said graciously and he didn't look gracious, his face red with frowning annoyance.

And Charles said simply, his voice curtly precise, 'My wife.'

Beth shuddered uncontrollably. She had never known he had a streak of possessiveness that was so wide and went so deep. He had no further use for her himself, and yet his pride wouldn't allow him to stand by and see another man pursue her. The knowledge made her cold.

'I'm sorry if you find the idea so repellent.' He had noted her shudder, of course he had. He didn't miss a trick. And he went on, the severely honed features demonic, 'But you are my wife. That is a fact.'

'But for how long?' Beth demanded thickly, fighting back. He had heard William's talk of marriage—after the divorce—and had decided, despotically, to nip that little notion in the bud, disregarding the fact that his impatience for his own second marriage had to be the foremost thought in his mind.

He wasn't to know that, even if she weren't pregnant by him, she would never have accepted William's proposal. How could she have done when the cruel fates had conspired to ensure that she would travel through life capable of loving only one man?

He disregarded her throaty question—it had probably hit too closely to home—and his voice was terse with a still, devastating command as he bit out, 'Get packed. We're leaving now.'

His statement hung on the sultry air, suspended by sheer disbelief, and Beth grated out, her nerves at screaming pitch, 'Legally, I may still be your wife. But you can't tell me what to do!' Shaking inside, she made the effort to gather herself together, stay calm. 'I have a job to do here, remember?'

And William, taking his cue from her, blustered, 'That's right, Savage! Beth is employed by me, and paid by me. She has unfinished secretarial duties—'

'Is that what you call them?' Charles queried contemptuously, then went on to tell him, his narrowed, steely eyes never moving from Beth's anguished features, 'The day after tomorrow I'll have a secretary on your doorstep. At my expense, she will finish whatever my wife has left undone. Any other leisure-time projects you might have in mind, Templeton—' his hard mouth curled scornfully '—will be left to her discretion. Now, get your things together, Beth, or leave without them. It's up to you.'

Although his control hadn't flickered by as much as a hair's breadth, Beth knew him well enough to judge the extent of his anger. Knew that at any moment his tightly reined rage could explode with devastating results.

It was there for anyone with the wits to see it, there in the white-knuckled fists bunched against the black fabric that moulded his taut thighs, there in the smoky glint in those normally inscrutable gunfighter's eyes, in the aggressive tightening of his hard, wide jawline.

But William hadn't the wits or the discretion to see that, as far as Charles Savage was concerned, he was simply someone who was in the way, someone to be trampled heedlessly underfoot if necessary, and Beth tensed with apprehension as her employer got to his

feet, blustering, 'Now look here—you can't barge into
my home and tell my secretary what to do. She may
be your wife—' his face went purple under the shaft
of icy contempt coming his way from the younger,
powerfully leashed intruder '—but, I can tell you this,
she doesn't want you, she wants a divorce. And I'm
not going to stand by and let you force her to do anything she doesn't want to do.'

The blustering bravado of his tone had drained
away, his voice tailing off, and Beth knew he was already regretting his hasty defence of her by the way
he suddenly sat down under the frozen threat of
Charles's eyes. And when Charles warned, 'Try to in-
terfere in my life, and you'll find yourself plastered on
the walls,' Beth stalked to the door, her body rigid with
tension because she knew he meant every word.

She paused, looking back at William, who refused
to meet her eyes and dropped his gaze to the floor.
'I'm sorry. I never had any intention of allowing you
to become embroiled in my domestic concerns. I'll
pack now. It's for the best.'

She made her way to her room, her legs stiff, as if
her body was in shock, and gathered her things together, hurling them haphazardly into her suitcase.
Pummelling them down with her tight little fists to
make them fit, she knelt to fasten the clasps and the
light went out, lightning hitting a power line somewhere, knocking out the supply. And that dark voice
said from the doorway, almost politely, 'Do you need
any help?'

'No!' she said quickly, and then her breath locked
in her lungs. She couldn't see him, only sense his dark

presence, like a nightmare, every last cell in her body totally and utterly aware of his nearness, and if he came closer she would scream.

Near or far, he represented a danger she could no longer hope to handle. Once she had believed in the power of her love, but that was futile now. It hadn't worked, and never would, and his draconian pursuit of her, his need to bring her to heel, was scaring her out of her wits.

But she wasn't going to let him see that. The one gain from their separation had been in the area of her pride, her self-respect. And she stood up, holding the suitcase in front of her like a shield, her voice tight with the outrage of what he was doing to her, what he was making her endure.

'You had no right to force your way in here, throwing your weight around. Apart from being the height of bad manners, you made me feel cheap, tawdry.'

'I have every right when I hear another man proposing marriage to my wife. I told you I'd be back, and if you feel cheap and tawdry then maybe that's down to the liberties you've been allowing Templeton to take over the last few weeks.'

His voice came thickly through the enveloping darkness, more oppressive than the storm-laden atmosphere, and the thunder growled and prowled, a fitting accompaniment, and she bit down on her lip, ignoring that disgusting insult, because who was he to dish out abuse when he was no doubt thoroughly enjoying an intimate relationship with the woman he intended to make his second wife? She hurled at him instead, 'OK, so you said you'd be back. I've been shaking in my shoes! So what took you so long?'

As if she didn't know! Why should he tear himself away from his south of France romantic interlude with the bewitching Zanna, the company of his child, to bother with his redundant wife? And why he had bothered to turn up eventually she would never know, unless it was to demonstrate how well he could wield the big stick!

'I doubt if the explanations would interest you,' he told her drily. 'You have shown yourself to be remarkably short on interest and concern—except for yourself.'

And she was still trying to get over the gross unfairness of that taunt when lightning jagged through the sky, throwing the grim lines of his devilish features into sharp relief, and he stepped forward, silently covering the space between them, one hand wrenching the suitcase from her, the other taking her arm, his grip inescapable.

'Let's go. I can think of better places to talk this through.'

In the darkness he was too close and Beth's blood thundered, the storm inside her outstripping the storm beyond the stout farmhouse walls. It was difficult negotiating their way through the house in the thick blackness, but Beth wasn't thinking about that, every sense, every thought unwillingly concentrated on the man at her side.

And once, as she blundered into the kitchen table, he slid an iron-hard arm around her, hauling her back against the tense warmth of his body.

Beth gave an agonised gasp, the effect of being so close to him again, her body melting into his as if they were two parts of a whole, hurting her more than her painful collision with the edge of the table.

But after a brief, smothered expletive, he moved on, taking her with him, and because they were so close she could feel the hammerbeats of his heart, hear his rapid breathing. Even so, he seemed able to see in the dark, like a cat, in spite of his being in unfamiliar surroundings, and when he released her to drag open the door that led to the courtyard she sagged against the old oak frame, pulling in lungfuls of the rain-sweet air.

And only then did her thought processes come together sufficiently to enable her to ask the question that should have been uppermost in her mind, but hadn't been.

'Where are we going? And why?' Why insist on taking her away from here when everything could have been dealt with by solicitors? And he surely didn't want her back at South Park when he would be taking Zanna and Harry there as soon as the divorce came through.

And his terse answer bore that out.

'Nowhere you know. Just a place I've found where we can settle this without interruptions, other people.'

There was little point in arguing. What could she say? That she refused to budge an inch? That would precipitate another scene, drenched with unspoken violence. And she couldn't do that to William. This was his home and this was her problem.

'No squeals of protest?' he enquired witheringly. 'You surprise me.' He took her arm and hustled her out into the rain, his breath hissing, 'No doubt you realise that it's no use running to Templeton for help. Your brave suitor has already thrown in the towel.'

His taunt infuriated her. She was simmering furiously as he hauled her along, her feet splashing through the puddles, the rain stinging her face, plastering her flimsy dress to her body. Who was he to jeer at the older man? William was decent and kind; he would never treat a woman the way Charles had treated her. And no man in his right mind would stand up to Charles Savage in this murderous mood, so his sarcasm, his taunt about throwing in the towel, were out of line.

And as they reached his car she told him so, wrenching her arm from his punishing grasp and informing him roughly, 'William is twice the man you'll ever be; he's—'

'I really don't want to know,' he drawled in return. 'Just get in.'

Which, helped by an ungentle shove from behind, Beth accomplished in seconds and, dripping wet, fuming, sat rigidly in the passenger-seat while the rain lashed the windscreen and Charles tossed her case into the boot before getting in beside her.

Wordlessly, he removed his sodden shirt and threw it on to the back seat, then, flicking on the courtesy light, he turned to her, his face all hard lines, instructing, 'Take your dress off.'

'No.' She started to shiver but felt her body go hot, remembering all too vividly that episode in the woods when their child had been conceived, knowing that her defences against him were all too few, and very tottery.

She was already painfully aware of his semi-nudity, the hair-roughened skin covering hard muscle and bone, the almost overpowering need to touch, to run her fingers over the wide thrust of his shoulders, trace the tight nipples with the tips of her fingers and follow the thick hairline to where it disappeared intriguingly beneath the low waistband of his jeans.

And he told her with quiet menace, 'Take it off, or I'll do it for you.' And he meant it, he meant it all right, and there was a sob in her throat, choking her, as her shaking fingers went slowly to the top button nestling between her breasts.

'And you can stop looking like a petrified virgin, my dear. I have no lustful intentions, believe me. I don't want you coming down with pneumonia, that's all.' He reached over to the back and hauled up a car blanket. 'You can placate your modesty with this.' His mouth was cruel as he lashed, 'I've seen your naked body before, remember? And right now I'm not in the mood to feel remotely interested.'

That should have reassured her, but it didn't. How could it when those narrowed, steel-grey eyes watched her every movement as she undid buttons and wriggled out of the clinging wet fabric, fastening on the betraying peaks of her breasts as they flaunted their shaming arousal through the delicate lace of her bra?

And when she made a shaky grab for the rug, to hide herself and the all-too obvious signs of her arousal, he held it back, his voice raw as he commanded roughly, 'And the rest.' But she couldn't move. How could she when her whole body was turning to boneless, aching receptivity, burning for his hands and mouth to touch her as his eyes were doing?

She made a small mew of distress, her pulses going into overdrive. She didn't know which was worse, her self-disgust or knowing that he had to be fully aware of how much she still wanted him. And he made an impatient sound, low in his throat, and swiftly dealt with the front fastening of her bra, his knuckles brushing against the hard, rosy velvet of her nipples before his hands slid to her rounded hips, dragging the matching lacy briefs down the length of her slender legs, his burning eyes resting for one tormenting moment on the riot of darkness that covered her throbbing womanhood before he tossed the rug over her.

'Cover yourself.' His voice was abrasive. And she whimpered, doing just that, shrinking into the soft fabric, hating herself for the way he made her feel, for the way he could so easily make her betray herself. Hating him, too, when he started the engine and asked, almost academically, 'Did you turn on so easily for Templeton? Was that the way you got him begging you to marry him?'

A hard lump of anger pushed against the inside of her chest and she could have wept, but she didn't. Instead, as the headlights of the powerful car cut a glittering swath through the darkness, she told him forcefully, hating him at that moment more than she'd ever hated anyone or anything before, 'You disgust me! You know nothing about my relationship with William. You know nothing! Do you hear me?'

'Oh, I hear you,' he countered rawly, swinging the big car on to the wet surface of the meandering lane.

'And getting to know all about your relationship with Templeton—among other things—is exactly what I have in mind. And where we are going, we'll have all the time it takes. And there won't be another man in miles for you to practise your seductive wiles on. Except me.'

And that was a promise she could do without.

CHAPTER SIX

'WHAT is this place?'

They had been driving for about an hour, the last quarter of which had been spent negotiating a roughly made forest track, straight as a die and probably a firebreak, and now the headlights revealed a small building huddled at the centre of a clearing, the tall trees crowding on every side.

'A shack,' he told her drily. 'Rented and basic it may be, but you may look on it as your temporary home.'

The dim green light from the dash made his face look unearthly, carved from some alien lunar stone and, to counter the terrifying feeling that she no longer knew him at all, had never truly known him or realised just what he was capable of, she snipped back sarcasticly, 'Gee—thanks! What have I done to deserve such a treat?' ending tartly, 'Where are Zanna and Harry?' Not here, for sure. Charles might have proved himself willing to do anything for the woman he loved, go to the ends of the earth, but the sophisticated Zanna wouldn't spend a moment under the roof of a hovel in the heart of a forest, miles from anywhere.

'Where the hell do you think?' he bit back tersely, the underbrow look he shot her saying he thought her mad, or despicable. Or both.

Beth shrugged, huddling deeper into the rug. His

reply told her nothing, of course. He hadn't meant it to. But she could guess. Living the life of Riley in some top international hotel in the south while Zanna waited for him to complete any unfinished business he had with his wife.

She shuddered then, beginning to panic as she wondered what that business would be. Everything could have been dealt with in a civilised way, through solicitors. Why his need to drag her here, subject her to the torment of being near him?

And the panic became almost uncontrollable as he cut the engine and headlights. The darkness was thick, impenetrable, the only sound the pattering of her heartbeats. She was sure he must be able to hear it, able, too, to read the chaos and confusion of her thoughts. But he pocketed the ignition key and told her, 'Stay where you are while I open the place up,' and she was able to breathe more easily as his dark form disappeared into the enveloping blackness. And by the time she saw the orange glow of light shining out from one of the tiny windows she had herself more or less under control.

If she'd been working for a woman, or if Charles hadn't seen what she'd been too blinkered to notice regarding the way William was beginning to feel about her, then he wouldn't have gone to these lengths in order to discuss their pending divorce. She would never have believed his possessiveness to be so deeply ingrained that it extended to the wife he no longer wanted if she hadn't borne the brunt of it.

Having sorted that out, she felt less confused, more able to face the coming twenty-four hours. Whatever it was Charles wanted to discuss with her personally couldn't take longer than that and he would be anxious to rejoin Zanna and their son. And the only way to handle what was to come was to behave with dignity, use her common sense and try to hide the way she was hurting.

Beginning right now.

Clutching the rug tightly around her, she opened the car door and slid out her long, naked legs. Thankfully, it had stopped raining, but she could still hear the storm grumbling away in the distance, a dark counterpoint to the steady drip-drip of raindrops from the eaves of the forest, and she had only gone two slithery paces towards the little light from the cottage when Charles appeared as if out of nowhere, his tall shadowy figure forbidding.

'Where the hell do you think you're going?'

His sudden, silent appearance had shocked the breath out of her lungs, making her doubt her ability to handle this at all, but pride came to her rescue again, had her hauling herself together, helping her to inject a note of sarcasm as she flung back witheringly, 'Out on the town, where else?' and made to walk past him, heading for that square of orange light, but he muttered a harsh expletive and scooped her up into his arms and she pummelled furiously against the hard bones of his shoulders, yelping,

'Put me down. I am capable of walking a few yards!' Being held so very close to him was seriously undermining her mental stability, she told herself, cursing the fragility of her resolve where he was concerned. This close she could easily find herself melting against

him, all liquid invitation, begging him to allow her to
try, once again, to teach him to love her.

'Suit yourself. If you want to wade through ankle-
deep mud, so be it,' he snapped out, then slid her down
the length of his body which, she decided in miserable
confusion, rated even higher in erotic stimulation than
being carried in his arms.

Biting her lip, she watched him stride ahead of her,
sure-footed as a cat. What did she have to do to turn
the tide of her emotions? How could she stop loving
him, wanting him, and begin the long haul back to the
peace of mind she craved?

Unable to find the answer, fearing she never would,
she began to follow, ignoring the drag of mud, intent
only on staying on her feet now, keeping the rug tightly
wrapped around her body.

'The power's out,' he informed her curtly as she
stepped over the threshold and closed the thick plank
door behind her. And, rather than look at him, meet
those clever, steely eyes, she peered about her.

It was a small room, the stone tiles beneath her feet
cracked and uneven with age, the walls roughly plastered, painted white, the furniture mostly pine, cottage
antiques. There were logs laid in the open hearth ready
for firing, and the two oil-lamps he had lit cast a warm,
intimate glow. A narrow wooden staircase led up from
one corner of the room and he must have been following the direction of the assessment she had tried to
make appear cool and only vaguely interested because
he told her acidly,

'We have two rooms. This and the bedroom above.
The kitchen and bathroom are tacked on. Primitive, but

adequate. I imagine it was once a woodsman's hut; it's not large enough to have been a hunting lodge.'

'I can't imagine why you bothered.' A nice touch of derision there. She bent to remove her muddy shoes, careful to keep her grasp on the enveloping rug firm, still keeping her eyes averted from him, then padded past him, making a show of opening the door which led into the built-on kitchen.

Basic, as he had said, but, as they wouldn't be here for more than a few hours tomorrow, adequate enough. And then, because she could sense his eyes on her, watching her every movement, she told him coldly, 'If, for some unknown reason, you wanted to discuss the details of the divorce personally, instead of through solicitors, you could have done it by phone. Don't you think dragging me out here was a touch melodramatic?' Oh, nicely said, she congratulated herself hollowly. She was at last getting the hang of presenting a cool, almost disinterested façade around him.

But the small success didn't make her feel any better; worse, if anything. She heard the deep pull of his indrawn breath and she did look at him then, hoping there was no trace of her inner anguish in her eyes. And what she saw made her heart turn over because he looked like a man who had recently travelled to hell.

His skin was taut across his facial bones, the character lines more deeply drawn, and there was a brooding savagery in his eyes that she had only seen once before. And that had been when Zanna had left him that first time.

First time? She shook her head unconsciously, pushing that unbelievable thought aside. She dared not allow herself to believe that the woman he loved, always would love, had once again walked out on him. But why else should he look as though the light had gone out of his life?

And then the moment was gone, pushed away by his tempered steel voice. 'And left you happily where you were—enjoying Templeton's lovemaking, drawing up cosy little plans for when you could be married? Sorry, my dear,' his voice became a menacing drawl, 'but I don't operate that way. And neither, as my wife, do you.'

Pointless to remind him that she wouldn't be his wife for much longer, or to tell him that William had never made love to her, that she would have run a mile if he'd tried it. That he might have proposed but that she would never have accepted in a million years. Pointless.

Suddenly Beth felt tears sting at the back of her eyes, making her throat burn. And she felt incredibly weary of the whole sorry mess, incredibly tired. She said numbly, 'If it's all the same to you, I'd like to get out of this rug,' then wished she'd kept her mouth firmly closed, a slow burn of colour covering her face as she remembered the way he'd looked at her naked body when, at his insistence, she'd removed her sodden clothing. Recalled how he'd asked if she turned on as easily for William. He must think she was a sex-starved tramp.

Besides, he had to remember her passionate, uninhibited response to his lovemaking before the loss of their child. The way he had refused to come near her, touch her, in the empty months that had followed. He would be putting two and two together and drawing the conclusion that sexual frustration had led her to jump into bed with William Templeton, not to mention wholeheartedly enjoying a sexual romp on the floor of the forest with the husband she had professed not to want, had walked out on!

His face was white, his mouth clamped in tight disgust, a muscle working sporadically along his hard jawline and, to dispel what he was obviously thinking, she said sharply, 'Don't worry, I'm not offering anything. I'd simply like to have a hot bath, if there is such a thing, and turn in. Whatever you have to say to me can wait until tomorrow.'

He didn't say a word. He gave her a long, complicated look then picked up her suitcase and walked up the narrow stairs. Beth followed, reluctantly and only because she had to, had no other option, clutching at the rug, hoisting it above her knees, afraid she might trip.

The stairs gave directly into a bedroom with a sloping ceiling. It was basically and simply furnished with a double bed she thought she might need a step-ladder to climb on to, a pine chest of drawers and a chair, and no door except one in narrow, white-painted pine boards, set into the opposite wall.

'The bathroom, such as it is, is through there.' Charles put the case down and gestured towards the white-painted door. 'No bath, but there is a shower and if the power's gone out recently there should still be some hot water.' He turned and took a dark navy sweater from one of the drawers, pulling it over his head.

She snapped out, all too revealing, 'About time, too!' Half naked, he presented a problem, especially so in the confines of the small room. She only had to look at his bronzed, hair-roughened skin to ache to touch it, to feel the vital warmth of flesh and blood, the hardness of bone and sinew, to feel his body respond to her as once it had done.

And one brow arched darkly, as if he knew what lay behind her snapped retort, but his mouth was unsmiling, the look he gave her long and hard before wide shoulders rose in a slight, dismissive shrug beneath the clinging, expensive wool. 'It's gone colder. I'll put a match to the fire before I make supper. Soup and rolls be enough?'

It had gone colder. The storm had cleared the air and the interior of the cottage felt chilly. Still Beth's slight body was burning, every cell, every nerve-end ignited by the mere fact of his presence, but she wasn't going to admit to that. And she wasn't going to prolong the torment of this crazy evening.

Tomorrow morning, after a night's sleep, would be soon enough to get to grips with his reasons for bringing her here, listen to whatever it was he had to say that couldn't have been discussed by letter or over the phone.

'I don't want anything.' She turned her back, opening her suitcase and rummaging around for the old, worn T-shirt she had taken to wearing to bed since leaving him.

Before then, before that fateful day when Zanna had reappeared, she had always worn the finest satins and silks at night, the most seductive nightwear money could buy, because she had never given up hoping that he would change his mind and come to her...

'Just one thing...' The harshness of his tone made her spine go stiff, her fingers rigid among the muddle of her hurried packing. 'Did you meet up with Templeton before, arrange to leave me and go to him? Or was it sheer coincidence that you went to work for him and made him fall in love with you?'

She did move then. Moved in one swift, fluid movement, totally oblivious of the way the rug pooled at her feet. And her head came up, her eyes sparking emerald defiance, clashing with his icily narrowed, probing gaze.

'Don't tar me with the same brush that blackened you!' Throughout their married life he had secretly yearned for the woman he really loved, had at some stage met up with her, arranged for her, Beth, to be tossed aside like an old rag. Must have done. Zanna had already known that his marriage was over. He had to have told her. Had he pleaded with Zanna to return to him, promised to get rid of his unwanted wife?

'Talk about double standards!' she spluttered on, furious now, forgetting her vow to remain calm, in control, act as if she no longer cared, had stopped caring a long time ago. 'But no, I had never met William before I went to work for him. And no again, I didn't ''make'' him fall in love with me.'

She was in a prime position to know how cold-bloodedly he'd married her, making no secret about his desire for a family, young children to fill the empty rooms at South Park, to inherit his considerable wealth. He had never even pretended to love her. Simply decided, after that six months' probationary period, that she would make an acceptable mother of his children, a good hostess, a biddable wife. So, knowing all that, she couldn't help tacking on, her short upper lip curling scornfully, 'Do you really see me as the sort of woman who could go around seducing every man she meets into falling in love?'

The very idea was risible, insane, and Charles was at last showing himself in his true colours, revealing the tortuous reasoning behind his strange behaviour.

He hadn't followed her to France to discuss their divorce, dragged her here because he had some complicated settlement to talk out. The cunning devil was trying to turn the tables, to make her seem the guilty party. How he must have rubbed his hands when he'd walked in and witnessed William's proposal of marriage!

He was sneaky and devious and—

And he was looking at her, a small smile tugging at the corners of his mouth, his eyes caressing her heaving breasts, sliding over her narrow waist, the gentle curve of her belly, down her long, slender legs, then slowly up again. And the smile became very slightly cruel as he told her, 'Very capable indeed. Capable of seducing any man who's once looked on that delectable body and is fool enough to think he can hold on to you.'

And only then, at last penetrating her fury, came the knowledge that she was stark naked!

She swooped, almost toppling over in her panic, her fingers scrabbling for the protective covering she hadn't, in her blind anger, realised she'd lost, dragging it up in front of her, colour scalding her face.

And when her stormy eyes at last locked with his she was sure she could detect the cruel light of amusement in the stony depths, and he said, slowly and very deliberately, 'That's one thing straight. Something we can begin to work on tomorrow.' Then turned on his heels. And although she couldn't make sense of what he had said she could swear she could hear his silent, derisive laughter ringing inside her head as he went swiftly down the stairs.

As soon as he'd gone she made a determined effort to pull herself together and began to hurry. She wouldn't put it past him to come back up, and having him walk in on her while she was in the shower was something she could do without.

Thankfully, he'd left the lamp he'd carried upstairs and as she put it down carefully on a marble-topped washstand in the tiny bathroom she reflected that he might also decide to share her bed. The thought made her go cold.

They hadn't shared a bed since her miscarriage and if he decided he wouldn't be able to sleep on the small, hard-looking sofa downstairs and took it into his head to join her she didn't know what she would do.

Throw him out? Physically, she was no match for him and if he'd made up his mind there would be nothing she could do or say to make him change it. And if she tried to leave him to it, sleep on the uncomfortable sofa herself, he would be angry and she knew what could happen then.

It was anger, nothing less, that had sparked off his

arrogant male desire that afternoon in the forest... And her control was still too fragile to be relied on...

He hadn't been near her. Which shouldn't have surprised her, given his track record during the latter part of their marriage. But it did, she thought, struggling into a sitting position, her knees up to her chin, the duvet huddled around her.

Or was it disappointment? asked a snide little voice from deep inside her. But she pushed the notion away, quickly. No, of course not. If he'd joined her in bed she'd been planning on feigning sleep but knew that if he so much as touched her—even accidentally—she would have jumped like a scalded cat or melted straight into his arms. Either way, the ending would have been the same.

And although having him make love to her would be nothing short of ecstasy it would also be a massive stumbling-block where her resolve to get on with her life without him, never looking back, was concerned.

Besides, on his part, it would only be animal lust. He didn't love her, never had. He'd never stopped loving Zanna. So, it would be lust, allied to his desire to stamp her in his own mind as a tramp, always willing, whatever the occasion, whoever the man!

She was quite sure now that he was intent on making her out to be the guilty party, finding all the evidence he could to point to that—hence the lovemaking on the first occasion he'd tracked her down. She could be turned on by anyone—the first man she'd come into contact with after leaving, the man who happened to be her employer—even the husband she'd asked for a

divorce only had to touch her to get her half crazed
with desire, begging for more!

Oh, yes, she thought sourly, running her fingers
through her rumpled hair, she knew he intended making her out to be a shameless tramp, the guilty party
in the break-up of their marriage. And, what was more,
she knew why!

The Savage family had been at South Park for gen-
erations, owning most of the land, most of the property,
for miles around. They were looked up to, almost revered as good landlords, local squires noted for their
compassion and concern, interested in the lives and
problems of the village and surrounding scattered-farm
population.

Reciprocally, the community returned that interest,
and with a vengeance! Nothing the Savage family did
escaped the notice of at least one villager, who would
then proceed to pass it on to everyone willing to listen.
And most were more than willing, although her father
had once grunted, 'Gossip may be a normal human
failing, but this time it's going too far. I pity the poor
devil, having to lead his life in the full glare of public
scrutiny and mindless tittle-tattle—he's having a hard
enough time, without knowing that every last move he
makes is avidly discussed on every doorstep.'

And even now she could still hear her mother's patient reply. 'The gossip isn't malicious. People are
sorry for him—especially now that James is working
abroad. Poor Charles has simply gone in on himself,
shutting himself away in that great empty house,
brooding. He was obsessed by that Zanna Hall, every-

one knew it. And now she's left him. People say she refused point-blank to marry him and tie hersef down.'

'"People say"!' her father had repeated scathingly. 'They might well say, but how much do they actually know?'

'You'd be surprised.' Her mother had quietly continued with her knitting. 'Anyway, you can't hide something as obvious as an all-out obsession. Everyone said no good would come of it. And it hasn't, has it?'

No, no good had come of it, Beth reflected sourly. And Charles would be perfectly well aware how tongues would wag—with utter disgust this time—if the gossips were to get hold of the information that he'd thrown little Beth Garner-that-was, the respected local GP's daughter, out on her neck to make room for Zanna Hall and their ready-made family. Which was why he would move heaven and earth to make himself seem the injured party! He wouldn't want to lose his standing with the local population, many of whom were his tenants, she decided cynically.

And he seemed to be sleeping late, she thought, swinging her legs over the side of the high, old-fashioned bed. Though how he could do that, on the small, uncomfortable sofa, she hadn't the least idea. But she was utterly thankful that there was no sound of him moving around when, as her feet touched the floor, the familiar morning nausea hit her.

She only just made it to the bathroom in time and emerged ten minutes later, grey-faced, to pull on a pair of well-worn jeans and an emerald-green cotton blouse. After a glass of water and a slice of dry toast she would be fine. Ready to face what the day had in store. That it would be nothing pleasant, she knew full well. But, somehow, she would handle it.

At least Charles hadn't surfaced to witness her violent bout of morning sickness, she consoled herself as she picked her way downstairs. She had no intention of telling him about the child they had conceived. It would smack of emotional blackmail.

If he preferred Zanna, and of course he did, then she wasn't going to use their unborn child as leverage to make him stay with her. The thought of tying him to her, knowing he was in love with someone else, made her feel ill. Besides, he already had a child, a son to carry his name, given him by the woman he had never stopped loving, a son who would soon legitimately bear his name.

It was something she had already accepted and the sooner this day was over and she was free to get on with the rest of her life, the better it would be. And the very first thing to do was to tackle Charles head-on, tell him she knew what he was up to, what he was trying to prove.

And then, she thought, she would tell him to go to hell! Because maybe, just maybe, she was at last beginning to get some sense! How could she possibly love a man who could do that to her? And when they came face to face she would tell him precisely how despicable he was, not worth a moment's thought. And by saying it out loud she might make it the truth.

But easier said than done. A thorough search of the tiny cottage—which didn't take longer than a couple

of minutes—told her he wasn't around. And his car
had gone.

As she stood in the centre of the clearing, the mud
now rapidly drying out in the morning sun, her green
eyes clouded with exasperation. Where the hell was
he?

And half an hour later she was still asking the same
question, but more with anxiety now because surely he
wouldn't have gone to the trouble to bring her here,
only to disappear into thin air himself?

A sudden thought sent relief spurting through her
and she dived for the small fridge, pulling it open then
closing it slowly, something more than disappointment
making her shoulders slump.

So he hadn't gone to the nearest village for supplies,
she thought drearily. The fridge was fully stocked. And
he must have spent some time here, she thought, pouring a glass of water and sipping it reflectively. The
store cupboards, too, were well stocked with tinned and
dried food and she knew he had a few changes of
clothing in the drawers upstairs. And it couldn't have
been his intention to bring her here and dump her
goodness knew how many miles from another human
being, no means of transport and no phone!

But worse than that uncomfortable thought—so very
much worse—was the tight ache inside her chest that
came from missing him! And that knocked her former
theory that her pride wouldn't allow her to go on loving him right on the head, didn't it just!

At the sound of a car drawing into the clearing she
went weak with relief. He was back! She fled over the
room and out through the door, her heart racing. No

need to wonder why she suddenly felt so light-hearted, she thought drily, why the relief that he had not, as she had begun to fear, been taken ill in the night and had driven away, looking for medical assistance, was almost intoxicating. She still loved the swine. Her foolish heart refused to listen to the wisdom of her head.

She stood watching him as he got out of the car, his movements relaxed and smooth, and she pushed her hair back out of her eyes. Her hand was shaking. And something of what she was feeling must have got through to him because he walked slowly towards her, stopping, towering right over her, and he said lightly, his mouth curling upwards just a little, 'Missed me?'

Totally unable to deny what she was sure any fool could read on her face, she said thickly, 'Where were you?' and suddenly felt claustrophobic, as if the tall trees were moving nearer, crowding her, smothering her. But it had nothing to do with the forest. He was doing the crowding. He hadn't moved, he hadn't needed to, his very presence was suffocating her.

And there was more than a smile in his eyes right now.

The narrowed grey slits were knowing as they rested for a lingering moment on her wide, shocked green eyes then drifted slowly down, assessing the suddenly soft trembling vulnerability of her parted lips, and down again to the revealing peaks of her breasts as they pushed in aching invitation against the fine cotton of her blouse.

And there wasn't even a hint of a query now as he moved a pace nearer and repeated, a shocking glint of something triumphant, alive and deep in his eyes, 'You missed me.'

She picked up the danger and desperately tried to negate it, shaking her head, her denial too vehement as her pulses suddenly changed gear, racing.

'You're crazy! I thought you'd dumped me. Wondered how far I'd have to walk, dragging a heavy suitcase, before I got back to civilisation—that's all.' Her eyes met his defiantly, impressing the lie, but she saw the soft insolence of his smile and shuddered.

He didn't believe a single word, and the angry reaction to the way she had actually worried about the brute had her snapping out, 'Where the hell were you, anyway?'

'Finding a phone and arranging for one of my secretaries to present herself on your former boss's doorstep to deal with your unfinished professional business.' He laid slight stress on the 'professional' but his shrug was minimal as he moved in, stating, 'It's not important.'

And what was? she wondered chaotically, as those narrowed, steely eyes undressed her, absorbing the fine tremors that invaded her skin. That she had missed him, worried about him? Did he get his kicks out of making her emotions go into a state of aching confusion? Turning her into a gibbering wreck while he stayed so calm, so coolly aloof?

But there was nothing aloof about the slow burn she glimpsed behind his eyes, nothing aloof about the way he brought his hand up, the tanned skin of his long, hard fingers brushing against the peachy softness of her cheek, lingering for one tantalising moment against the fullness of her lips, making them part, revealing her trembling vulnerability.

Oh, nothing aloof at all.

Beth shuddered, watching her control slide out of existence with a strange detachment. He only had to touch her...

Touch her. The warm pads of his fingers were resting now on the tiny pulse that was beating so frantically at the base of her throat and he said thickly, 'You are so beautiful.'

He had never said that to her before and, for a brief space of time, for a few glorious, heady moments, she believed him. Could believe nothing else as his mouth took hers, his strong, inescapable arms drawing her so close to the hard length of his body that they seemed to be fused together, divided only by the thin superfluity of clothing, paradoxically made whole by the very separateness of their sex.

And her senses went haywire as his hands shaped her body, making it blossom beneath the sliding sensuality of his touch.

Greedily, lost in the wanton responsiveness only he could call forth, her body moved against his, soft breasts crushed against the heated masculinity of his chest, hips pressing urgently on to his, the obvious strength of his arousal making her mindless, boneless, utterly receptive. And her head was spinning, her brain functions on hold, as he swept her up into his arms and carried her back to the cottage, his long stride purposeful. And her head fell back against the taut breadth of his shoulder, her lazy eyes sweeping languorously to his profile, and her heart almost exploded with rapacious sensation as the glint of resolve in those predatory, narrowed eyes, the dull flush of naked desire that brushed the taut skin across his angular cheekbones, the sensual curve of that hard, bold mouth told a story that was as old as time...

CHAPTER SEVEN

IN A daze of receptive sensuality, Beth felt as if she were being wafted upstairs on the wings of a dream. In reality, Charles's arms were holding her close, his dark head dipped as his mouth curved erotically over the exposed skin of her long white throat, the delicate angle of her jaw, the sensitive hollow just below her ear. And that was so much better, infinitely more satisfying than any dream.

And a drugging mist of fantasy kept her pinned to the bed, her body so boneless that she felt as if she were drowning in honey, and languorously she became plastic beneath the sureness of his hands, her breath swelling within her as he slowly unbuttoned the green cotton blouse, pulling it away from the gleaming slenderness of her shoulders as if it were a thing of no substance, dissolving in the heated, narcotic sexual tension that throbbed and sighed in the air.

A tension that inexorably began to tighten. She could feel the build-up, the spiralling heat so deep inside her, felt it and caught the echo of it coming from him, calling her, binding her. And as the last of her clothing disappeared beneath the wicked magic of his hands, he straightened, the heat of desire marking the high slash of his cheekbones, the brooding intensity of his eyes holding hers captive as his hands went to the buckle of his belt.

And he said thickly, 'You want me. That has to prove something.'

And something sharp, very painful, exploded darkly in her brain. It killed the wanting, the overpowering need, made all that magic turn to dust, translating into a raw sob as she twisted round on the bed, burrowing beneath the covers as if she could hide from the hateful, shameful knowledge that he had deliberately set out to prove just how easily she could be turned on— by any passable man who happened along, regardless of emotion. That she didn't care who that man was, that even the man she had repeatedly asked for a divorce could make her delirious, begging for sexual release!

'Just go away—leave me alone!' she howled, self-disgust and the icy knowledge that she was just part of a vile experiment, part of his plan to discredit her, making her voice a disjointed, anguished sound beneath the smothering duvet.

Merciless hands dragged the unlikely shield away from her body, his voice no less unyielding as he told her rawly, 'Never. And you'd better believe that.'

And then he was on the bed beside her, one long, hard-muscled, hair-roughened leg across her, pinning her down, and she raised her white-knuckled fists to beat him off, her blood pounding in burning outrage, but one of his hands, quite slowly and oh, so effortlessly, pulled those totally ineffective little fists above her head and his voice was silky as he told her, 'Don't make me fight you for what we both know we want.'

His dark head dipped, his daunting mouth fastening around one pulsatingly aware nipple, playing with it until she thought she would go out of her mind before he gave his exquisitely tormenting attention to its twin. And his voice sounded strangely muffled, reaching her consciousness in wave upon wave of disorientating sensuality. 'I only have to touch you—like this, and this…' And her treacherous body gave up the fight.

And then the last of the small bright flame of resistance, of common sense, was quenched in the heat, in the moist and sultry pool of desire. And her body instinctively relaxed, moving, arching beneath his, opening to receive his throbbing need, answering it, matching it with the passionate flowering of the silken sheath of her womanhood.

'Are you hungry?' Beth opened her love-drugged eyes slowly to find Charles propped on one elbow, looking at her. And she stretched, supple as a cat, a voluptuous smile curving her kiss-swollen lips. She could tell him she was hungry for him, again and again, but he might think her immodest.

The slow smile twitched into a wide grin at that much too belated notion and he knew her thoughts— of course he did. He made a small, rough growling sound in his throat and circled one erect nipple with the tip of a finger.

'Later, my insatiable little cat. Later, and more, and better.'

More. The very thought made her womb pulsate, that low, telling heat beginning to throb again, and she squirmed over on to her stomach, burying her face into the pillow that smelled of him, of the spicy cologne he wore, the musky scent of masculinity that was his alone.

And it couldn't possibly be better, she thought, feeling him leave the bed, hearing the rustle of his clothing, the faint scratchy sound as he dealt with the zip of his jeans. So many times during the long summer morning, so many times, all of them revealing a different aspect of his sexuality—savagely masterful, tender, slow, so slow with the sensuality of the true voluptuary. So many times and all of them beautiful...

A light tap on her naked backside, a tap that almost lingered, hovered, just, and so tantalisingly, on the edge of a new discovery, pulled her out of drugging memory and he said, 'Food. Ten minutes. OK?'

And she simply nodded, on a plane too divorced from reality to speak because that tap had lingered, full of promise—if promises were needed...

Twenty minute later, showered, dressed now in a full filmy cotton skirt with a toning peacock-blue sleeveless blouse tied just beneath her breasts, she wandered down to the tiny kitchen. She still felt disorientated, as if she had beeen drugged, reality blurred and suspended. But her nostrils quivered appreciatively at the aroma of grilled bacon and she said lightly, 'So you mastered the stove. You deserve a medal!'

It was a cranky-looking monster, and ran on bottled gas, and to Beth's jaundiced eye it looked about a thousand years old, but Charles gave her an odd, tight smile, hunched one shoulder and turned to yank at the door of the oven. And she looked at him, weak still with the ecstasy of what had happened, a weakness compounded by what her lingering eyes drank in—the

tall, lean strength of him, the wide, rangy shoulders
covered in the dark cotton of his shirt, the worn jeans
that snuggled to spare hips, neat buttocks and long
sexy legs.

But he wasn't looking at her as he extracted two
plates from the oven, holding them with a cloth. And
he walked quickly over to a ramshackle apology for a
breakfast bar which, she saw, he had taken the trouble
to spread with a checked tablecloth and had set out
with fruit conserves, a crock of butter, a rack of fresh
toast and a big brown pot from which he began to pour
steaming, fragrant tea.

'I'm starving,' she admitted, pulling up a stool and
sitting down to a plate mounded with bacon and mush-
rooms.

He joined her, picking up his cutlery, and instead of
agreeing he said, 'Tell me exactly why you decided to
walk out on our marriage.'

It was like being flung into a bath of cold water. It
took her breath away and, for a moment, she couldn't
reply because they were back to reality again.

And, suddenly, she didn't think she could face it,
not the cold, hard reality of him and Zanna and Harry.
Yet, staring down at her plate, she knew she had to.
What had happened this morning had to be firmly
placed right at the back of her mind, along with the
consequences of their lovemaking over six weeks ago.

Somehow she was going to have to make a life for
herself and the child she was going to bear, and now
was the time to start, she informed herself tartly, not
feeling too brave about it.

So she said, in what she hoped was a tone of level

reasonableness, 'I told you why, before I left. Surely you can't have forgotten.'

She couldn't bring herself to mention Zanna. She had already told him how she'd overheard that damning conversation, and he might begin to put two and two together if she as much as mentioned that woman's name.

Her pride, or what was left of it, demanded that he should believe that she was the one to abandon their marriage. She was not, in his eyes at least, willing to appear as the spurned and discarded wife!

'I haven't forgotten a single damn word,' he replied heavily. Then, 'What I want to know is why. You lacked nothing. We were good together.'

Her mouth tightened, her fingers knotted together in her lap. Did he think that material things counted for anything? Did he want blood? Did he really want her to confess that her already wounded pride had made her leave before he got the opportunity to throw her out? Would his male ego continue to be piqued until he had wrung just such a confession from her? And she snapped at him heatedly, 'Good together? I disagree. For three months you didn't come near me, stayed away more often than not—you couldn't bear to touch me.'

His face was a battleground of warring emotions, the conflict graphically painted in the hard slash of his mouth, the tightness of skin over jutting cheekbones and jaw, the deep dark silver glints in those narrowed, brooding eyes, and she looked at him compulsively, her heart beating heavily because the truth was here, between them, a cruel, cold and hurting thing.

She said quickly, 'You don't really want me. You never did. I got tired of being second-best.' And that was more of the truth than was wise to release. He could pick it up, examine it, and maybe find the knowledge of her long and hopeless love.

But he said rawly, 'I don't know what the hell you're talking about!' and strode over to the stone sink, tipping his unfinished meal into the waste bin. Then he turned and faced her, his shoulders rigid with tension, his eyes hard as he grated out, 'Didn't our recent lovemaking tell you anything about how much I want you?'

Their lovemaking. That beautiful, beautiful phantom happiness. It hurt too much to think about it. And if he looked back on it, too, he would recognise her unrestrained responsiveness for what it was, understand how much it revealed about her true feelings for him.

And so she made her face blank, lifted her chin and fixed her gaze on a point just above his head because if she met his eyes she would be defeated utterly, and told him with a tiny dismissive shrug, 'You couldn't bring yourself to touch me during the final months of our marriage—that tells me how much you want me. The other—well—' She schooled the wobble of misery out of her voice, replaced it with a throwaway nonchalance that surprised even herself. 'I've already written that off as frustration.'

It wasn't true, of course it wasn't. But it was slightly easier than admitting to the bleak suspicion that he had been simply using her to convince himself of her latent promiscuity.

She expected exasperation, perhaps annoyance, even, over what he would see as a blasé comment.

Expected that, but not the white-hot rage which had him covering the small distance between them after one long, deadly moment of silence.

His face was tight with it, those narrowed eyes spitting fire, his hands cruel as he dragged her off her precarious perch on the rickety stool and set her on her feet. And his voice was murderous, low and clipped.

'You little bitch! Just thank your lucky stars I don't hit women.' His hands dropped away abruptly, as if physical contact with her disgusted him. But a stroke of hot colour burned across his high slanting cheekbones as he grated, his voice raw with emotion, 'I didn't touch you because I bloody well couldn't! I was full of guilt. Ridden with it, do you hear me?'

She heard. Oh, she heard. But she didn't understand. She shook her head, stepping back, her face white with misery, and the silence was heavy, thick with things she didn't understand, and she didn't know why he was doing this to them, why he was complicating the dreadful simplicity of his need to be free of one wife to take another.

He said sharply, each word cutting her like a knife, making her change her knowledge of him, of herself and her reactions to him, 'You were expecting our child. You were light with joy, a complete and confident woman.' His mouth twisted in a bitter line. 'And I changed all that. You lost the child and, for all we know, lost the opportunity of conceiving another. And I was behind the wheel.' He swung on his heels, as if unable to look at the beaten creature he believed she had become, and walked to the door.

Beth began to say he mustn't feel guilty, not over

that, but the words were stopped in her throat when he whipped round again, facing her, telling her, 'I hired this place for a couple of weeks. I thought we needed and deserved at least that much time to resolve our future.' His voice was toneless now, totally without life, or even, seemingly, interest. 'But now I find I can't wait that long. I can't command the necessary patience and ingenuity to work it through.' He moved out of the door, into a shaft of sudden sunlight, but even that brilliance failed to thaw the ice in his eyes. 'I want you to return to South Park, where, as my wife, you should be. I want no further talk of separations—trial or otherwise—and certainly not of divorce.'

'But what about—?'

'No buts.' He made a slashing gesture with one hand, blocking her tumbling questions about where Zanna and Harry would fit into that particular arrangement. 'It's straightforward enough. Come back to England with me and we'll try to forget the past couple of months ever happened. Or tell me you don't want me at any price. Then we can both wipe the slate clean. I won't beg—I don't even want to. It's entirely your decision, and I want it by tonight.'

He walked away then and Beth stood watching his tall, broad-shouldered figure stride purposefully across the sunlit yard and on to a forest track, the trees swallowing him, taking him away, leaving her feeling more empty and alone than she had ever felt in her life.

Blindly, she walked back into the centre of the small kitchen and began to clear up, hurling her untouched breakfast into the bin, her movements clumsy and uncharacteristically uncoordinated.

No prizes for guessing why Charles had made that ultimatum. Her earlier, and quickly dismissed, idea that Zanna had once again walked out on him had proved to be correct. She could kill the bitch! How dared the hateful creature hurt her darling time and time again?

Then, realising that her feet were planted on the path to hysteria, she took herself in hand and, her soft mouth compressed, gushed a tepid stream from the ineffectual water heater on to the plates in the sink.

Despite everything, she loved Charles. And love could make a fool of the most sensible soul alive. She had been made a fool of once, through loving more deeply than wisely, and it mustn't happen again.

She had to think of herself, acknowledge the impossibility of remaining the wife of a man who was obsessed by another woman. That the other woman was a bitch, incapable of true and abiding love, uncaring of how much torment and pain she inflicted on the father of her child, had nothing to do with the case, she assured herself tightly as she dealt with the breakfast dishes.

Her failure to win his love in the past had taught her a lesson she would be a fool to forget. That their relationship had degenerated abysmally, with little hope of salvation and no hope at all for a return to the civilised and caring thing it had been during the early months of their marriage, had been clearly demonstrated by his ultimatum.

Obviously, with the feckless Zanna out of his reach yet again, he would prefer her to return to South Park and take up her duties as his wife. It would save him from having to face the unsavoury gossip which would

undoubtedly follow on a divorce, and, she thought cynically, stowing the last of the cutlery away in a drawer,
she had made a career out of being his wife, had been
good at the job. Yes, he would prefer her to go back
with him but wouldn't much care if she didn't.

Even if she had been tempted to stay married to him,
his blunt ultimatum, his careless take-it-or-leave-it attitude, his open admission that he didn't have the patience to try to persuade her—which would entail making love to her at every opportunity until she was
utterly seduced into mindless acquiescence—would
have put an end to that!

And his insensitive comment about forgetting the
past couple of months demonstrated exactly how little
he thought of her. How could she ever possibly forget
Zanna's return—with their son tucked under her arm—
and his obvious desire to get rid of his existing wife
in order to marry the woman he couldn't stop loving?

Her chores finished, she wandered outside and sat
on a wooden bench near the front door, closing her
eyes and allowing the green and golden peace to sur-
round her. She would face her future alone. When
Charles came back she would tell him so.

It was all over. Except for one last thing. If they
parted tomorrow, or even later tonight, never saw each
other again, she had to rid him of those feelings of
guilt about the loss of their child.

Slow tears trickled from beneath her closed eyelids,
the last she would ever shed for either of them, because
if she had known his feelings she wouldn't have felt
so worthless and rejected herself, and they could have
helped each other through those dreadful days and

lonely nights, and the last few months of their ill-fated no-hoper of a marriage would not have spawned the bitter memories they were both going to drag into their separate futures.

CHAPTER EIGHT

BETH was calm, very calm. At least, she thought she was, until Charles walked in on her and every cell in her body went on red alert.

He appeared in the open doorway of the kitchen and he must have walked for miles. His shirt was wet with sweat, sticking to his body, his dark hair damp, unruly, as if he'd pushed his hands through it time and time again. She met the brooding intensity of his eyes and shuddered. He looked exhausted, driven, and her love for him made her tender heart twist in unwilling compassion.

Almost, she was ready to do whatever he asked of her, be whatever he wanted her to be. But only almost. Unconsciously shaking her head, she dismissed the aching temptation. The raw, emotional savagery coming from him had to be down to the pain of having Zanna reject him yet again. It assuredly had nothing to do with whether or not she was willing to forget the divorce she'd told him she wanted.

'We'll eat in half an hour.' The banality of his words was negated utterly by the low harshness of his tone, riven with a pain as dark as it was unknowable, and she nodded mutely, unable to speak, her mouth gone dry, and turned blindly back to the sink where, just before he'd returned, she'd been washing salad.

She heard him move behind her, on his way through

to the tiny sitting-room, and felt her whole body tense with her unstoppable, helpless awareness of him. And only when she heard him mount the stairs, heard the sound of his movements in the bathroom overhead, the gush and rattle of the nightmarish plumbing, did she feel herself relax, her body sagging with reaction.

Closing her eyes, she leant against the sink and willed herself to recapture the calm acceptance, the stoicism she had found during the long green and golden day. She wasn't prepared to take second place in his life and she couldn't help him come to terms with what Zanna had done to him. No one could. He would have to call upon his own deep reserves of mental strength to accomplish that. And he, above all men, was strong enough to do it.

Fleetingly, she wondered why the other woman had taken off again. She had seemed determined to replace her as Charles's wife, more than happy with the situation, had agreed that yes, her intention was to legitimise their son, allow him to bear his father's name.

Motherhood had obviously failed to tame the wild and reckless streak that was such a strong part of Zanna Hall's wayward character. She wouldn't be tamed and she wouldn't be caged and she went through life doing exactly as she pleased, utterly regardless of who got hurt in her selfish, flamboyant progress.

Beth pushed herself away from the sink and straightened her shoulders. She refused to think about it any more. She had enough to do to keep herself calm. Telling Charles that she wanted that divorce was going to require a single-minded strength of purpose she only hoped she possessed.

She had a meal to produce and she would concentrate on that, but even so the steaks she had found in the fridge were only just beginning to sizzle when Charles came down and she shot him a quick, questioning look—which told her nothing about his mood, about anything, except that he had showered, changed into a black cotton sleeveless T-shirt and hip-hugging denims.

'Anything I can do to help?' he offered blandly.

She made her voice crisp and did her best to look extremely efficient as she bustled about, spreading the breakfast bar with the checked cloth, setting out the bread and the salad, telling him, 'No, not really. Thanks,' meaning that the only thing he could do for her was give her permanent amnesia, make her forget that she had ever met him, ever loved him.

'In that case, I'll open the wine.' Toneless. Polite. She wondered frenziedly when he would ask for her decision, then mentally slammed that enervating thought out of existence. He would ask when he was ready and in the meantime there was something she could do for him. One last thing.

She turned the steaks and took the glass of red wine he held out to her, drank it down in two long swallows and immediately felt better. Dutch courage was better than no courage at all, she informed herself sagely as she reached into the wall cupboard for the mustard and marmalade.

'Templeton's lavish hand with the champagne must have given you a taste for the bottle,' he said drily. 'The most I've ever seen you put back before is half a glass, and you've made that last all evening.'

Nevertheless, he refilled her glass and she ignored that taunt about the Pol Roger he must have noticed when he'd walked into William's home and dragged her out. It wasn't important. What she had to say to him was.

Forking the steaks on to two plates, she carried them over, sucked in her breath and told him, not quite meeting his eyes, 'What you said earlier—about feeling guilty. You mustn't. What happened wasn't your fault. No one could have avoided that accident.'

She did look at him then because the silence was so long, burdened with tension, and when her green eyes locked with his narrowed grey gaze she turned her head quickly because what she had seen was compassion, pity. She couldn't handle that.

And he said huskily, 'You were so happy until then. I knew how badly you wanted that child. How could I not have felt the burden of guilt? It was like a ton weight.' He seated himself beside her and reached for her, tilting her small chin between the thumb and forefinger of one hand, forcing her to meet the shadowed power of his eyes. 'And I was right, wasn't I? It was something you couldn't spring back from. Your jealousy of Harry cut me like a knife. During that weekend I watched you freeze, die a little more inside. You can't imagine what it did to me. Culpability isn't easy to live with.'

Culpability. A draining word, defeating them, slicing through the tenuous bonds there had once been between them. Little wonder he had shut her out of his life, had sought out the warmth and vibrancy of the woman he had been unable to stop loving. And discovering she had borne him a son had only fuelled his obsession.

Compressing her lips, she twisted her head away and picked up her cutlery. Jealous of young Harry she had been, but only because the little charmer was his son. His and Zanna's. Not for the reasons he had manufactured in his head. She didn't know how he could be so blind, so insensitive to her feelings.

On the other hand, she knew very well, she thought drearily as she cut into her meat, suddenly and inexplicably ravenous. Even during their most intimate moments he had never pretended he loved her. And, because of that, she had never been able to confess how she felt. Protestations of love on her part would only have embarrassed him, made him feel trapped by the weight of it. And increased her own sense of vulnerability, which had been terrifying enough as it was.

And nothing she had said, it seemed, had lessened his unreasoning sense of guilt over the loss of their child. She didn't know how she could further help him over that hurdle, except by telling him that the consultant's dire prognosis had been unfounded, that she had, in fact, conceived again.

From the corner of her eye she saw him begin his own meal. He didn't seem to have much of an appetite. She sighed. She could help him to lose some of that sense of guilt, but she had no intention of doing so. Not yet. Perhaps not for a long time to come. Because for the first time in her life she was going to be utterly and completely selfish.

She was going to keep the fact of her pregnancy secret until she had sorted out a new life for herself and was better able to handle the future ramifications of the visiting rights, the watchful interest he would insist on taking in his child. It would be appalling to have to meet him at regular intervals. The only way she could kill off her futile, hopeless love for him was to cut him completely out of her life, never see him again. If he knew about the coming child he would make that impossible.

'The steak's good.' She had to say something, didn't she? Something, anything, to break the aching silence. Any moment now he would ask for her decision. And she would give it. And that would, irrevocably, end the marriage that had once been her whole existence.

But she wasn't going to think of that right now. Her metabolism was demanding sustenance and the meat was good, but needed something...

Her mouth watering, she reached for the marmalade she had unconsciously put out and unthinkingly spread it thickly over her steak, cut into it and popped a morsel into her mouth. Delicious.

And at her side Charles said tightly, 'You're pregnant.'

Beth swallowed convulsively, her face going scarlet. She felt as if she had been discovered doing something shameful. And unbidden, swift memory blazed across her mind.

Two months pregnant the last time. She and Charles dining out. Both choosing Châteaubriand. And then that sudden craving for, of all crazy things, marmalade on her meat...

The discreet lilt of the waiter's eyebrows had, to give him his due, been hardly discernible. But Charles had lounged back in his chair, and even now, in memory, she could see the indulgent curve of his mouth, the warm pride in his eyes as he'd drawled amusedly, 'My wife is in what is politely known as an interesting condition, and has developed a few outrageous eating habits.'

And she had glowed then, then and for the remainder of the evening, secure with him, so secure...

Her eyes winged up to his, her cheeks still stained with hectic colour, and she saw a blaze of something she could only translate as that one closely shared memory in those narrowed grey depths, and she couldn't for the life of her, even attempt to lie to him.

'You've always blushed easily,' he said with soft irony, his shadowed eyes dropping from her warm, shell-shocked face, down over her rounded, thrusting breasts to her narrow little waist. 'When were you going to tell me? Or weren't you?'

'I—' Oh, lordy, how could she answer that? 'When I'd got used to the idea myself,' she temporised after a frantic search through her scrambled brain.

But all he said, his voice dark, was, 'I wonder.' He gave her a tight cynical smile before he got to his feet, removing her glass of wine. 'In your condition, you don't drink,' he told her in a hard, accusatory tone. 'Eat. I'll make the coffee.'

Although he had left the greater part of his own meal, she saw the sense in what he had said. She had eaten nothing all day and mixing alcohol with pregnancy wasn't the best of ideas. But already he was taking over and she dragged her mind together and began using it furiously while she ate as much as she could, the food she had been so ravenous for now tasting like so much sawdust.

And she knew she had been right to concentrate on working things through when he carried their coffee-mugs through to the sitting-room, gestured her to the only comfortable chair the cottage boasted, and straddled the hearth.

'There is no question now of a divorce, a trial separation, whatever.' His eyes were harder than she'd ever seen them. 'No matter how little it seems to mean to you, you are my wife, and you are carrying my child. And you are coming home to South Park with me, tomorrow, where you will be watched over with merciless attention by the best consultant I can find. And if you have any irresponsible notions about bringing up our child on your own, forget them. I would apply for custody. Make no mistake about that. Do you understand?'

Perfectly. It was what she had expected, the reason she had kept her secret. There was no way he would let her go now. And yes, he would have no hesitation in applying for custody, and with his financial clout, his standing, her own seemingly flighty desertion of him, he might just win. In any case, she dared not take that risk.

Zanna had done another of her disappearing acts, taking Harry with her. And although he could demand access to his son, it could be tricky. But she, as his legal wife, would be allowed no such freedom. The coming child was his legitimate offspring. And what he had, he kept.

His reason for marrying her in the first place had

hinged upon his desire for a family to inherit the newly affluent Savage dynasty, to enjoy the fruits of his hard labour, his clever brain, to carry on the line.

So she said, 'Yes, I understand you,' her voice emerging rustily as she mentally injected a dose of stiffening into her backbone. He might have her neatly trapped, but there was no way he was going to make her *feel* trapped, no more than by the bounds of her living space, anyway.

At one time she would have agreed to anything and everything he asked of her, because of the love she bore him. But not now. Not any more. She would wean herself away from the dependency of her love for him. And she said crisply, 'I agree to go back to South Park with you, to run your home as you expect me to, entertain your guests. But, in return, I have stipulations of my own to make.'

Uncrossing her slender legs, she got to her feet, moving restlessly over the tiny room to put her coffee-mug down on a table. The dark intensity of his un-wavering regard was making her feel overwhelmed. And that, the disturbing sexual magnetism that was such an intrinsic part of his make-up as far as she was concerned, was something she was going to have to get to grips with, fight, emerge, if not exactly a winner, not a victim either.

'And those are?' His cool, almost indifferent tone made her shudder. She knew him well enough to rec-ognise the concealed threat. Tilting her chin, she dis-regarded it, pacing the room with a swirl of soft skirts, aware of the way his guarded eyes followed every movement she made, yet desperately pretending she wasn't.

'I need to work. To achieve something in my own right. I need to be more than your appendage.' Needed something to hold on to, something to take her mind off the empty sham of their relationship. Something to blunt the pain of knowing that her old dream of teaching him to love her was completely hopeless.

'I see. And just how will that be achieved?'

'No hassle.' Stoically, she ignored the patronising tone. He had only ever seen her as someone who could be useful to him. Run his lovely home, entertain his weekend guests, bear him the sons and daughters he had decided he needed. He had never seen her as a woman who had needs that could not be satisfied by a gracious home to live in, beautiful clothes to wear, his attention in the bedroom when he felt so inclined.

Ignoring the knot of pain that had so annoyingly planted itself behind her breastbone, she continued coolly, 'Allie has often asked me to go back into partnership with her. We made a good team. And she wants to expand the area of the agency's activities. It's the sort of challenge I'd enjoy.'

Enough of a challenge to take her outside the closed and unsatisfactory arena of their marriage. True, she would have their child, and she would love him or her to distraction. But she would need something more, something outside the sterile boundaries of her marriage, if she were to keep her self-respect, her sanity.

'And the child?' He had finished his coffee and was pouring more of the wine for himself, the unspoken tension in him translating itself into the terse rattle of the neck of the bottle against the glass. 'If you are harbouring any delusions of putting on your business suit and prancing out to the office each day, leaving our child to the mercies of a hired nanny, then you can forget them.'

Which pulled her mouth into a straight line, made her eyes glitter like bright green glass, equalling the hardness she saw in his.

'I have no delusions,' she spat. None at all, not now. Not a single one was left to cloud the issue, which, she reminded herself, just in time, just before she lost her temper, was all to the good, wasn't it? 'I would be working purely in an administrative capacity and could do that from South Park. You worked from home often enough. Or used to,' she tacked on snidely, unwisely, she saw, recognising the slight upwards drift of one dark male brow. He wasn't a fool and would ferret out all her hang-ups if she didn't keep a more careful watch over her tongue.

Making herself relax because she was fighting for the chance to make a life for herself, distance herself from him and destroy the soul-draining, all-consuming love he so unconsciously called from her, she slowly walked to the chair she had vacated and resumed her seat, tilting her head in his direction, her expression so very carefully bland, tossing the ball straight back at him. 'Well? You agree?'

He gave her a coolly sardonic look then took a hard-looking pinewood chair from the chimney corner, swivelled it round and straddled it, resting his arms along the back, his wine glass held loosely in one long-fingered hand. All this before he told her with soft scorn, 'We seem to be reaching the heart of the matter. You should have been honest about this before. Am I so much of a tyrant?'

He lifted one wide, hard-boned shoulder in a shrug so minimal as to make it practically non-existent, the insouciant gesture clearly telling her that whether she regarded him as a tyrant or not was not of any particular interest to him. Then his hard, incredibly sexy mouth curved into a smile that held no humour at all as he stated, 'So you want to fly. You were so greedy for some sort of freedom outside our marriage that you used the grimy little pretext of a trial separation in order to stretch your wings. Our marriage, so it would seem, was not enough of a challange.' He drained his glass, setting it down carefully at his feet, turning the cold scrutiny of his eyes back to her, his chilling assessment making her shake inside because she was sure he could see beneath the calmness of the relaxed front she presented to the mass of miseries deep inside.

Desperately, she bit back the scathing words of bitter condemnation that crowded on her tongue. How could she now explain that the conversation which he knew she'd overheard between him and Zanna had been the reason for the way she'd walked out on their marriage?

How could she, when she had been so determined to get in there first, leading him to believe—for the sake of her self-respect—that she had decided on a separation, pushing home that concept because she hadn't been able to bear the final humiliation of having him ask her to divorce him, leaving him free to marry the mother of his son?

She had spiked her own guns in that respect and she

was damned if she was going to tell him the truth now. And he said, 'Your pregnancy, of course, has put an end to all that. However, within the boundaries of what you have outlined, I agree.'

Was she supposed to curtsy, or genuflect? she asked herself acidly, trying to make herself hate him because her next stipulation, his agreement so necessary, was going to be far harder to make.

It was growing darker now, the forest trees cutting out the last of the evening sunlight, casting a dark green shade that made the small room like an underwater cavern. Charles got to his feet, going to light one of the oil-lamps, and she said quickly, before her already shaky resolve could desert her, 'There is one last thing. I want us to have separate rooms. I don't want to sleep with you again.' She saw him go very still, the honed features having a demonic quality in the orange flare of lamplight.

The eyes he turned on her as he straightened were deep in their shadowed sockets, unreadable, his mouth thinned, accentuating its fascinating cruelty, but his voice was casual to the point of boredom as he thrust his hands into the pockets of his jeans and told her, 'You surprise me. Your response to my recent love-making has been, frankly, cataclysmic. Not to mention your avid initiation of the process on one or two quite memorable occasions earlier today. However, my dear, you can be assured that I would never waste my sexual energies on an unwilling woman.'

A furious scarlet stain covered her entire body at his calculatedly cold description of what had happened this morning, but she was shivering inside because she knew he would feel perfectly free to seek his sexual pleasures elsewhere. Preferably finding emotional and physical release with Zanna, who obviously still found him sexually exciting even if she balked at the constraints of marriage.

But it was a stipulation she had had to make. His lovemaking might be everything she craved, but for him it was meaningless, a mere assuaging of a natural appetite. And having him share her bed would only leave her feeling degraded, leaving her just as far away as ever from falling out of love with him, finding the self she had once lost in her unreasoning love for him and would be in danger of losing again.

'I'm tired.' Her small face was pale with the strain of knowing herself trapped by her own unthinking revelation of her pregnancy, of the sheer effort of determination that had led her to make the stipulations that would enable her to keep her self-respect.

She got to her feet, pushing the wings of dark hair away from her forehead, gesturing to the hideously unyielding sofa he had to have used last night. 'If you're not up to facing the rigours of that thing again, then I'm willing,' she said, making it clear that her insistence on separate sleeping arrangements was already in operation. And he lifted one straight black brow cynically.

'I'm flattered to hear that there's at least one area in our life where you're willing. I shall manage adequately; you take the bed.'

And then, before weak tears could betray her, she turned to the stairs, but his voice, cold and hard, stopped her, froze her in the ice of disgust.

'There is one thing, my dear wife—before we embark on the future of your choosing. I would like to be sure that the child you are carrying is mine, not Templeton's.'

CHAPTER NINE

FOR a moment Beth was too shocked and furious to move. Her heart beating like a drum, she felt a tide of angry colour flush over her face before it receded, leaving her feeling cold with a rage deeper than she had ever known before.

How dared he?

Hauling her shoulders back, scarcely knowing what she was doing, she marched rigidly back across the room, brought her hand up and cracked it across his hard mouth, using every last ounce of strength.

The harsh sound of the contact, emphasised by the silence of the room, gave her a small, momentary stab of satisfaction, but not enough to assuage the anger boiling inside her, not nearly enough.

Charles didn't even flinch and the brief flare of something that looked, oddly, like triumph died quickly and left his eyes like stone, betraying nothing. She might not have touched him, let alone slapped him with all the energy she possessed, and she raised her hand again, her already stinging palm ready to deliver one more blow, and then another—until she had worked the torment of her anger, her passionate disgust of what he had said, right out of her system.

But, without even seeming to move, he captured her wrist in one of his hands and held it between them, the dark red stain already spreading over his face in stark contrast with the pinched whiteness of the skin around his nostrils.

'A wife is allowed to slap her husband just once in her life. That option is no longer open to you. Try it again and I'll hit you back.' He released her hand then, stepping back as if he couldn't bear to be this close, and the grey of his gunfighter's eyes had turned to black and she knew he meant what he said.

Her own head came up, her green eyes defiant in the small pale oval of her face. And the clamour of her heartbeats pushed the breath from her lungs as she realised how she would almost have welcomed his physical violence, because it would at least be contact, of a kind, an indication that his emotions were involved, and that—anything—would be better than the cool scorn with which he now regarded her, the light sarcasm he had used to her when discussing the future of their marriage.

And that thought, more than anything else, made her draw back, lose the taste for confrontation. It was sick, and she disgusted herself. Physical violence had always been loathsome to her and, as far as she knew—and she knew him well—to him.

And then, with a cold sarcasm that made her shiver, and go on shivering, he told her, 'I take it that your reaction means you haven't slept with him. You'll have to forgive me for asking, but I did hear him propose marriage. And, being a cynic, I assumed you had given him the necessary encouragement.'

Beth turned away, all her mental and physical reserves brought into play in her effort to cross the room and walk up the stairs without breaking down completely. And, this achieved, by some large miracle, she lay awake for most of the night wondering how she was going to cope with the rest of her life.

'Oh, it is nice to be home!' Molly Garner heaved a sigh of pure pleasure, took her teacup and saucer from the low table and leaned back in her armchair, sipping contentedly. 'I don't care what country you're in, you can't get a decent cup of tea. Not that we didn't have a lovely time, of course, but—'

'It is nice to be home!' Beth supplied with a wide and wicked grin as she gathered her parents' holiday photographs together and stacked them neatly.

The windows were open and the distant sound of a lawn-mower was vaguely hypnotic in the somnolent late-summer afternoon and just outside the windows a bee buzzed drowsily in the voluptuous heart of a blowsy red rose.

For the first time in weeks Beth felt a layer of contentment close around her heart. And she said, meaning it more than her mother would ever know, 'It's nice to have you home. I've missed you both.'

In the few weeks she'd been back at South Park she had felt lonelier and emptier than she had ever done in her life. True, Allie had welcomed her suggestion of renewing their partnership with a whoop of delight and they'd been busy sorting out the legalities, future working procedure, and turning a little-used study which was tucked away behind the impressive library at South Park into an office for her use, complete with a computer link-up, filing cabinets and the like.

But nothing, not even starting back to work again,

could ever make up for the cold sham of her marriage, and she shuddered involuntarily and her mother asked quickly, 'Cold, pet? Let me close that window.'

'I'm fine. Just a goose walking over my grave.' She found a smile for her spherical mother who was already struggling out of the depths of her chair, and went on smiling until her face felt stiff with the effort as Molly scoffed,

'It's nice of you to say it, but you wouldn't have had time to miss us, running around like that. France, wasn't it?'

Her parents hadn't been back home for five minutes before the gossips had gone to work. Nothing could be kept a secret in this close-knit community. So Beth had little option but to bend the truth.

'Near Boulogne. Charles was so often away at that time and Allie had a client she couldn't fix. It was only a short-term temporary thing, so I stepped into the breach. Charles managed to visit a couple of times.'

'Well, he must have done, mustn't he?' Mrs Garner responded drily. 'Otherwise I wouldn't be looking forward to a grandchild.'

Beth summoned a shaky smile but inside she was giving a sigh of relief. She was back now, keeping up appearances as Charles's wife, and if her mother ever got to know that she was doing so only because he had threatened to apply for custody of their child, with all the attendant publicity the court case would create, doubts cast upon her daughter's fitness for bringing up a child—no doubt with salacious tales of her sojourn in France with a man who had ended up proposing to her—she would be more than horrified.

She had been against the marriage in the first place. Not because Charles Savage was so far above the doctor's daughter both financially and socially—she wasn't that old-fashioned—but because of Zanna. Only a week before the wedding she had said worriedly,

'Have you really thought it out, pet? I don't want to spoil things for you, but I don't want to see you unhappy, either. Don't you think it's a little soon? He could be marrying you on the rebound, you know. Have you thought about that? No one could miss seeing the way he was with that Zanna Hall woman. She'll be a hard act to follow.'

But Beth hadn't thought about it, or only inasmuch as to convince herself that although he had made no pretence of being in love with her, spouted no pretty words, she, with her own deep and long-developing love for him, could teach him to need her as much as she needed him. It had been the supreme self-confidence of untried youth, the supreme folly. And, in the circumstances, the less her mother knew about the present situation, the better.

And now that lady was saying complacently, 'Your good news couldn't have been a better homecoming present. I'm going to have to buy lots of baby wool.'

Beth winced inside. Could her mother really have forgotten all those tiny jackets and caps, carefully folded away in tissue paper, which she'd knitted with such enthusiasm for the baby they'd lost?

No one ever mentioned the accident, and its tragic aftermath. Everyone had been traumatised. They seemed to think that if it wasn't mentioned it hadn't really happened.

'And do tell...' Mrs Garner leaned forward to pour them both another cup of tea. 'I heard that Hall woman turned up at South Park—brazen as ever, with her two-year-old son. Did you give her short shrift? I know I would have done. That woman has no sensibilities whatsoever! She's not married, apparently.'

'I didn't see much of her,' Beth said, feigning indifference. 'We had a houseful of guests for the weekend and I was leaving for France almost immediately.' Any minute now her mother would be relaying the news that young Harry bore a remarkable resemblance to Charles Savage, and Beth didn't know quite how she was going to skirt round that one. She could feel perspiration begin to break out on her brow, in the palms of her hands but, thankfully, her father walked in through the door.

'Any tea in the pot? I'm parched.' He flopped down on the sofa next to Beth, running his hands through his thinning grey hair. 'Soon be autumn, and I can put the garden to bed. I know exercise is good for me— drummed it into my patients often enough, but—'

'But you'll spend the winter evenings reading through the seed catalogues, mapping out new borders, ordering plants, fretting to get out there again,' his wife cut in drily, passing him a cup of tea. 'Do you know, Beth, he paid Johnny Higgs a small fortune to keep everything trim while we were away, and no sooner had he dumped the suitcases in the kitchen than he was out there, on his hands and knees with a magnifying glass looking for imaginary weeds, trimming hedges, mowing lawns...'

Amid the rueful laughter Beth got to her feet,

smoothing down her skirts, making her excuses.
'Charles was away last night, but he said he'd be back
by teatime. I must rush, if I'm to be there to meet him.'

They kept up the pretence, even in front of each
other, treating each other politely, like strangers. He
worked more from home now but every now and then
had to go up to town, staying overnight to give himself
two clear days at head office. And she always made
sure she was around when she knew he was due,
emerging from her office in time to tidy herself, ready
to greet him with polite if stilted enquiries about the
journey, offering him a drink to help him unwind, passing on snippets of local news she thought might interest him. No one would ever be able to accuse her of
not keeping to their bargain.

'Well, don't rush too much,' her father advised
gruffly as he walked with her to the door, an arm
around her shoulder. 'Got to handle yourself with kid
gloves from now on.'

It was the nearest either of her parents had got to
mentioning her miscarriage, apart from the initial flood
of shocked sympathy, and she wondered, belatedly,
whether more openness would have helped during the
long, distressingly miserable months that had followed.

Certainly, if Charles had been able to bring himself
to explain that his deep feelings of guilt had been responsible for the distance he had put between them,
then things would have been easier, and they would
have grown closer instead of further and further apart.
Especially if she had confided her own feelings of failure, the terrible feelings of inadequacy she'd gone

through after she'd learned she might never conceive again.

But any closeness they might have achieved would have counted for nothing from the moment that Zanna and Harry put in an appearance, she reminded herself tartly as she settled herself behind the wheel of her car. The past was over and all the might-have-beens in the world would make no difference to the future.

Winding down the window and pasting a smile on her face, she waved to her hovering parents, calling brightly, 'Dinner with us tomorrow. Don't forget— seven o'clock sharp. And bring your holiday snaps; Charles won't want to miss seeing them.' And she drove away slowly because sudden, stupid tears were blurring her vision. She had a long way to go before she could calmly accept her life for what it was.

She entertained a great deal, worked hard for the agency, put on a bright face. And if her parents expressed concern over her pallor, the dark smudges beneath her eyes, she told them truthfully that she was being looked after by one of the leading obstetricians in the country—at Charles's instigation—and that he pronounced himself satisfied, said she was doing fine.

And when she and Charles were together, which happened as little as she could arrange it, she sometimes glanced up to find him watching her and, just for a moment, their eyes would hold. And there was something there she could not read, gave up even trying to, and pigeon-holed the enigmatic expression under the label of resentment.

He had to resent her presence, her nominal position

as his wife. They both knew he had been willing to divorce her, to take the woman he loved as his wife, and they both knew that she, Beth, was only here because she was carrying his child, because the impossible-to-pin-down Zanna had walked out on him yet again.

His heart was with the flamboyant, vibrantly alive redhead; always had been, always would be. Every time he looked at her, Beth, he would resent her for not being Zanna.

She was a second-best wife, and knew it. But was learning to handle it, learning to make the most of her organising abilities and put them to good use in the build-up of the agency. Learning, slowly and painfully, to erect an impenetrable wall around her heart.

Christmas and the New Year festivities came and went and Beth congratulated herself on handling everything perfectly. The big house was decorated with branches of holly cut from around the estate, the huge open hearths alight with blazing logs, the hospitality lavish—right down to the silver bowls of Mrs Penny's aromatic punch.

Charles's brows had drawn together in a frowning black bar when he'd scanned the guest list he'd asked to see, but she'd ignored the obvious signs of his displeasure, knowing that he possessed enough self-control to be the perfect host, knowing that she had to fill the house with guests to be able to get through the season at all because she wasn't yet strong enough, self-contained enough, to be alone with him at this supposedly happy, family time.

But she was getting there, she assured herself, learn-

ing to live with his icy, slightly mocking politeness,
learning to match it, learning not to care. And when
he told her, 'There will be no more entertaining, apart
from when your parents come for dinner, no more huge
parties,' she simply dipped her head in cool submission
and turned back to her work, feeding fresh data into
the computer.

He had come to her office, which was unusual, and
his interference in the way she ran the social side of
their lives more unusual still. And the veneer of cool
indifference was peeling along the edges of his voice
as he bit out, 'You're running yourself ragged. If you
don't give a damn about your own health, you should
think about the child. From now on, you're going to
do just that because, if you don't, I'll damn well make
you.' And left the room, slamming the door behind
him.

The child. Of course. The new life she was carrying
inside her was his prime concern. The only reason she
was here. But she couldn't feel resentful, couldn't wish
the baby had never been conceived. It was all she had
to live for now.

In all truth, she didn't regret Charles's strict veto.
She was getting bulkier and slower, her body telling
her it was time to be quiet. Entertaining so frequently,
so lavishly, was, she recognised, becoming something
of a strain.

But that didn't mean she could be content to spend
much time alone with Charles. She knew, from the
bitter expression she sometimes surprised in the depths
of her eyes when she used her mirror, that she was on

the verge of accepting her life as it was, the polished, surface-bright sham of her marriage.

However, alone with him, who could tell whether some remnant of emotion she hadn't quite managed to kill off might rear to shocking life and rend her with the pain of all that would-be forgotten love? She simply couldn't trust herself enough to run that risk.

Love didn't die to order; you couldn't switch it off because you had been hurt and humiliated.

But she was getting there.

So, as January drew to its storm-swept, bleak close she devised other methods of distancing herself.

Her mother was more than happy to agree to her suggestion of a week in London, buying new maternity clothes, but still she said, 'You won't want too many, surely? Only a couple of months to go and if you're anything like I was...after you were born, I couldn't wait to donate those dreadful tents to the vicar's jumble sale! Mind you, I felt guilty afterwards because they might have come in again. But, as it turned out, you were the only one—we did so want you to have a brother or sister. But, with any luck, you and Charles will have lots of babies—South Park needs filling, don't you think?'

Beth closed her eyes on the pain of that artless remark. The child she was carrying would be the only one. That her marriage to Charles was in name only, physical intimacies relegated to the past, was her bitter secret. South Park's empty rooms would remain so.

Nevertheless, her chin came resolutely up. As an only child herself she had never felt deprived or lonely. She'd always had lots of friends in the village and at

school and she would make sure that her child had
them too.

And of course the week away stretched to just over
two. There were plenty of shows Beth suddenly found
she had to see, exhibitions which would be a pity to
miss.

'Pity not to pamper ourselves now we're here,' she
told her mother when she pointed out that their week
was up. 'It's nice to see all we want to see in a leisurely
fashion. You're not fretting about Dad, are you?'

'No, of course not.' Molly Garner smiled up at the
hotel waiter who had brought a rack of fresh toast to
their breakfast table. 'He manages very well on his
own. He probably enjoys the silence. He's always accusing me of talking too much! No, Beth, it's you I'm
worried about. Is everything all right?'

'Of course!' she answered, too quickly, and made a
great production of buttering toast she didn't want.
Beneath the prattling inconsequentiality of her
mother's conversation there was an astute mind. And
she'd always been a little over-protective of her only
offspring. She would do well to remember that. So she
tacked on offhandedly, 'Whatever makes you ask?'

'You've changed. I can't quite put my finger on it.
But there's a sadness in your eyes that sometimes
makes me want to cry.'

'Idiot!' It was an effort to achieve a light tone, to
force a smile. If her mother had remarked on a new
hardness, she would have privately agreed with her and
silently congratulated herself on the achievement of her
aims. But sadness?

Did what she had gone through really show that

much? Did her eyes say one thing even as her brain
was saying another? Had she still such a long way to
go in her determination to wrench all that ill-begotten
love for her husband out of her heart? It didn't bear
thinking about. So she smiled resolutely at her troubled
parent and passed it off.

'You're imagining things. You're looking at a
woman who has backache, frequent heartburn, puffy
ankles and bruises to show where a certain little monster is playing football with its mother's insides! Now,
what shall we do today? The exhibition of Victorian
jewellery? Or shall we go back to Harrods to look at
that suit I almost talked you into buying on
Wednesday?'

But she couldn't stay away forever, and, certainly,
Charles gave her no indication that he had missed her.
But, then, why should he? They had stopped pretending when his feelings for Zanna had been brought out
into the open.

Besides, she had plenty to occupy herself. She had
the excuse of the agency work to catch up on and so
was able to shut herself in her office each day, emerging to share a hasty and largely silent dinner with
Charles, going immediately after to her room on the
pretext of tiredness.

Not that it was a pretext, of course. She was tired,
her body ached with it. But her mind wouldn't let her
rest. And, one early March night, with the icy rain
lashing her window panes, she gave up all attempt to
capture elusive sleep, pulled a wrap over her increasing
girth and waddled as quietly as she could to the nursery.

Although Charles had said nothing—one raised brow had been enough to tell her he thought her crazy but was willing to pander to the whims of the pregnant—she had insisted on having the room re-done.

It was here that Harry had slept—not that she blamed the little innocent, but she couldn't forget how she had seen his parents hovering over him as he lay in the cot that had been bought with such excitement for the baby she had lost.

And even now, if she allowed the forbidden memory over the wall she had built in her mind, she could see Zanna in that clinging satin nightdress, Charles holding her, hear again those fervent words of welcome for the child she had brought him...

Wandering around, touching things, she felt herself begin to relax and sat down on the edge of the single bed she had had one of the gardeners bring into the room. She would sleep here for the first few months of the baby's life as she had every intention of feeding it herself and no intention whatsoever of asking Charles to vacate the adjoining master suite.

The thought of him, now, lying sprawled in the huge double bed, did nothing to help her determination to relax so she thrust it unceremoniously away and hauled herself back to her feet.

Mrs Penny had insisted on carrying up the packages of baby clothes she'd spent an extravagant small fortune on in London, saying, with some justification, that there was enough stuff here already to clothe an army of infants before pushing the new consignment on to the top of the series of open shelves that ran down one side of the cream-painted nursery cupboards.

They had been there for weeks now and needed sorting, placing on the right shelves, and, even standing on tiptoe, Beth couldn't quite reach. Not willing to give up the attempt, she caught hold of the low nursing chair and dragged it across the floor. Clambering up on it, she could just reach, her fingers closing around the piles of tiny, tissue-wrapped garments, the boxed baby toys she hadn't been able to resist.

And the first intimation she had that she was not alone was the rough sound of a crude oath and the strength and warmth and power of the male arms circling her body.

'Just what the hell do you think you're doing?' His voice cracked like the lash of a whip and her whole body went on fire as his arms tightened, swinging her gently down from the chair and setting her on the ground. He was still holding her, but loosely, and she twisted round within the circle of his arms and then wished she hadn't.

He was wearing one of his short towelling robes, hastily tied, and she knew from experience he would be naked beneath it. He never wore anything between the sheets. And just looking at him, at the severely carved angles and planes of his unforgettable features, the dusting of crisp body hair that coarsened the olive-toned skin of his exposed chest and long, firmly muscled legs, her heart began to thunder and her thought processes lay down and died.

'Well?' he demanded, his eyes flaying hers, making her lower her thick lashes very quickly to deny him the knowledge of the effect he could still have on her.

Pushing her tongue over her dry lips, she managed,

'I still haven't sorted out the baby things I bought in London.' She had to stay calm, she had to. Now wasn't the time to throw a wobbly. But after months of conducting limited conversations in tones of lightly veiled sarcasm or, what was probably worse, with polite boredom, his sudden anger, that show of real emotion, had her running scared, unsure of how to handle it.

It didn't fit into her undeviating delineation of what their type of marriage should be, and without her carefully drawn-up guidelines to cling on to she was in danger of drifting woefully off course.

'So you decided, after weeks, to do it right now. Couldn't it have waited until you could have asked someone else to reach the stuff down?'

He had released her now, stuffing his hands into the pockets of his robe, rocking back a little on the heels of his bare feet. And she stepped back, away from his overpowering sexual appeal, knocking against the back of the chair and earning herself an impatient scowl.

'I couldn't sleep.' Did she have to sound so overwrought? she asked herself edgily. And why was she so suddenly aware of how truly awful she looked, her bulky, clumsy body forcing her to stand with her feet planted wide apart, the weight she had put on extending to her face, giving her the beginnings of a double chin?

'Neither could I,' he admitted, his rarely seen smile flickering briefly along his beautiful male mouth. 'That's why I heard you blundering about in here.'

Blundering. She bit down on her lip at his choice of word. He might as well come right out with it and tell her she looked and moved like a whale out of water.

She swung quickly away, furious with herself. Why did it matter? Women in her condition shouldn't care if they were unattractive, and minding that he should describe her as blundering was surely abnormal, especially since he had never really wanted her at all, but had simply used her because she was his wife and was available.

But his cool fingers caught her hand, trapping it beneath the tensile strength of muscle and bone, and the intonation of gentleness in his voice was something she hadn't heard since she had run out on him to go to France.

'As neither of us can sleep, why don't we do the job together?' His hands went to her shoulders, exerting a soft yet firm pressure as he sat her down in the nursing chair then turned in one fluid movement to reach the pile of packages and carriers from the top shelf. 'You unwrap them and tell me where to put them.'

The old, almost forgotten warmth and tenderness was right back in his voice, in the dark grey eyes that slanted an understanding smile towards her, and she sat there, feeling like a beached sea mammal, wondering at the ease with which he breached her carefully erected wall.

But only a small breach, surely, she informed herself, the merest trickle of all that she shouldn't allow getting through her defences. So she said, to put the matter right, 'There's really no need for you to bother,' her voice carrying just the right amount of disparagement, not enough to sound offensive.

He gave her a quick underbrow look, sucked in his

breath, then responded lightly, 'No bother. I'd like to get acquainted with my heir's wardrobe.'

That figured, she thought, attempting to stir an inner resentment that simply wasn't there to stir, so she gave up trying and the coil of tension inside her was slowly released, and she went with it, letting her guard down because her brain had gone on hold, she recognised, not really caring much at all.

And she actually found herself enjoying unwrapping the tiny garments, running her fingers over the soft wool, the tiny silken ribbons, gurgling with laughter as he held a minute bootee between his long fingers, his expression wholly perplexed male.

'You wouldn't think anything could be small enough to fit into this.'

'You could be right.' Tomorrow she would regret the lowering of her defences, but right now she was simply allowing herself to relax, to enjoy the closeness that had been growing over the last half an hour. 'The way he kicks, he could emerge wearing soccer boots—size twelve,' she said then winced as a hefty movement served to prove her point.

'What is it, Beth?' With a swiftness that took her breath away, Charles was on his knees beside her, his brow darkly furrowed as he took her hands in his. 'Are you in pain?'

The amazing thing was, he looked as if he cared, Beth thought on a dizzying wave of stunned disbelief. In the space of half an hour he had reverted to being the warm, caring man who had been her much loved husband before that accident, before Zanna's return. It made her nervous; she didn't know how to handle it.

She had been so sure she was at last schooling all that hopeless love for him out of her heart, and yet...

'No.' She shook her head, the soft wings of her hair flying around her flushed face. 'He's decided to go in for disco dancing, I think.'

Relief washed his anxious features but his eyes held a hesitancy that was completely new in her experience of him as he asked huskily, 'I'd like to feel our child move. Would you mind?'

In her experience of him, he had always taken what he wanted, and right now she was seeing a side of him she hadn't known existed. And, gently, she took his hand and laid it over the bulge of her stomach and the look of incredulous wonder in his dark eyes as Junior obliged with a well aimed kick brought tears to her eyes.

Still kneeling, he moved closer, an arm around her, his hand still resting gently, reassuringly, over her stomach, and for long, timeless moments his eyes held hers, her stupid heart leaping and jumping like a wild thing as he told her quietly, 'You are beautiful, Beth. Never more so, in my eyes, than you are right now.' And then the moment was gone as he grinned, his brows rising. 'There he goes again! No wonder you can't sleep if he keeps this up all night!' Lifting his hand, he tilted her chin between his thumb and fore-finger, holding her eyes with his. 'Tell me something— we keep referring to the baby as "he". Will you be disappointed if we have a daughter?'

She shook her head, half dazedly, scarcely compre-hending. This was the type of intimacy she had written out of their marriage—for the sake of her self-respect, her sanity. And here she was, lapping it up, weak fool that she was. Her condition must be making her especially vulnerable. But she managed huskily, 'No. Will you?'

'Of course not.'

And, silently, she echoed his words in her head. Of course not. He already had a son. He would feel no driving desire to sire a male child to rear in his image. But, strangely, even that thought had no power to wound and she dismissed it, every cell in her body melting as he stood up, pulling her with him, a muscle working at the side of his jaw as he told her, his voice thick with something nameless, something that made her bones go weak, 'I want to sleep with you tonight. Just to hold you in my arms, you and our child, nothing else.'

Beth couldn't speak for the emotion clogging her throat, and his wide, sexy mouth firmed with determination as he swept her up in his arms, telling her, 'The world went black for me when I saw you teetering around on that chair. Tonight I need the reassurance of holding you close, keeping you safe.'

And as if he would listen to no argument, no protest, he carried her through the partly open door into the master suite and gently laid her on the huge double bed, tucking the soft duvet carefully around her.

Beth blinked back tears, snuggling into the warmth, her face burrowing into the soft down pillow, breathing in the faint, slightly spicy scent of the aftershave he used, the heady, musky male presence of him.

It had been a year since she had shared this room with him, this bed. It felt like coming home and fresh tears glittered in her eyes because he had never, ever admitted a need for reassurance before.

Finding her tottering around on that nursery chair, reaching for packages, had brought back bad memories of the accident that had caused her miscarriage, brought back the feelings of guilt he had no right to have. And when she felt the mattress dip beside her, his arms reach out for her, she knew why she had made no protest and snuggled herself into the protective curve of his body, promising herself that they both needed this one night out of time.

Tomorrow, she thought, as his deep and regular breathing told her that he had drifted immediately off to sleep, things would be back to where they were, because, knowing what they both knew, how could they be different?

CHAPTER TEN

BETH came awake quickly. She knew she was alone in the big double bed. She hadn't slept so deeply, so peacefully in months and she levered herself up, stacking the pillows behind her and leaning back.

A smile spread unstoppably over her features and she chewed on her lower lip to prevent it getting out of hand. Slowly, she admonished herself. Take it slowly.

But her thoughts were running around like mice, rushing onwards as if she'd pushed the fast-forward button in her brain. They wouldn't be stopped, so she let it all happen, all the tenuous hopes and needs coalescing into one great big beautiful whole.

Last night Charles had demonstrated that he was still capable of caring for her. Even if she wasn't Zanna, she was his wife, the soon-to-be mother of his child. And they had taken comfort and reassurance from each other, despite her stipulation that theirs should be a marriage in name only, despite the way their lives had been compartmentalised, never touching each other.

But it needn't go back to being that way, need it?

Daylight was struggling to get through the thickness of the lined velvet curtains but Beth was going to stay right where she was until she had everything sorted out in her mind.

She would have to have a long and serious talk with

him, because maybe she'd been wrong to try to im-
mure herself behind the wall of her own painstaking
construction. If they could speak openly about his feelings for Zanna then maybe they could reach a better
understanding.

Perhaps the wayward redhead's second desertion of
him had killed his obsession? She could only hope and
pray it had. Because if it had, and she was able to stop
living on the knife-edge of wondering just when the
other woman would walk back into his life, and take
him away, then she needn't tell herself that her love
for him was self-defeating, masochistic. She would
have no need to try to kill it.

She had been afraid to question him before. He had
known she knew the truth about Harry and Zanna, his
desire to be with them, and digging down into it all
would only have heaped more pain and humiliation on
her head, and she hadn't been brave enough, strong
enough to face that.

But the way he had been with her last night, so
gentle, admitting his own vulnerability, his need for
her comfort and reassurance, had given her an injection
of courage, and, somehow, she had found more of the
same inside herself. Enough courage to ask him to talk
this whole thing through.

An extremely perfunctory tap on the door heralded
Mrs Penny's arrival with a breakfast tray, and, her
thoughts disrupted, Beth beamed and called out a
bright good morning.

She was actually feeling more hopeful now than she
had ever done, even during the first months of their
marriage when she'd been sure she could make him

love her. Now, though, she wasn't asking for the moon, the sun and the stars. Just to reach a new understanding, a hope that they could build on the foundations of their marriage and, eventually, create something of enduring strength. So the moon alone would do for starters!

'Breakfast in bed, and you're to stay right where you are until noon. Charlie-boy's orders.' The housekeeper put the tray on her knees and rushed around pulling back the curtains. 'He's gone to the bank and he said to tell you he'll be back before lunch and you're to take it easy until then. And about time, too, if you ask me.'

'I'm not,' Beth responded wryly. 'Not that it matters. You'll tell me, anyway.'

'Too right. Eat your eggs.' Mrs Penny shot her a huffy look which was quite at variance with the gleam in her eyes. 'And while we're at it, I'm happy to see you back where you belong. I don't hold with married folks having separate rooms.' She planted her hands on her hips. 'It may be considered sophisticated and civilised in some circles but I call it plain unnatural! And mind you drink your orange juice.'

There wasn't much that escaped Mrs Penny's gimlet eye, Beth thought as she dutifully consumed scrambled eggs and toast. She would have tied her disappearance and her subsequent strained relationship with Charles up with Zanna's arrival, back in June.

And she'd made no attempt to hide her disapproval when she'd remarked on the unmissable likeness between Harry and his father. She'd been at South Park so long that she regarded herself as one of the family and wasn't afraid to speak her mind...

Beth put the tray to one side and slid out of bed. Looking over her shoulder, back into the past, wasn't going to help her attempts to build a new future with Charles. They needed to talk; she had to tell him that if she could be sure his obsession with Zanna was a thing of the past, with no danger of any future resurrection, then she was willing to forget everything that had happened and try to make their marriage something of value for both of them.

She had tried so hard to stop loving him, and had believed she had succeeded. But one show of tenderness from him, a night spent held so gently in his arms, had shown her how wrong she had been. She could no more stop loving him than stop breathing.

As if to reinforce her mood of hopefulness the weather had changed, producing a day that was the perfect harbinger of spring. Unable to settle to work or to take the rest Charles had prescribed, Beth slipped a coat over one of the light wool maternity dresses she'd bought in London and had not got round to wearing yet, and slipped outside.

The wind was chilly but light enough to be disregarded and the sun was shining, the sky an aching, beautiful blue, dotted with small, fluffy white clouds. It would be another month before the buds on the trees began to swell and unfurl their leaves, but there were already drifts of small wild daffodils spreading their gleam of golden promise beneath them.

Deciding to pick a few of the blooms and make an arrangement for the dining-room table—which, she acknowledged wryly, would help pass the time before Charles returned and they could have that talk, the thought of which was producing butterflies of nervous excitement inside her—she set off across the wide gravelled drive, only to leap for the safety of the grass verge as a small scarlet sports car howled round the bend.

Her bulk made leaping for safety both undignified and difficult, and she scrabbled up from her hands and knees, her face scarlet with outrage and humiliation as she brushed the clinging particles of damp grass and soil from her hands and coat, turning annoyed green eyes to the car which had jerked to a gravel-spattering halt just past her and was now reversing at a ridiculous speed.

Through the side-window of the low-slung sports car Beth could see an expensive piece of luggage on the passenger-seat, a glimpse of long, silk-clad legs, the soft emerald-green fabric of a suit skirt riding high on lush thighs. And she knew, she just knew, and she could only stare woodenly as the other woman slid quickly out from behind the wheel and tossed out over the low roof of the vehicle,

'I broke all speed records getting from Heathrow only to run you down on your own driveway! Mind you, your size makes you almost impossible to miss—I never did get that big carrying Harry!'

Disparaging, heavily made-up eyes swept over Beth, taking in the grass stains on the front of her coat. 'You didn't hurt yourself, did you?'

Beth shook her head impatiently, ignoring the sudden pain in her side. Her heart was hurting too much to let a little thing like stitch bother her. Zanna was here again—the thing she had dreaded had actually happened.

As lovely as ever, as vibrantly alive and charismatic as always—would Charles be able to resist her?

She closed her eyes briefly as Zanna began to walk around the back of the car and when she opened them again she was standing directly in front of her, running long, scarlet-tipped fingers through the tumbling riot of her red-gold hair.

There was no sign of Harry. Beth wasn't going to ask where the little boy was. And all she could say, thinly, was, 'Heathrow? You flew over from France?' Surely Charles didn't know about this. Surely he didn't? He would be as dismayed and annoyed as she was herself—of course he would, she told herself forcefully.

'Spain, actually. We've been in Spain for the last few months.' Zanna twisted round, inspecting the seams of her stockings, twitching at the pencil-slim skirt of the obviously designer-made suit she was wearing. And Beth wondered if she'd left the little boy behind, in the care of some Spanish child-minder while she obeyed the waywardly irresponsible impulse to fly over and see Charles again, boost her already over-inflated ego by proving, yet again, that he was hers for the asking…

But he wasn't! she screamed silently inside her head. He'd been obsessed by Zanna—everyone knew that— willing, at one time, to throw out his wife for her sake. But he was too strong-minded, too sensible, to allow himself to be put through that kind of hell all over again. Of course he was!

So when Zanna gave a theatrical shudder and said, 'I'm too exotic for the English climate; hop in, I'll give you a lift back to the house,' Beth was able to give her a cold, hard stare and refuse.

'I'd rather walk. Why are you here?' As if she couldn't guess, she scorned, her soft mouth twisting, and Zanna returned her glare, her lovely head tipped on one side as she came right back.

'God, but you're a frigid bitch. No wonder Charles—anyway...' She shrugged, obviously thinking better of whatever it was she had been going to say, which, Beth reflected bitterly, didn't need spelling out, did it? 'Look at me as if I'm poison if you want to— just as you did back in June—you'll find out why I'm here soon enough.' She turned to flounce back to the car but stopped as the Range Rover Charles was driving braked to a halt as he rounded the bend.

'Charles—darling!' Zanna, her arms outstretched, ran towards the parked vehicle and Beth went icy cold, clutching her coat collar tightly around her throat, the race of her heartbeats threatening to choke her. Everything hinged on his reaction, the way he greeted the woman who had twice walked out of his life, leaving him devastated.

She saw him leave the car, heard the slam of the door as he closed it behind him, saw the brief interrogatory glance he shafted in her direction, the slight shrug of those impressively broad shoulders, covered in impeccable tweed, and then his austere features were irradiated by a smile of sheer pleasure as he held out his own arms and caught the flying, green-suited figure, pulling her into the hard curve of his body.

Jealousy knifed wickedly through Beth's veins. She couldn't stand here on the sidelines, overlooked, one moment longer. She couldn't watch, but she couldn't help hearing Zanna's shriek of delight, her breathless, 'Darling—I've come back! Isn't it wonderful? Kiss me, do!'

It was unbelievable, incredible, and yet it was happening all over again. Zanna only had to put in an appearance to have the so adult, so controlled Charles Savage acting like a besotted schoolboy. Beth couldn't cope with it and, fighting back a tide of nausea, forced her trembling legs to carry her back to the house.

The moment—the very moment—she got him on his own she would give him a huge chunk of her mind! And then walk out. No court in the land would give custody to a man who could behave as he did!

Reaching the hall, she closed the main door behind her and ground her small teeth together in temper. Anger was the only way to stop herself bursting into broken-hearted tears. All her foolish hopes for the future had been ground into the dust because Zanna Hall had chosen to flick an eyelash in his direction!

So much for last night's gentle interlude. The other woman only had to give him that gorgeous smile and he conveniently forgot everything else—his wife, his responsibilities, his marriage vows!

Stamping towards the stairs, she made it halfway up before she bent double, gasping in pain. And below her, Mrs Penny, with an armful of freshly ironed sheets, called anxiously,

'What is it? Are you all right?'

'Oh, fine,' Beth answered, catching her breath. She sat down on the stairs. 'I think the baby's on its way.'

'Not to panic.' Mrs Penny put the bundle of sheets on a side-table. 'Better early than overdue. Where's that husband of yours?'

'I haven't the least idea.' The outright lie was better than having to admit that he was still devouring the love of his life in the middle of the drive! She was through with him. Through! Rage was the only salvation she could look for.

'Typical,' Mrs Penny muttered, hurrying up the stairs towards her. 'When you need them they're missing. When you don't they're crawling all over you, getting underfoot. Come on.' A helping arm heaved Beth to her feet. 'Phone your dad, he'll get you to the hospital. And I'll pop up and fetch your bag. Not to worry.'

Giving birth was the least of her worries, Beth thought sourly as she picked up the phone while the housekeeper rushed upstairs to fetch the bag Beth had packed a week ago. She would rather her father drove her. She didn't want Charles anywhere near her because she would only bawl him out, rip him to shreds with her tongue. And that wouldn't do her blood-pressure much good.

She began to punch numbers but hadn't got beyond the first two when a second contraction, much stronger than the first, had her dropping everything in sheer amazement.

And, of course, it was Charles who drove her. He had walked into the hall, one arm casually draped around Zanna's shoulders, and had sized up the situation immediately.

Putting the dangling receiver back on its rest, he'd taken the bag from the panting Mrs Penny and ushered her out of the door, lifting her into the passenger-seat of the Range Rover, which was parked at the front, right beside Zanna's showy sports job.

'You can drive me, because it will be quicker,' Beth told him, tight-lipped, as he swung in beside her, firing the ignition. 'But after that I don't want you near me.' She wiped the beads of perspiration from her upper lip with the back of her hand, meeting his narrowed, sideways glare defiantly. 'I wouldn't want the responsibility of keeping you from your little playmate. I'm sure she's got lots of lovely games for you to enjoy while I'm out of the way!'

'And what the hell is that supposed to mean?' His hands were tight on the wheel as they shot out of the main gates and on to the narrow country road, and his voice was a threat. But Beth had other things to think of right now and she tossed back exasperatedly,

'You know what it means! I overheard you talking, remember?' She winced, holding on to the edges of her seat as they flew over a hump-backed bridge. Perspiration dewed her small pale face all over again, but it had nothing to do with the speed. He was driving fast, but it was a controlled speed. He knew these roads like the back of his hand and wasn't taking any risks. And when she'd regained her breath she castigated, 'When she brought your son to meet you, back in June, you'd have divorced me like a shot to marry her. I only agreed to come back to you because I was pregnant—'

Again the spiking, clawing pain, but she howled straight through it. 'She walked out on you again, didn't she? Oh, I know she told you she was tired of being a single parent, and Harry needed his father, but she still walked out in the end. And I hoped you'd think twice about letting her do that to you again. But no, oh, no!' Her even, white teeth showed in a mirthless smile. 'The minute she shows again you're all over her like a rash—holding her, kissing her. You make me sick!'

He shot her a dark, complicated look. There were so many different emotions colouring his eyes black, too many to untangle, and she wasn't interested in trying, was she? she questioned herself snappily as he turned his attention back to the road and told her heatedly, 'You've got more than a few wires crossed.'

'Is that so?' Cool indifference might be more telling than any amount of justifiable ire and she turned her head to look out of the window at her side.

They had left the village behind and were on the main road and it wouldn't take longer than another five minutes to reach the exclusive private maternity home where she was booked in. She couldn't wait—in more ways than one!

'Beth—'

'Don't try to soft-soap me!' she grated through whatever it was he was beginning to say. 'And don't think I can't see through you. If you want to keep your options open, fine. But don't look to me. Whether

Zanna stays or goes, it's all one to me because I won't
be coming back. Not this time.'

For some crazy reason her throat clogged, unshed
tears stinging at the backs of her eyes. She blinked
furiously, aware of his hard sideways stare, the harsh
intake of his breath.

And just for a moment his foot eased on the accel-
erator, as if he was contemplating pulling out of the
traffic on to the side of the road, the better to give his
full attention to the row they were having. But as a
fresh spasm gripped her she gave a shuddering gasp
and closed her eyes and his foot went down again. And
all he said was, with a kind of bitter calm, 'We'll talk
this over in a day or two. Right now I suggest you save
your energy. You're hysterical.'

He could be right, Beth anguished, her eyes glued
shut. Finally bringing things out into the open, speaking her mind, showing her utter disgust at the way
things were between him and Zanna, had helped to
take her mind off the horrible thought of having her
baby in a lay-by. And now, in the tense silence, she
wasn't so sure she was going to be able to avoid such
an undignified happening!

In the event, it was the early hours of the following
morning before the tiny, red-faced bundle was laid in
her arms. Beth's heart went out instinctively, irredeem-
ably and eternally and as her fingers stroked gently
over the velvety cheek she whispered, 'Your name is
Aidan John, my precious.'

'No "Charles"?' Soft-footed, Charles stood in the
open doorway, the look in his eyes unrevealing. He

advanced very slowly. 'Let's see—Aidan, because you like the name, I presume. John, for your father. But nothing for me, his father?'

Although she had told him she didn't want him near her, he had insisted on staying and, if she was honest, she had been more than merely grateful for the way he'd offered his hand for her to mangle, the way he'd stroked something cool and slightly fragrant over her heated skin. He'd never been more than inches away, completely supportive, and now, although she made a half-hearted attempt to come up with a withering comment, she couldn't find one.

She was tired but completely euphoric and now, with her hour-old son in her arms, wasn't the time to start another unholy row. But her unresisting capitulation, the tenderness in her smile as she glanced from her tiny son to his father, surprised her, and she acknowledged huskily, 'Charles Aidan John Savage—to be known as Aidan to avoid confusion.'

'Ah. Of course.' He had reached the bedside and was hunkering down, unfurling his son's tiny fingers, and devils were dancing in his sexy eyes as he murmured, 'I think it's time you got some rest, Mrs Savage. I'm glad to see you've worked your way through your own particular confusion.'

As if on cue, one of the nurses came in, took the sleeping baby and dimmed the light.

'Rest now, Mrs Savage,' she echoed, 'and if there's anything you need, just press the bell. Mr Savage...?' The tilt of a blonde eyebrow was frankly flirtatious, the blue eyes full of female assessment, and Beth felt a sleepy smile drift across her mouth. Maybe she should feel jealous, but she didn't. Women had been giving Charles Savage the come-and-get-me since he'd reached his late teens and there was no room for jealousy or resentment, just a glorious sense of pride. Which was strange, she pondered exhaustedly as she heard him reply,

'Is staying put until his wife falls asleep,' and felt the rough, needing-a-shave brush of his cheek against hers as the dark waves of sleep pulled her under and her last conscious thought was that maybe he was right. Maybe her confusion was over.

In the early afternoon, holding court among a positive bower of hot-house flowers—the largest and most lavish of which had come from Charles—Beth knew that nothing was over, certainly not her 'confusion', if that was what he'd thought her decision to remove herself from his life to be.

He had phoned much earlier, full of supposedly loving enquiries, but she'd cut him short, saying her room was full of gabbling visitors, which was true—except for the gabbling bit—and that she couldn't hear herself think—which wasn't true at all because she'd heard the hard bite in his voice when he'd said he'd be with her later.

And now her parents were on their way out, taking Mrs Penny with them because she'd begged a lift to see the new arrival. And Allie inched her way in as they were going out, and although Beth would have welcomed the opportunity to have a good long thinking session, planning exactly what she would say to Charles when he got his two-timing, louse-like person here, she greeted her best and oldest friend with pleasure.

After the obligatory peek into the cradle, and enthusiastic cooings, Allie laid her offering of spring flowers on the counterpane and grimaced.

'Coals to Newcastle, I see! Never mind, I've got something you might appreciate more.' She put a bulky package on Beth's knees. 'It came to the agency this morning. There was a covering letter so I know what it is. Go on, open it!'

It was, it transpired, after she had dealt with Sellotape and brown paper, bound proofs of William's latest book, the one she had worked on with him. And her face went pink with embarrassment as she read the accompanying card:

If you ever need your job back, or anything else, don't hesitate. I'll always be here. Yours, Will.

Which was misguided of him, but sweet, and not at all helpful when a narrow-eyed Charles walked into the room and enquired, so silky-smooth, 'Someone sent you a book? Hi, Allie.' He glanced in the other girl's direction, but only briefly; he was intently reading the message on the piece of pasteboard he'd taken from Beth's nerveless fingers.

And then his eyes went black as outer space as he tossed the card back on the bed and took the two strides necessary to have him hovering over the cradle.

Beth knew, she just knew what was going on in his twisted, devious mind and a wildness took over her brain as she hissed, regardless of Allie's presence, 'If you're looking to see if there's any likeness—forget it. And if you mention tests to establish paternity, I'll kill you!'

He slewed round on his heels, his face granite, the impeccable cut of the dark suit he was wearing making him seem unapproachable, the menace in him distancing him from his surroundings as he clipped out coldly, 'Save your breath. Your reaction to my accusation, back in France, convinced me. You wouldn't have put a foot back over my doorstep if I'd had the slightest doubt.'

'I'll—I'll be off, then.' Allie's fluttery, awkward words were lost to them both as Beth sniped back at him.

'You do have a nice trusting nature, don't you?' she said, and didn't even flinch when his brows came down in a threatening bar.

'So it seems. I'd appreciate it, though, if you could acquire one, too.'

His effrontery took her breath away and she opened her mouth on a howl of protest. But he covered her lips with a none-too-gentle hand and warned her darkly, 'Don't utter another sound until I've had my say.' Leaving her propped amid the pillows, her lips compressed but her chin at a defiant angle, he put the 'Do Not Disturb' sign on the outside of the door, tossed Allie's flowers and William's bound proofs on to the floor, and lay on the bed, his arms folded behind his head, ignoring her snort of outrage.

'I've been trying to figure your behaviour out ever since you came up with the stupid idea of a trial separation.'

'It was one of the most sensible things I'd ever done.' He might have commanded her to keep quiet, but he couldn't make her keep her mouth shut. And she wished he'd get off the bed. He was far too close. So she tacked on viperishly, 'You hadn't come near me in months. I could have been a lodger, an octogenarian one at that, for all the interest you showed in me.' She gave him a fulminating sideways glare then stared sniffily at the ceiling, her arms folded beneath her breasts. She hadn't finished with him yet—she had barely begun!

'I've explained why.' For the first time, there was a trace of weariness in his voice and Beth's heart twisted sickeningly as he went on, 'If you knew how guilty I felt, you wouldn't have needed to ask why.'

No matter what he was; never mind if he would always put Zanna first, she had to acknowledge that he had been sincere about that. There had been no mistaking the pain in his voice when he had told her how he had blamed himself during those dreadful months after the accident. Her taunt had been unnecessary and out of order, and, to make up, she said diffidently, 'How could I have known, if you didn't tell me? And if it helps at all, I felt the guilt, too. You'd married me to have children—primarily, at least. I felt I'd let you down. Knowing I was unlikely to conceive again made me feel a failure, inadequate.'

He twisted suddenly on the bed, forcing her to look at him.

'You should have told me. Correction.' His hard mouth indented wryly. 'We should have told each other. Talked it through.' His eyes softened; his mouth did, too, as he brushed his lips over the suddenly sensitised skin of the shoulder her sleeveless nightgown left bare.

Beth shuddered helplessly. This confrontation wasn't going as she'd planned—she felt as if she'd been left in a mire of non-communication. If only they'd talked, not kept their guilt locked away inside themselves.

But that was all in the past, and they couldn't go back there, and he made that patently clear when he hoisted himself up on one elbow, his inescapable eyes on a level with hers as he informed her with studied patience, 'As I've been trying to explain, working out the motives for your behaviour has been beyond me. Until, that is, you came out with that hysterical spiel on the way here.'

'Hysterical?' she bridled, stung. 'It had nothing to do with what I was saying. You'd have been hysterical, too, if you'd thought you wouldn't make it in time to give birth in the proper place!'

'Rather more than that, I'd say. I would have been having a few rather serious doubts about my role in life.'

Unwillingly, her lips twitched. And then she remembered that jettisoning a husband was utterly serious. And, strangely, frightening, too. She sighed, very sober now, cold inside and, despite the peacefully sleeping baby, very alone. And Charles told her, 'It was only when you gabbled some nonsense about Harry being my son that I was able to put the facts together. Tell me, what exactly did you overhear, back in June?'

Nonsense? Beth's heart leapt then settled down to a sombre, heavy beat. She had heard what she had heard, and there was no way he could get round that. And, surely, he wouldn't want to, would he?

She ran the tip of her tongue over her dry lips, and husked out accusingly, 'She called you darling.'

'Is that all? She calls everyone darling.' He turned on his back again and closed his eyes, as if totally bored. Beth dug him sharply in the ribs.

'No, not all—not by a long chalk, and you know it.'

A small mew, followed by a hiccuping screech, had Beth scrambling down from the bed, lifting the tiny, protesting scrap of humanity from the cradle and scrambling back, Charles Aidan John tucked comfortably at her breast. And Charles muttered, 'Well, go on, then. Tell me.'

'I don't think this is the time or the place to be discussing the breakdown of our marriage,' Beth replied repressively. She would not let herself be upset. Not now. Later, perhaps. Or tomorrow. But now now.

Charles shifted round again, his eyes on the greedily suckling infant, his gaze slowly lifting to the softly vulnerable curve of her lips, the dreamy green of her eyes, and he said thickly, 'My God—I think I'm jealous of my own son!' And then he went on, taking in her fiery blush, 'When you took that job in France and told me you wanted a separation, I nearly went out of my mind. Things had been going badly for us—I knew how much you wanted children. I think, on the whole, that desire was responsible for turning the tide in my favour when you agreed to marry me.'

'You said you wanted children, too. Hordes of them,

to fill South Park,' she reminded him defensively, and
he held up a quietening hand.

'Only because I knew how keen you were. I wanted
you, only you. If you gave me children, great. But if
you hadn't been able to I wouldn't have gone into a
decline, believe me,' he told her drily. 'And I believed
seeing young Harry, in our home, was the final straw,
the thing that sent you away. I'd been responsible—in
my own mind at least—for the way you'd lost your
baby. And, for all we knew, lost all hope of having
any more. I tried to make you believe that there would
be more for you—more to comfort you than to ease
my own conscience. I could see how Harry's presence
was hurting you, making you bitter. I hadn't been able
to touch you, you see. Partly because of my feelings
of guilt and partly because I knew if we shared the
same bed I wouldn't be able to keep my hands off you.
I felt you needed time to come to terms with what had
happened, without my making that sort of demand.'

She had been thinking about his words, words about
wanting her, and only her, allowing them to linger on
her mind like soothing balm, and about him saying
he'd tried to comfort her, telling her there would be
more children for her when, at the time, she'd believed
he'd meant men! But his statement about the effect his
son had had on her jolted her out of the dangerous
fool's paradise. Of course Harry's presence had hurt,
made her bitter and jealous!

'I was hurt because Harry was—is—your son,' she
told him tightly, feeling the ache of loneliness and loss
build up inside her again. 'I heard Zanna call him ''our
son'', say she'd had to come to you again because the

boy needed to get to know his father. Tell you she'd
heard our marriage was over, which it was to all intents
and purposes—and only you could have told her that.
And I saw you together that night, in the nursery, and
Mrs Penny said Harry was the spitting image of you,
which he is, and—'

'Mrs Penny always did know more than is good for
her,' Charles interrupted, lifting a hand to gentle away
the tears she hadn't been able to prevent escaping from
beneath her closed eyelids. 'Don't upset yourself, my
love. There really is no need. Because you do love me,
don't you?'

The deep note of triumph in his voice made her
shiver. And she nodded, too emotional now to speak,
to even try to salvage the pride that had become so
important to her.

He took the now sleeping baby from her arms and
tucked him gently back in his cradle, then sat on the
bed, pulling her into his arms, telling her huskily, 'I
worked that out for myself, in between ministering to
you while you were so gallantly producing our son and
heir! From what you'd told me, I knew you couldn't
have overheard all that conversation, as I'd believed.
If you had, you would have known that Harry is
James's son, not mine! You left because you believed
Zanna had come back to me, bringing our son, and I
was going to turn you out.'

'James's son?' Beth lifted her face from the haven
of his broad chest, her eyes incredulous. 'But she was
having an affair with you—everyone knew how obsessed you were with her.'

He dropped his mouth to her parted lips, whispering

against them, 'I never had an affair with Zanna. And as for being obsessed, I suppose I was, in a way. Obsessed by the need to keep her away from James.'

An imperious rap on the door heralded the arrival of a nurse, ignoring the 'Do Not Disturb' notice which was for the benefit of visitors only.

'Has Baby been fed, Mrs Savage?' she asked briskly, and, at Beth's bemused nod, whisked him out of his comfortable nest. 'Then it's time he was changed, isn't it? You only had to press that bell.'

Watching the starched, retreating back, Beth shook her head bemusedly. Was she being accused of being an uncaring mother? She rather thought she was! But, instead of being justifiably indignant, she curved her mouth in a soft smile. Already she loved her tiny son more than life. But she loved his father even more, and it was beginning to make sense, some of it...

Had everyone been wrong about his tempestuous affair with the gorgeous redhead?

'Explain,' she commanded, drawing away from the arms which were still holding her so close.

'I'll have to, won't I?' His eyes gleamed with devilry. 'But all I can really take in is the fact that, after all the traumas, you love me.' His lips took hers, but gently, savouring her, the hint of tightly leashed, underlying passion making her head spin. And long, delicious minutes later, he cradled her head against his shoulder and told her, 'To go back years, our family have always known the Halls. Zanna's father and mine were at the same schools together. She was always a minx—lovely, granted, but totally uncontrollable. I found her more annoying than intriguing. And then,

five years or so ago, she came to stay with us. Her
parents were sick of her behaviour, the way she went
through men. There were always broken-hearted ex-
men-friends littering their doorstep, apparently. What
they didn't know, though, was that James had been
secretly smitten for years. But I knew it, and maybe I
was being over-protective, but I didn't want to see him
go the way of all the others, so I took it on myself to
squire the woman around, letting James think I was the
current lover. Unfortunately...' He ran his hands over
her back, his fingers burning through the thin silk of
her nightgown, making her melt against him. 'Everyone else believed it, too,' he continued. 'It was the
most misguided thing I'd ever done in my life. It
caused a rift between us, James and me, and it's only
recently been healed. At the time, I believed I'd done
the right thing, especially when James, who had gone
to work on a project in France, married Lisa. Zanna
was still hanging around and, to be fair, she did make
herself useful, acting as my hostess when I needed
her—in between flitting hither and thither, doing her
own thing. Crunch time came when she told me she'd
visited James and Lisa—she actually had the gall to
tell me she'd fallen in love with him, that they'd had
an affair, practically under Lisa's nose. Needless to
say, I threw her out, told her never to darken my doorstep again, et cetera. I think the whole village believed
the boot was well and truly on the other foot, that she'd
given me my marching orders. Everyone, all of a sudden, became remarkably sympathetic!'

'She's hateful!' Beth exploded hotly.

Charles said drily, 'She can be. But I think she's

changed. She'll always be headstrong, always hog the limelight, but she's a good mother—and that surprised me—and she and James love each other. If he can handle her temperament, they'll be OK.'

'So James really is Harry's father,' Beth whispered, hardly able to believe that at last everything was beginning to fall into place. 'And you thought I knew that all along, and wouldn't discuss it when you and she invited me to. I just walked out. You and Zanna must have thought me a prize bitch.'

'Never that, my love.' He smiled into her troubled eyes, lifted her hands and kissed both palms with a lingering tenderness that made her want to weep with the depth and the beauty of her love for him. 'I believed you were troubled, and hurt—that seeing young Harry had brought back all you had missed out on. And when you went I was determined to get you back. I knew my life wouldn't be worth living without you.'

'Then what were you doing with her in France?' Beth, with an effort, stopped herself from melting against him and gave him an angular look, and he shook his head, lifting his eyes.

'Patience, woman. I'm trying to tell you. We were going to find James. But the first I knew of Harry's existence was when Zanna turned up at South Park with him that day. She was putting a brave face on it—trying to be her old, flamboyant self—but boy was she worried underneath. She told me that Harry was my nephew and that, having heard of Lisa's untimely death, she needed to contact him but had no idea where he was. Harry had a right to get to know his father, and James, now free, might still care enough for her to marry her. She still loved him. Which, quite frankly, knowing her track record, I could hardly credit. Anyway—' he shrugged wide shoulders '—there was no doubt that the boy was James's; the family likeness was too strong to overlook. So I promised I'd do what I could. I knew he was still working with the same firm of civil engineers in France and managed to track him down to a small town in the south. But first I had to find you. As you know, I learned where you were from Allie, phoned James to warn him we were arriving—and when—and stopped off at Boulogne, much to Zanna's annoyance, because, having arranged that meeting with James, she hated the thought of delay.

'I found you and intended to talk things through with you, ask you to give me the opportunity to try again. But, as you know again, things got out of hand and the day I'd given myself to persuade you was over. But I knew where you were, knew you would stay put with that William guy, and what with helping to sort things out between James and Zanna, sorting out a few pressing business affairs of my own to give me the time to spend with you, hiring that cottage and stocking it, it was weeks before I could come for you again—knowing I'd have enough time, hopefully, to persuade you to my point of view.'

'Which is?' Beth prompted, resolutely pushing the misery of the last year out of her head, knowing that the present and the future she had with this one man was the only thing that mattered.

'To teach you to love me,' he answered simply. 'I'd loved you almost from the moment you came to South Park as my temporary housekeeper. You were so

warm, so natural, so caring. I couldn't believe my good
fortune when you agreed to marry me.'

'You didn't tell me you loved me,' Beth accused,
but softly. She recalled how she'd ached to hear him
say those words, but that was all behind her now, and
nothing mattered because she knew the truth.

The surprise in his eyes made her want to shake him
for being so cussedly male, but she kissed him instead
when he told her, 'I showed you, didn't I? Every time
I held you in my arms I showed you how much I loved
you. And when I get you home, after a suitable interval
for your recovery, of course, I'll show you again, and
again...' He gathered her slowly into his arms and
brushed his mouth against hers, invoking a response
she should have been too exhausted to give, all things
considered, she thought dizzily, and she twined her
arms around his neck, intent on showing him how exhausted she was not, when he lifted his head and said,

'And before you ask, Zanna and James are back in
England to break the news of their marriage to Lisa's
parents. James thought it politic to go on ahead, with
Harry, to break the ice as it were. Zanna came to South
Park to beg a bed for the night. Even now she's on her
way up north to join the others.'

'Blow Zanna!' Beth muttered hoarsely, pulling his
head down to hers, and things were starting to get out
of hand when the starchy nurse—so different from the
fluttery blonde from the night before—announced
stiffly,

'Baby thinks he needs feeding again, I do believe.
He's been bathed and changed and weighed and—'

'Thank you.' Charles was on his feet, taking his

wide-eyed, grumbling son into the crook of his arm, ushering the nurse on her way.

He drew Beth to her feet, his other arm around her, supporting and cherishing her, holding her close, and his voice was deep with emotion as he murmured, 'Can you feel it, Beth? The love that surrounds us? I swear there's enough of it here, in this room, to make the world go round for a thousand years.'

And she looked deep into those hard gunfighter's eyes, and saw love, and silently pledged her love to him for the rest of her life. And he understood—he read the message that was too deep to put into words and brushed his lips across hers as she took the protesting infant into her arms, settled him to her breast and held out her free hand to her husband, her wonderful, tough, soft-centred, exasperating Charles. And her smile was glorious.

MILLS & BOON®

Makes any time special™

Mills & Boon publish 29 new titles every month. Select from...

Modern Romance™   Tender Romance™

Sensual Romance™

Medical Romance™ Historical Romance™

MAT2

Christmas is a time
for loving...

A Tender
Christmas

Available at branches of WH Smith, Tesco, Martins, Borders, Easons,
Volume One, James Thin and most good paperback bookshops

Historical Romance™
Two brand new titles each month
...rich, vivid
and passionate.
Available at most branches of WH Smith, Tesco,
Martins, Borders, Easons, Volume One/James Thin
and most good paperback bookshops
GEN/04/RTL2

Together for the first time
3 compelling novels by
bestselling author

PENNY JORDAN

The *Bride's* BOUQUET

One wedding—one bouquet—
leads to three trips to the altar

Published on 22nd September

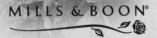

MILLS & BOON®

0010/116/MB6